Network
Analysis and
Synthesis

Network Analysis and Synthesis

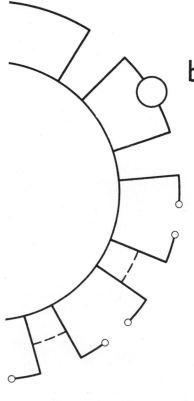

by Franklin F. Kuo

Bell Telephone

Laboratories, Inc.

Murray Hill,

New Jersey

John Wiley and Sons, Inc.

New York, London

Library of Congress Catalog Card Number: 62-10924
Printed in the United States of America

To My Father and Mother

Preface

This book is an introduction to the study of electric networks based upon a *system theoretic* approach. In contrast to many present textbooks, the emphasis is not on the form and structure of a network but rather on its *excitation-response* properties. In other words, the major theme is concerned with how a linear network behaves as a signal processor. Special emphasis is given to the descriptions of a linear network by its system function in the frequency domain and its impulse response in the time domain. With the use of the system function as a unifying link, the transition from network analysis to synthesis can be accomplished with relative ease.

The book was originally conceived as a set of notes for a second course in network analysis at the Polytechnic Institute of Brooklyn. It assumes that the student has already had a course in steady-state circuit analysis. He should be familiar with Kirchhoff's laws, mesh and node equations, standard network theorems, and, preferably, he should have an elementary understanding of network topology.

A brief description of the subject matter follows. Chapters 1 and 2 deal with signal representation and certain characteristics of linear networks. Chapters 3, 4, 5, and 6 discuss transient analysis from both a time domain viewpoint, i.e., in terms of differential equations and the impulse response, and a frequency domain viewpoint using Fourier and Laplace transforms. Chapter 7 is concerned with the use of poles and zeros in both transient and steady-state analysis. Chapter 8 contains a classical treatment of network functions.

The final five chapters deal with network synthesis. In Chapter 9, the elements of realizability theory are presented. Chapters 10 and 11 are concerned with elementary driving-point and transfer function synthesis procedures. In Chapter 12, some fundamental concepts in modern filter design are introduced. Chapter 13 deals with the use of scattering matrices in network analysis and synthesis. In addition, there are three appendices covering the rudiments of matrix algebra, complex variables, and proofs of Brune's realizability theorems.

The book is intended for a two-semester course in network theory. Chapters 1 through 7 can be used in a one-semester undergraduate or beginning graduate course in transient analysis or linear system analysis. Chapters 8 through 13 are to be used in a subsequent course on network synthesis.

It was my very good fortune to have studied under Professor M. E. Van Valkenburg at the University of Illinois. I have been profoundly influenced by his philosophy of teaching and writing which places strong emphasis upon clarity of exposition. In keeping with this philosophy, I have tried to present complicated material from a simple viewpoint, and I have included a large number of illustrative examples and exercises. In addition, I have tried to take a middle ground between mathematical rigor and intuitive understanding. Unless a proof contributes materially to the understanding of a theorem, it is omitted in favor of an intuitive argument. For example, in the treatment of unit impulses, a development in terms of a *generalized function* is first introduced. It is stressed that the unit impulse is not really a function but actually a sequence of functions whose limit point is undefined. Then, the less rigorous, intuitive notion of an impulse "function" is presented. The treatment then proceeds along the nonrigorous path.

There are a number of topics which have been omitted. One of these is network topology which seems to be in vogue at present. I have purposely omitted topology because it seems out of place in a book that de-emphasizes the form and structure approach to network analysis.

In an expository book of this nature, it is almost impossible to reference adequately all the original contributors in the vast and fertile field of network theory. I apologize to those whose names were omitted either through oversight or ignorance. At the end of the book, some supplementary textbooks are listed for the student who either wishes to fill in some gaps in his training or wants to obtain a different point of view.

It is with much pleasure that I acknowledge with gratitude the help and advice given to me by my colleagues at the Bell Telephone Laboratories and by my former colleagues at the Polytechnic Institute of Brooklyn. I wish to express my sincere appreciation to the many reviewers whose advice and criticism were invaluable in revising preliminary drafts of the manuscript. Professors R. D. Barnard of Wayne State University and R. W. Newcomb of Stanford University deserve specific thanks for their critical reading of the entire manuscript and numerous helpful suggestions and comments.

In addition, I wish to thank Mrs. Elizabeth Jenkins and Miss Elizabeth La Jeunesse of the Bell Telephone Laboratories for their efficient and careful typing of the manuscript.

Finally, to my wife, Dora, I owe a special debt of gratitude. Her encouragement and cooperation made the writing of this book an enjoyable undertaking.

F. F. Kuo

Murray Hill, New Jersey,
January, 1962

Contents

chapter I

Signals and systems

This book is an introduction to electric network theory. The first half of the book is devoted to network analysis and the remainder to network synthesis and design. What *are* network analysis and synthesis? In a generally accepted definition of network analysis and synthesis, there are three key words: the *excitation*, the *network*, and the *response* as depicted

FIG. 1.1. The objects of our concern.

in Fig. 1.1. Network analysis is concerned with determining the response, given the excitation and the network. In network synthesis, the problem is to design the network given the excitation and the desired response. In this chapter we will outline some of the problems to be encountered in this book without going into the actual details of the problems. We will also discuss some basic definitions.

1.1 SIGNAL ANALYSIS

For electric networks, the excitation and response are given in terms of voltages and currents which are functions of time, t. In general, these functions of time are called *signals*. In describing signals, we use the two universal languages of electrical engineering—*time* and *frequency*. Strictly speaking, a signal is a function of time. However, the signal can be described equally well in terms of *spectral* or *frequency* information. As between any two languages, such as French and German, translation is

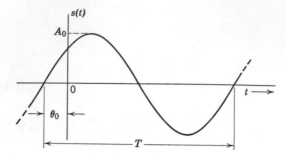

FIG. I.2. Sinusoidal signal.

needed to render information given in one language comprehensible in the other. Between time and frequency, the translation is effected by the *Fourier series*, the *Fourier integral*, and the *Laplace transform*. We shall have ample opportunity to define and study these terms later in the book. At the moment, let us examine how a signal can be described in terms of both frequency and time. Consider the sinusoidal signal,

$$s(t) = A_0 \sin(\omega_0 t + \theta_0) \tag{1.1}$$

where A_0 is the *amplitude*, θ_0 is the *phase shift*, and ω_0 is the *angular frequency* as given by the equation,

$$\omega_0 = \frac{2\pi}{T} \tag{1.2}$$

where T is the period of the sinusoid. The signal is plotted against time in Fig. 1.2. An equally complete description of the signal is obtained if we let the angular frequency ω be the independent variable. In this case, the signal is described in terms of A_0, ω_0, and θ_0, as shown in Fig. 1.3a, where amplitude is plotted against frequency, and in Fig. 1.3b, where phase shift is plotted.

Suppose now, the signal is made up of $2n + 1$ sinusoidal components,

$$s(t) = \sum_{i=-n}^{n} A_i \sin(\omega_i t + \theta_i) \tag{1.3}$$

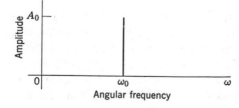

FIG. I.3a. Plot of amplitude A_0 versus angular frequency ω_0.

FIG. 1.3b. Plot of phase θ_0 versus angular frequency ω_0.

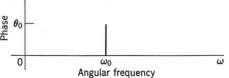

The spectral description of the signal would then contain $2n + 1$ lines at $\pm\omega_1, \pm\omega_2, \cdots, \pm\omega_n$, as given in Figs. 1.4a and b. These discrete spectra of amplitude A versus ω and phase shift θ versus ω are sometimes called *line spectra*. Consider the case when the number of these spectral lines becomes infinite and the intervals $(\omega_{i+1} - \omega_i)$ between the lines approach zero. Then there is no longer any discrimination between one frequency and another, so that the discrete line spectra fuse into a *continuous* spectra, as shown by the example in Figs. 1.5a and b. In the continuous case, the sum in Eq. 1.3 becomes an integral,

$$s(t) = \int_{-\infty}^{\infty} A(\omega) \sin\left[\omega t + \theta(\omega)\right] d\omega \qquad (1.4)$$

where $A(\omega)$ is known as the *amplitude spectrum* and $\theta(\omega)$ as the *phase spectrum*.

As we shall see later, periodic signals such as the sine wave in Fig. 1.2 can be described in terms of discrete spectra through the use of Fourier series. On the other hand, a nonperiodic signal such as the triangular pulse in Fig. 1.6 can only be described in terms of continuous spectra through the Fourier integral transform.

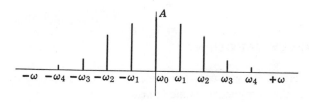

FIG. 1.4a. Discrete amplitude spectrum.

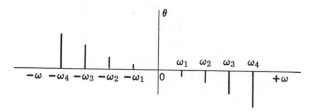

FIG. 1.4b. Discrete phase spectrum.

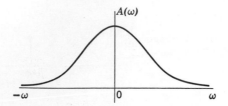

FIG. 1.5a. Continuous amplitude spectrum.

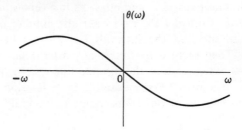

FIG. 1.5b. Continuous phase spectrum.

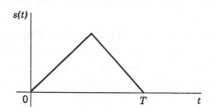

FIG. 1.6. Triangular signal.

1.2 COMPLEX FREQUENCY

In this section, we will consider the concept of *complex frequency*. As we shall see, the complex frequency variable,

$$s = \sigma + j\omega \tag{1.5}$$

is a generalized frequency variable whose real part σ describes growth and decay of the amplitudes of signals, and the imaginary part $j\omega$ is angular frequency in the usual sense. The idea of complex frequency is developed by examining the cisoidal signal,

$$\mathbf{S}(t) = Ae^{j\omega t}, \tag{1.6}$$

when $\mathbf{S}(t)$ is represented as a rotating phasor,* as shown in Fig. 1.7.

---

* A phasor **S** is a complex number characterized by a magnitude and a phase angle (see Appendix A).

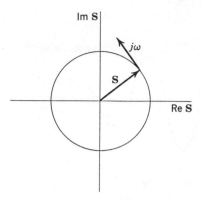

FIG. I.7. Rotating phasor.

The angular frequency ω of the phasor can then be thought of as a *velocity* at the end of the phasor. In particular the velocity ω is always at right angle to the phasor, as shown in Fig. 1.7. However, consider the general case when the velocity is inclined at any arbitrary angle ψ as given in Figs. 1.8a and 1.8b. In this case, if the velocity is given by the symbol s, we see that s is composed of a component ω at right angle to the phasor S, as well as a component σ which is parallel to S. In Fig. 1.8a, s has a component $-\sigma$ toward the origin. As the phasor S spins in a counterclockwise fashion, the phasor decreases in amplitude. The resulting wave for the real and imaginary parts of S(t) are *damped sinusoids* as given by

$$\text{Re } S(t) = Ae^{-\sigma t} \cos \omega t$$
$$\text{Im } S(t) = Ae^{-\sigma t} \sin \omega t \qquad (1.7)$$

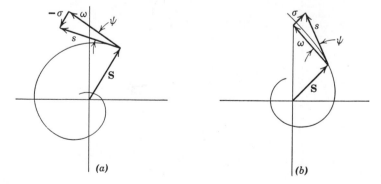

FIG. I.8. (a) Rotating phasor with exponentially decreasing amplitude. (b) Rotating phasor with exponentially increasing amplitude.

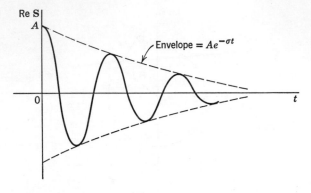

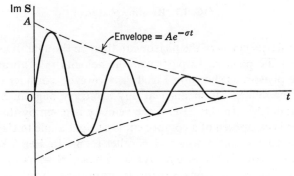

FIG. 1.9. Damped sinusoids.

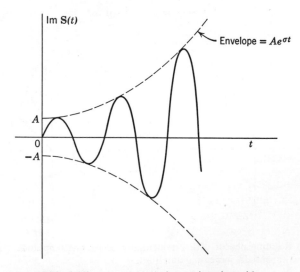

FIG. 1.10. Exponentially increasing sinusoid.

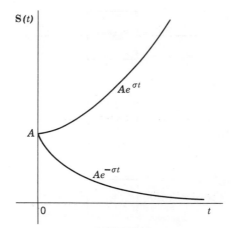

FIG. I.II. Exponential signals.

which are shown in Fig. 1.9. Note that the damped sinusoid has an exponential envelope decay, $Ae^{-\sigma t}$. In Fig. 1.8b, the phasor is shown with a positive real component of velocity $+\sigma$. Therefore, as the phasor spins, the amplitudes of the real and imaginary parts increase exponentially with an envelope $Ae^{+\sigma t}$, as shown by Im $S(t)$ in Fig. 1.10.

From this discussion, it is apparent that the generalized cisoidal signal

$$S(t) = Ae^{st} = Ae^{(\sigma + j\omega)t} \tag{1.8}$$

describes the growth and decay of the amplitudes in addition to angular frequency in the usual sense. When $\sigma = 0$, the sinusoid is undamped, and when $j\omega = 0$, the signal is an exponential signal

$$S(t) = Ae^{\pm \sigma t} \tag{1.9}$$

as shown in Fig. 1.11. Finally, if $\sigma = j\omega = 0$, then the signal is a constant A. Thus we see the versatility of a complex frequency description.

I.3 NETWORK ANALYSIS

As mentioned before, the characterization of the excitation and response signals in time and frequency makes up only part of the analysis problem. The other part consists of characterizing the network itself in terms of time and frequency, and determining how the network behaves as a signal processer. Let us turn our attention now to a brief study of the properties of linear networks and the general characteristics of signal processing by a linear system.

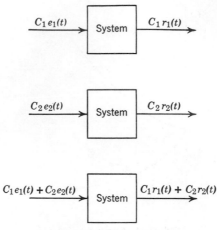

FIG. 1.12. Linear system.

Consider the block representation of the system shown in Fig. 1.12. Let us suppose that an excitation, $C_1 e_1(t)$ produces a response $C_1 r_1(t)$, and $C_2 e_2(t)$, in turn, results in a response $C_2 r_2(t)$. Then the system is *linear* if a superposition of the signals $C_1 e_1(t)$ and $C_2 e_2(t)$ produces a response equal to the sum of the individual responses, $C_1 r_1(t) + C_2 r_2(t)$.

Other adjectives which may describe a linear system are *inert* and *time invariant*.* We say a system is inert if

$$e(t) = 0 \qquad t < T \qquad (1.10)$$

then

$$r(t) = 0 \qquad t < T$$

In other words, a system is inert if before an excitation is applied at $t = T$, the response is zero for $-\infty < t < T$.

To understand the concept of time invariance in a linear system, let us suppose that, initially, the excitation is introduced at $t = 0$, which gives rise to a response $r(t)$. If $e(t)$ is introduced at $t = T_1$, and if the shape of the response waveform is the same as in the first case but delayed by a time T_1, then we say that the system is time invariant. In mathematical terms, if $e(t)$ produces the response $r(t)$, then $e(t \pm T_1)$ would produce the response $r(t \pm T_1)$ if the system is time invariant, as illustrated in Fig. 1.13. Another way of looking at this concept is through the fact that a time-invariant system only contains elements whose values do not change with time.

From the time-invariant property we can show that, if $e(t)$ at the input gives rise to $r(t)$ at the output, (Fig. 1.14) then, if the input were $e'(t)$, i.e., the derivative of $e(t)$, the response would be $r'(t)$. The proof is quite

---

* Note that linear systems need not be inert or time invariant.

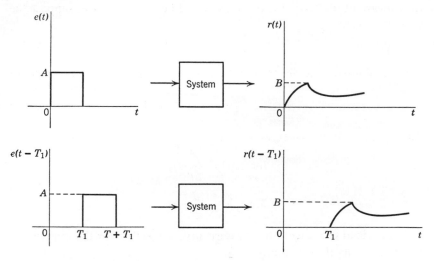

FIG. 1.13. Time-invariant system.

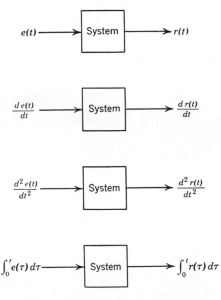

FIG. 1.14. Some implications of time-invariant systems.

simple. Consider an excitation $e(t + \epsilon)$ where ϵ is a real quantity. By the time-invariant property, the response would be $r(t + \epsilon)$. Now suppose the excitation were

$$e_1(t) = \frac{1}{\epsilon}[e(t + \epsilon) - e(t)] \qquad (1.11)$$

then according to the linearity and time-invariant properties, the response would be

$$r_1(t) = \frac{1}{\epsilon}[r(t + \epsilon) - r(t)] \qquad (1.12)$$

Taking the limit as $\epsilon \to 0$, we see that

$$\lim_{\epsilon \to 0} e_1(t) = \frac{d}{dt}e(t)$$
$$\lim_{\epsilon \to 0} r_1(t) = \frac{d}{dt}r(t) \qquad (1.13)$$

We can extend this idea to higher derivatives as well as for the integrals of $e(t)$ and $r(t)$, as shown in Fig. 1.14.

Let us examine now some idealized models of linear systems. The systems given in the following all have properties which make them very useful in signal processing.

1. *Amplifier:* An amplifier scales up the magnitude of the input, i.e., $r(t) = Ke(t)$, where K is a constant (Fig. 1.15).

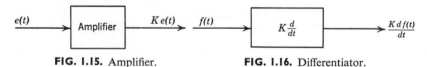

FIG. 1.15. Amplifier.   **FIG. 1.16.** Differentiator.

2. *Differentiator:* The input signal is differentiated and possibly scaled up or down (Fig. 1.16).

3. *Integrator:* The output is the integral of the input, as shown in Fig. 1.17.

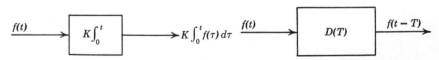

FIG. 1.17. Integrator.   **FIG. 1.18.** Time-delay network.

4. *Time delayer:* The output is delayed by an amount T, but retains the same wave-shape as the input (Fig. 1.18).

Suppose we take the triangular pulse in Fig. 1.19 as the input signal. Then the outputs for each of the four systems described above are shown in Figs. 1.20a–1.20d.

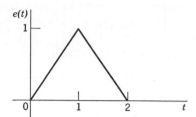

FIG. 1.19. Excitation function.

In the analysis of electric networks, we use idealized linear mathematical models of physical circuit elements. The elements most often encountered are the resistor R, given in ohms, the capacitor C, given in farads, and the inductor L, expressed in henrys. The endpoints of the elements are called *terminals*. A *port* is defined as any pair of two terminals into which energy is supplied or withdrawn or where network variables may be measured or observed. In Fig. 1.21 we have an example of a two-port network.

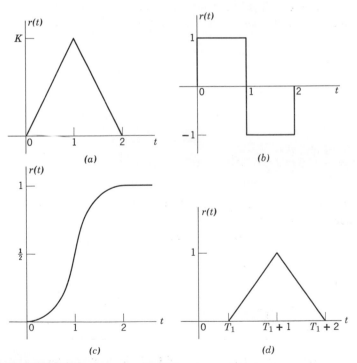

FIG. 1.20. (*a*) Amplifier output. (*b*) Differentiator output. (*c*) Integrator output. (*d*) Delayed output.

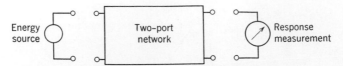

FIG. I.21. Two-port network.

The energy sources that make up the excitation functions are ideal *current* or *voltage sources*, as shown in Figs. 1.22a and b. The polarities indicated for the voltage source and the direction of flow for the current source are arbitrarily assumed for reference purposes only. An ideal voltage source is an energy source that provides, at a given port, a voltage signal that is independent of the current at that port. If we interchange the words "current" and "voltage" in the last definition, we then define an ideal current source.

In network analysis, the principal problem is to find the relationships that exist between the currents and voltages at the ports of the network. Certain simple voltage-current relationships for the network elements also serve as defining equations for the elements themselves. For example, when the currents and voltages are expressed as functions of time, then the R, L, and C elements, shown in Fig. 1.23, are defined by the equation,

$$v(t) = R\, i(t) \qquad \text{or} \qquad i(t) = \frac{1}{R}\, v(t)$$

$$v(t) = L \frac{di(t)}{dt} \qquad \text{or} \qquad i(t) = \frac{1}{L} \int_0^t v(x)\, dx + i(0) \quad (1.14)$$

$$v(t) = \frac{1}{C} \int_0^t i(x)\, dx + v(0) \qquad \text{or} \qquad i(t) = C \frac{dv(t)}{dt}$$

where the constants of integration $i(0)$ and $v(0)$ are *initial conditions* to be discussed in detail later.

Expressed as a function of the complex frequency variable s, the equations

FIG. I.22a. Voltage source.   **FIG. I.22b.** Current source.

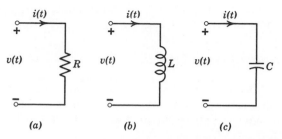

FIG. 1.23. (a) Resistor. (b) Inductor. (c) Capacitor.

defining the R, L, and C elements, shown in Fig. 1.24, are (ignoring initial conditions for the moment)

$$V(s) = R \, I(s) \qquad \text{or} \qquad I(s) = \frac{1}{R} V(s)$$

$$V(s) = sL \, I(s) \qquad \text{or} \qquad I(s) = \frac{1}{sL} V(s) \qquad (1.15)$$

$$V(s) = \frac{1}{sC} I(s) \qquad \text{or} \qquad I(s) = sC \, V(s)$$

We see that in the *time domain* (i.e., where the independent variable is *t*) the voltage-current relationships are given in terms of differential equations. On the other hand, in the *complex-frequency domain*, the voltage-current relationships for the elements are expressed in *algebraic* equations. Algebraic equations are, in most cases, more easily solved than differential equations. Herein lies the *raison d'être* for describing signals and networks in the frequency domain as well as in the time domain.

When a network is made up of an interconnection of linear circuit elements, the network is described by its *system* or *transfer function* H(s). The response R(s) and the excitation E(s) are related by the equation

$$R(s) = H(s) \, E(s). \qquad (1.16)$$

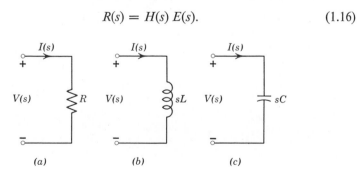

FIG. 1.24. (a) Resistor. (b) Inductor. (c) Capacitor.

In network analysis, we are given $E(s)$ and we can obtain $H(s)$ directly from the network. Our task is to determine $R(s)$.

1.4 NETWORK SYNTHESIS

We will now briefly introduce some of the problems germane to network synthesis. In network synthesis, we are given the response $R(s)$ and the excitation $E(s)$, and we are required to synthesize the network from the system function

$$H(s) = \frac{R(s)}{E(s)} \tag{1.17}$$

Since $R(s)$ and $E(s)$ are voltages or currents, then $H(s)$ is denoted generally as an *immittance* if $R(s)$ is a voltage and $E(s)$ is a current, or vice versa. A *driving-point immittance** is defined to be a function for which the variables are measured at the same port. Thus a driving-point impedance $Z(s)$ at a given port is the function

$$Z(s) = \frac{V(s)}{I(s)} \tag{1.18}$$

where the excitation is a current $I(s)$ and the response is a voltage $V(s)$, as shown in Fig. 1.25. When we interchange the words "current" and "voltage" in the last definition, we then have a *driving-point* admittance. An example of a driving-point impedance is the network in Fig. 1.25, where

$$Z(s) = \frac{V(s)}{I(s)} = R \tag{1.19}$$

Now suppose the resistor in Fig. 1.25 were enclosed in a "black box." We have no access to this black box, except at the terminals 1-1′ in Fig. 1.26. Our task is to determine the network in the black box. Suppose we are given the information that, for a given excitation $I(s)$, the voltage

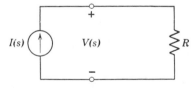

FIG. 1.25. Driving point impedance $Z(s) = R$.

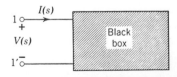

FIG. 1.26. Black box.

---

* IRE Standards on Circuits "Linear Passive Networks," *Proc. IRE*, **48,** No. 9 (Sept. 1960), 1608–1610.

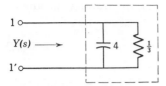

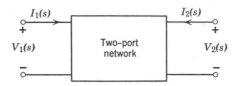

FIG. 1.27. Network realization for $Y(s)$.

FIG. 1.28. Two-port network.

response $V(s)$ is proportional to $I(s)$ by the equation

$$V(s) = K\,I(s). \tag{1.20}$$

An obvious solution, though not unique, is that the network consists of a resistor of value $R = K\,\Omega$. Suppose next that the excitation is a voltage $V(s)$ and the response is a current $I(s)$, and that

$$Y(s) = \frac{I(s)}{V(s)} = 3 + 4s \tag{1.21}$$

Our task is to synthesize a network equivalent to the network in the black box. From a close scrutiny of the driving point admittance $Y(s)$, we see that a possible solution might consist of a resistor of $\frac{1}{3}$ Ω in parallel with a capacitor of 4 fd, as seen in Fig. 1.27.

The problem of driving-point synthesis, as shown from the examples just given, consists of decomposing a given immittance function into basic recognizable parts (such as $3 + 4s$). Before we proceed with the mechanics of decomposition, we must first determine whether the function is *realizable*, i.e., can it be synthesized in terms of positive resistances, inductances, and capacitances? It will be shown that realizable driving-point immittances belong to a class of functions known as *positive real* or, simply, p.r. functions. From the properties of p.r. functions, we can test a given driving-point function for realizability. The Appendices present a short introduction to complex variables as well as the proofs of some theorems on positive real functions. With a knowledge of p.r. functions, we then go on to examine special driving-point functions. These include functions which can be realized with two kinds of elements only—the L-C, R-C, and R-L immittances.

Next we proceed to the synthesis of transfer functions. According to the IRE Standards on passive linear networks,* a *transfer function* or *transmittance* is a system function for which the variables are measured at different ports. There are many different forms which a transfer function might take. For example, consider the two-port network in Fig. 1.28.

---

* Loc. cit.

If the excitation is $I_1(s)$ and the response $V_2(s)$, the transfer function is a *transfer impedance*,

$$Z_{21}(s) = \frac{V_2(s)}{I_1(s)} \tag{1.22}$$

On the other hand, if $V_1(s)$ were the excitation and $V_2(s)$ the response, then we would have a *voltage-ratio* transfer function,

$$H(s) = \frac{V_2(s)}{V_1(s)} \tag{1.23}$$

As for driving-point functions, there are certain properties which a transfer function must satisfy in order to be realizable. We shall study these realizability conditions and then proceed to the synthesis of some simple transfer functions.

The most important aspect of transfer function synthesis is *filter design*. A filter is defined as a network which passes a certain portion of a frequency spectrum and blocks the remainder of the spectrum. By "blocking" we imply that the magnitude response $|H(j\omega)|$ of the filter is approximately zero for that frequency range. Thus, an ideal *low-pass* filter is a network which passes all frequencies up to a *cutoff* frequency ω_C, and blocks all frequencies above ω_C, as shown in Fig. 1.29.

One aspect of filter design is to synthesize the network from the transfer function $H(s)$. The other aspect deals with the problem of obtaining a realizable transmittance $H(s)$ given the specification of, say, the magnitude characteristic in Fig. 1.29. This part of the synthesis is generally referred to as the *approximation* problem. Why the word "approximation"? Because frequency response characteristics of the R, L, and C elements are continuous (with the exception of isolated points called *resonance* points), a network containing these elements cannot be made to cut off abruptly at ω_C in Fig. 1.29. Instead, we can realize low-pass filters which have the magnitude characteristics of Fig. 1.30. In connection with the filter design problems, we will discuss certain problems in *magnitude* and

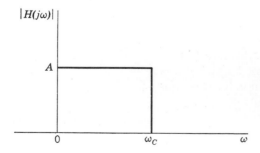

FIG. 1.29. Ideal amplitude spectrum for low-pass filter.

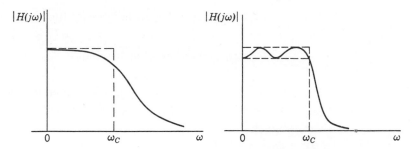

FIG. 1.30. Realizable low-pass filter characteristics.

frequency normalization, so that, in designing a filter, we deal with element values as $R = 0.5$ ohm and $C = 2$ farads instead of "practical" element values of, say, $R = 500,000$ ohms and $C = 2$ picofarads (pico $= 10^{-12}$). Also we will study a method whereby low-pass filter designs might be transformed into high-pass, band-pass, and band-elimination filters. The mathematical basis of this method is called *frequency transformation*.

Finally, we will discuss some aspects of analysis and synthesis in which the excitation and response functions are given in terms of *power* rather than of voltage and current. We will examine the power-transfer properties of linear networks, using *scattering parameters* which describe the incident and reflected power of the network at its ports.

1.5 BASIC DEFINITIONS

In this textbook we deal mainly with networks which are *linear*, *passive*, and *time invariant*. We have already examined the concept of time invariance. Now let us discuss the definitions of the other terms. First consider the definition of "linear."

Linear

A system (network) is linear if (*a*) the principle of *superposition* and (*b*) the principle of *proportionality* hold.

By the superposition principle, if, for a given network, $[e_1(t), r_1(t)]$ and $[e_2(t), r_2(t)]$ are excitation-response pairs, then if the excitation were $e(t) = e_1(t) + e_2(t)$, the response would be $r(t) = r_1(t) + r_2(t)$. By the proportionality principle, if the excitation were $C_1e_1(t)$, where C_1 is a constant, then the response would be $C_1r_1(t)$, i.e., the constant of proportionality C_1 is preserved by the linear network. The two conditions of linearity are summarized in Fig. 1.12.

Another definition of a linear network is that the excitation and response of the network are related by a linear differential equation. We shall discuss this definition in Chapter 3 on differential equations.

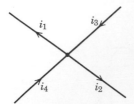

FIG. 1.31. Example for Kirchhoff's current law.

Linear passive network

A linear network is passive* if (a) the energy delivered to the network is nonnegative for any arbitrary excitation and (b) no voltages and currents appear at any port before an excitation is applied.

Finally, let us consider the basic Kirchhoff's current and voltage postulates before embarking on the course ahead. Kirchhoff's current postulate states that, at any point in the network which is a junction of current-carrying conductors, the sum of currents flowing toward the junction is equal to the sum of currents flowing away from the junction. If the currents flowing away from the junction carry a reference positive sign, and the currents flowing toward the junction carry a negative sign, then the algebraic sum of currents at that junction is zero. Thus, for the junction shown in Fig. 1.31,

$$i_1 + i_2 - i_3 - i_4 = 0$$

Kirchhoff's voltage law states that starting from any junction of current conductors and tracing through any closed path such that we arrive back at the original junction, the algebraic sum of the voltages around the closed path is equal to zero. Thus, for the network in Fig. 1.32,

$$V_0 + V_1 + V_2 + V_3 = 0$$

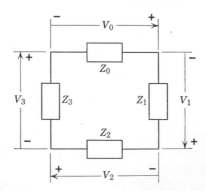

FIG. 1.32. Example for Kirchhoff's voltage law.

---

* G. Raisbeck, "A Definition of Passive Linear Networks in Terms of Time and Energy," *J. Appl. Phys.*, **25**, (Dec. 1954) 1510–1514.

Problems

1.1 Draw the line spectra for the signal

$$s(t) = 3 \sin \left(t + \frac{\pi}{4} \right) - 4 \sin \left(2t - \frac{\pi}{8} \right) + 6 \sin 3t$$

1.2 The magnitude and phase spectra for an ideal low-pass filter is given as

$$|H(j\omega)| = A, \quad |\omega| \leq |\omega_C|$$
$$= 0 \text{ elsewhere}$$
$$\theta(\omega) = -\omega_0 T$$

Draw the spectra.

1.3 Find the response to the excitation $\sin t$ into a *sampler* which closes every $K\pi/4$ seconds, where $K = 0, 1, 2, \cdots$. Draw the response for $0 \leq t \leq 2\pi$.

1.4 Find the response to the excitation shown in the figure when the network is: (*a*) an ideal differentiator; (*b*) an ideal integrator.

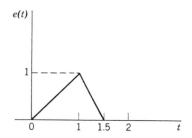

PROB. 1.4. Excitation signal.

1.5 If the current through a capacitor is given by

$$i(t) = 3e^{-2t}$$
$$i(0) = 3$$

find the voltage across the capacitor.

1.6 Discuss the significance of the variable x in the equation

$$i(t) = \frac{1}{L} \int_0^t v(x) \, dx + i(0)$$

1.7 If the system function of a network is given as

$$H(s) = \frac{1}{(s + 2)(s + 3)}$$

find the response $R(s)$ if the excitation is

$$E(s) = \frac{3}{s}$$

1.8   Given the driving-point functions

(a)
$$Z(s) = 3 + 2s + \frac{1}{3s}$$

(b)
$$Y(s) = 2s + \frac{3s}{s + 2}$$

(c)
$$Z(s) = 3 + \frac{s}{s^2 + 2}$$

(d)
$$Y(s) = \frac{1}{3s + 2} + \frac{1}{2}$$

find networks which correspond to the driving-point immittances.

1.9   The *Butterworth* low-pass filter has a normalized magnitude spectrum given by the equation

$$|H(j\omega)| = \frac{1}{(1 + \omega^{2n})^{\frac{1}{2}}}$$

Plot $|H(j\omega)|$ in the range $0 \leq \omega \leq 4$ for $n = 2, 4$.

chapter 2

Signals and waveforms

Our main concern in this chapter is the characterization of signals as functions of time and frequency. In previous studies we have dealt with d-c signals that were constant with time, or a-c signals which were sinusoids of constant amplitude such as $s(t) = A \sin(\omega t + \theta)$. In engineering practice, the class of signals encountered is substantially broader in scope than simple a-c or d-c signals. To attempt to characterize each member of the class is foolhardy in view of the almost infinite variety of signals encountered. Instead, we will deal only with those signals that can be characterized in simple mathematical terms and which serve as *building blocks* for a large number of other signals. We will concentrate on formulating analytical tools to aid us in describing signals, rather than deal with the representation of specific signals. In view of time and space limitations, we will cover only signals which do not exhibit random behavior, i.e., signals which can be explicitly characterized as functions of time. These signals are often referred to as *deterministic* signals. Let us first discuss certain qualitative aspects of signals in general.

2.1 GENERAL CHARACTERISTICS OF SIGNALS

In this section we will examine certain behavior patterns of signals. Once these patterns are established, signals can be classified accordingly, and some simplifications result. The adjectives which give a general qualitative description of a signal are *periodic*, *symmetrical*, and *continuous*. Let us discuss these terms in the given order.

First, signals are either *periodic* or *aperiodic*. If a signal is periodic, then it is described by the equation

$$s(t) = s(t \pm kT) \qquad k = 0, 1, 2, \cdots \qquad (2.1)$$

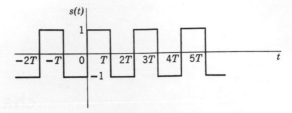

FIG. 2.1. Square wave.

where T is the period of the signal. The sine wave, $\sin t$, is periodic with period $T = 2\pi$. Another example of a periodic signal for $t \geq 0$ is the *square wave* given in Fig. 2.1. On the other hand, the signals given in Fig. 2.2 are aperiodic because the pulse patterns do not repeat after a certain finite interval T. Alternatively, these signals may be considered to be "periodic" with an infinite period.

Next, consider the symmetry properties of a signal. The key adjectives here are *even* and *odd*. A signal function can be even or odd, or neither. An even function obeys the relation

$$s(t) = s(-t) \tag{2.2}$$

For an odd function,

$$s(t) = -s(-t) \tag{2.3}$$

For example, the function $\sin t$ is odd, whereas $\cos t$ is even. The square pulse in Fig. 2.2a is even whereas the triangular pulse is odd (Fig. 2.2b).

Observe that a signal need not be even or odd. Two examples of signals of this type are shown in Figs. 2.3a and 2.4a. It is significant to note, however, that any signal $s(t)$ can be resolved into an even component $s_e(t)$ and an odd component $s_0(t)$ such that

$$s(t) = s_e(t) + s_0(t) \tag{2.4}$$

For example, the signals in Figs. 2.3a and 2.4a can be decomposed into odd and even components, as indicated in Figs. 2.3b, 2.3c, 2.4b, and 2.4c.

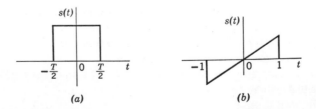

FIG. 2.2. (a) Even function. (b) Odd function.

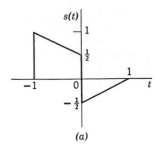

(a)

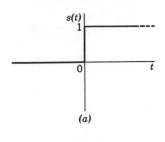

(a)

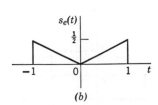

(b)

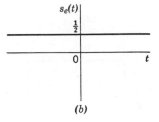

(b)

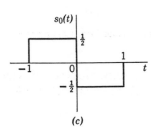

(c)

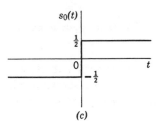

(c)

FIG. 2.3. Decomposition into odd and even components. (a) Original function. (b) Even part. (c) Odd part.

FIG. 2.4. Decomposition into even and odd components. (a) Unit step function. (b) Even part of unit step. (c) Odd part of unit step.

From Eq. 2.4 we observe that

$$s(-t) = s_e(-t) + s_0(-t)$$
$$= s_e(t) - s_0(t) \tag{2.5}$$

Consequently, the odd and even parts of the signal can be expressed as

$$s_e(t) = \tfrac{1}{2}[s(t) + s(-t)]$$
$$s_0(t) = \tfrac{1}{2}[s(t) - s(-t)] \tag{2.6}$$

Consider the signal $s(t)$, shown in Fig. 2.5a. The function $s(-t)$ is equal to $s(t)$ reflected about the $t = 0$ axis and is given in Fig. 2.5b. We then obtain $s_e(t)$ and $s_0(t)$ as outlined in Figs. 2.5c and d respectively.

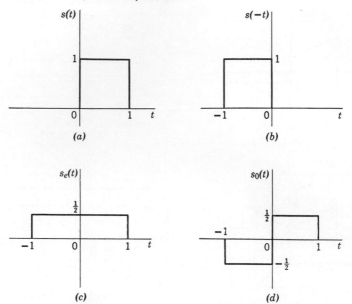

FIG. 2.5. Decomposition into odd and even components from $s(t)$ and $s(-t)$.

Now, let us turn out attention to the continuity property of signals. Consider the signal shown in Fig. 2.6. At $t = T$, the signal is *discontinuous*. The height of the discontinuity is

$$f(T+) - f(T-) = A \tag{2.7}$$

where

$$f(T+) = \lim_{\epsilon \to 0} f(T + \epsilon)$$

$$f(T-) = \lim_{\epsilon \to 0} f(T - \epsilon) \tag{2.8}$$

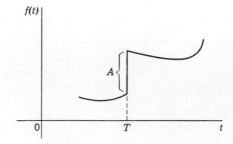

FIG. 2.6. Signal with discontinuity.

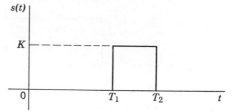

FIG. 2.7. Signal with two discontinuities.

and ϵ is a real positive quantity. In particular, we are concerned with discontinuities in the neighborhood of $t = 0$. From Eq. 2.8, the points $f(0+)$ and $f(0-)$ are

$$f(0+) = \lim_{\epsilon \to 0} f(\epsilon)$$
$$f(0-) = \lim_{\epsilon \to 0} f(-\epsilon)$$
(2.9)

For example, the square pulse in Fig. 2.7 has two discontinuities, at T_1 and T_2. The height of the discontinuity at T_1 is

$$s(T_1+) - s(T_1-) = K \tag{2.10}$$

Similarly, the height of the discontinuity at T_2 is $-K$.

2.2 THE STEP FUNCTION AND ASSOCIATED WAVEFORMS

The unit step function $u(t)$ shown in Fig. 2.8 is defined as

$$u(t) = 0 \qquad t < 0$$
$$= 1 \qquad t \geq 0$$
(2.11)

The physical analogy of a unit step excitation corresponds to a switch S which closes at $t = 0$ and connects a d-c battery of 1 volt to a given circuit, as shown in Fig. 2.9. Note that the unit step is zero whenever the argument (t)

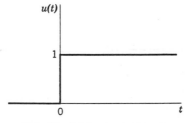

FIG. 2.8. Unit step function.

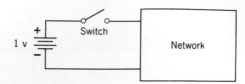

FIG. 2.9. Network analog of unit step.

within the parentheses is negative, and is unity when the argument (t) is greater than zero. Thus the function $u(t - a)$, where $a > 0$, is defined by

$$u(t - a) = 0 \qquad t < a$$
$$= 1 \qquad t \geq a \tag{2.12}$$

and is shown in Fig. 2.10. Note that the jump discontinuity of the step occurs when the argument within the parentheses is zero. This forms the basis of the *shifting* property of the step function. Also, the height of the jump discontinuity of the step can be scaled up or down by the multiplication of a constant K.

With the use of the change of amplitude and the shifting properties of the step function, we can proceed to construct a family of pulse waveforms. For example, the square pulse in Fig. 2.11 can be constructed by the sum of two step functions

$$s(t) = 4u(t - 1) + (-4)\,u(t - 2) \tag{2.13}$$

as given in Fig. 2.12. The "staircase" function shown in Fig. 2.13 is characterized by the equation

$$s(t) = \sum_{k=0}^{2} u(t - kT) \tag{2.14}$$

Finally, let us construct the square wave in Fig. 2.1. Using the shifting property, we see that the square wave is given by (for $t \geq 0$)

$$s(t) = u(t) - 2u(t - T) + 2u(t - 2T) - 2u(t - 3T) + \cdots \tag{2.15}$$

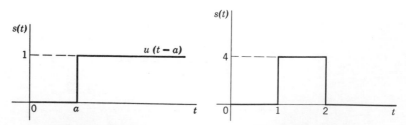

FIG. 2.10. Shifted step function.   **FIG. 2.11.** Square pulse.

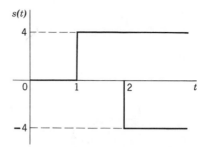

FIG. 2.12. Construction of square pulse by step function.

A simpler way to represent the square wave is obtained by using the property that the step function is zero whenever its argument is negative. Restricting ourselves to the interval $t \geq 0$, the function

$$s(t) = u\left(\sin \frac{\pi t}{T}\right) \tag{2.16}$$

is zero whenever $\sin (\pi t/T)$ is negative, as seen by the waveform in Fig. 2.14. It is now apparent that the square wave in Fig. 2.1 can be represented as

$$s(t) = u\left(\sin \frac{\pi t}{T}\right) - u\left(-\sin \frac{\pi t}{T}\right) \tag{2.17}$$

Another method of describing the square wave is obtained if we consider a generalization of the step function known as the *sgn function* (pronounced signum). The sgn function is defined as

$$\begin{aligned} \text{sgn}\,[f(t)] &= 1 & f(t) > 0 \\ &= 0 & f(t) = 0 \\ &= -1 & f(t) < 0 \end{aligned} \tag{2.18}$$

Thus the square wave in Fig. 2.1 is simply expressed as

$$s(t) = \text{sgn}\left(\sin \frac{\pi t}{T}\right) \tag{2.19}$$

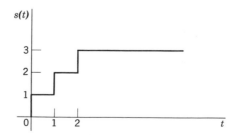

FIG. 2.13. Staircase function.

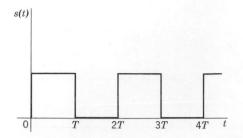

FIG. 2.14. The signal $u(\sin \pi t/T)$.

Returning to the shifting property of the step function, we see that the single sine pulse in Fig. 2.15 can be represented as

$$s(t) = \sin \frac{\pi t}{T} \left[u(t - 2T) - u(t - 3T) \right] \qquad (2.20)$$

The step function is also extremely useful in representing the shifted or delayed version of any given signal. For example, consider the *unit ramp function*,

$$\rho(t) = t \, u(t) \qquad (2.21)$$

shown in Fig. 2.16. Suppose the ramp is delayed by an amount $t = a$, as shown in Fig. 2.17. How do we represent the delayed version of ramp? First, let us replace the variable t by a new variable $t' = t - a$. Then

$$\rho(t') = t' \, u(t') \qquad (2.22)$$

When $\rho(t')$ is plotted against t', the resulting curve is identical to the plot of $s(t)$ versus t in Fig. 2.16. If, however, we substitute $t - a = t'$ in $\rho(t')$, we then have

$$\rho(t') = (t - a) \, u(t - a) \qquad (2.23)$$

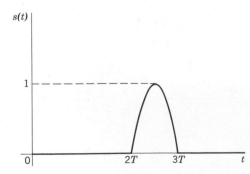

FIG. 2.15. Sine pulse.

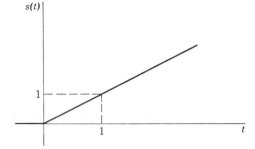

FIG. 2.16. Ramp function with zero time shift.

When we plot $\rho(t')$ against t, we have the delayed version of $\rho(t)$ shown in Fig. 2.17.

From the above discussion, it is clear that, if any signal $f(t)\,u(t)$ is delayed by a time T, the delayed or shifted signal is given by

$$f(t') = f(t - T)\,u(t - T) \qquad (2.24)$$

For example, let us delay the function $(\sin \pi t/T)\,u(t)$ by a period T. Then the delayed function $s(t')$, shown in Fig. 2.18, is

$$s(t') = \left[\sin \frac{\pi}{T}(t - T)\right] u(t - T) \qquad (2.25)$$

As a final example, consider the waveform in Fig. 2.19 whose component parts are given in Fig. 2.20. For increasing t, the first nonzero component is the function $2(t - 1)\,u(t - 1)$ which represents the straight line of slope 2 at $t = 1$. At $t = 2$, the rise of the straight line is to be arrested, so we add to the first component a term equal to $-2(t - 2)\,u(t - 2)$ with a slope of -2. The sum is then a constant equal to 2. We then add a term $-2u(t - 2)$ to bring the level down to zero. Thus,

$$s(t) = 2(t - 1)\,u(t - 1) - 2(t - 2)\,u(t - 2) - 2u(t - 2) \qquad (2.26)$$

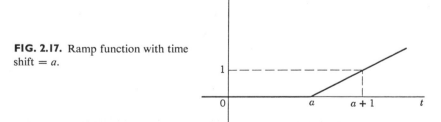

FIG. 2.17. Ramp function with time shift $= a$.

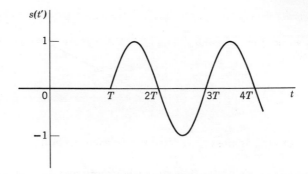

FIG. 2.18. Shifted sine wave.

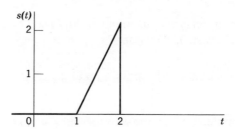

FIG. 2.19. Triangular pulse.

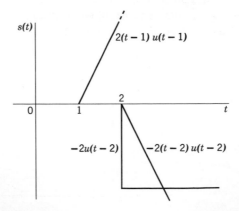

FIG. 2.20. Decomposition of the triangular pulse in Fig. 2.19.

2.3 THE RAMP AND IMPULSE FUNCTIONS

The integral of the unit step, known as the *unit ramp* function, is given by the equation,

$$\rho(t) = \int_0^t u(x)\, dx \tag{2.27}$$

From this integral definition of the ramp function, we obtain an alternative definition,

$$\begin{aligned} \rho(t) &= t; & t \geq 0 \\ &= 0; & t < 0 \end{aligned} \tag{2.28}$$

as plotted on Fig. 2.16. The ramp function possesses both the change of amplitude and time shift properties of the step. By multiplying the unit ramp by a constant K, we change the slope of the ramp function as given by the equation,

$$\begin{aligned} K\,\rho(t) &= Kt; & t \geq 0 \\ &= 0; & t < 0 \end{aligned} \tag{2.29}$$

If we delay the unit ramp by a units, as seen in Fig. 2.17, we can describe the shifted ramp as

$$s(t) = \rho(t - a) \tag{2.30}$$

From the previous section, we see that the unit ramp can also be written as

$$\rho(t) = t\, u(t) \tag{2.31}$$

and a delayed ramp of slope K can also be given as

$$s(t) = K(t - a)\, u(t - a) \tag{2.32}$$

We thus see that the formal definition of the ramp is of little practical value except to point out that the integral of a step function is a ramp function.

In contrast to the ramp function, the derivative of the unit step function known as the *unit impulse* or *delta* function is much more interesting. At first glance this statement is doubtful. After all, the derivative of the unit step is zero everywhere except at the jump discontinuity, and it does not even exist at that point! However, consider the function $g_\epsilon(t)$ in Fig. 2.21. It is clear that as ϵ goes to zero, $g_\epsilon(t)$ approaches a unit step function, i.e.,

$$\lim_{\epsilon \to 0} g_\epsilon(t) = u(t) \tag{2.33}$$

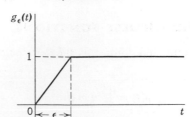

FIG. 2.21. Unit step when $\epsilon \to 0$.

Taking the derivative of $g_\epsilon(t)$, we obtain $g'_\epsilon(t)$ defined by the equations

$$
\begin{aligned}
g'_\epsilon(t) &= \frac{1}{\epsilon}; && 0 \le t \le \epsilon \\
&= 0; && t < 0, t > \epsilon
\end{aligned}
\tag{2.34}
$$

as shown in Fig. 2.22. Now let ϵ take on a sequence of values ϵ_i, such that $\epsilon_i > \epsilon_{i+1}$. Consider the sequence of functions $\{g'_{\epsilon_i}(t)\}$ for decreasing values of ϵ_i as shown in Fig. 2.23. The sequence has the following property:

$$
\lim_{\epsilon_i \to 0} \int_{t_1 < 0}^{t_2 > 0} g'_{\epsilon_i}(t)\, dt = 1
\tag{2.35}
$$

where t_1 and t_2 are arbitrary real numbers. For every nonzero value of ϵ, there corresponds a well-behaved function (i.e., it does not "blow up") $g'_{\epsilon_i}(t)$. As ϵ_i approaches zero,

$$
g'_{\epsilon_i}(0+) \underset{\epsilon_i \to 0}{\to} \infty
\tag{2.36}
$$

so that the limit of the sequence is not defined in the classical sense. Another sequence of functions which obeys the property given in Eq. 2.35 is the sequence $\{f_{\epsilon_i}(t)\}$ in Fig. 2.24. We now define the *unit impulse* $\delta(t)$ to be the class of all sequences of functions which obey Eq. 2.35. In particular, we define

$$
\delta(t) \triangleq \{g'_{\epsilon_i}(t)\} = \{f_{\epsilon_i}(t)\}
\tag{2.37}
$$

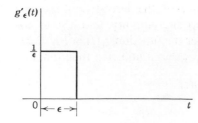

FIG. 2.22. Derivative of $g_\epsilon(t)$ in Fig. 2.21.

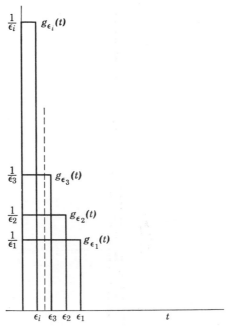

FIG. 2.23. The sequence $\{g_{\epsilon_i}(t)\}$.

The unit impulse as defined is thus any sequence of functions which obeys Eq. 2.35. For convenience, we will take the sequence of functions $\{g'_{\epsilon_i}(t)$ or $\{f_{\epsilon_i}(t)\}$ to be a "generalized function"* $\delta(t)$, which we will call the unit impulse or *impulse function*. The limit and integration process given in Eq. 2.35 can now be assigned a convenient symbolic representation in terms of the integral

$$\int_{t_1<0}^{t_2>0} \delta(t)\, dt = 1 \tag{2.38}$$

It must be emphasized that the functional representation of the unit impulse in Eq. 2.38 is more convenient than rigorous. Heuristically speaking, however, the unit impulse can be thought of as a "function" whose defining equation is Eq. 2.38 and which has the additional properties

$$\delta(0) = \infty$$
$$\delta(t \neq 0) = 0 \tag{2.39}$$

We see that the impulse "function" is equal to the limit as ϵ approaches zero of $g_\epsilon(t)$ in Eq. 2.34 and Fig. 2.22, i.e.,

$$\delta(t) = \lim_{\epsilon \to 0} g'_\epsilon(t) \tag{2.40}$$

---

* For a rigorous treatment of the unit impulse, see M. J. Lighthill, *Fourier Analysis and Generalized Functions*, Cambridge University Press, New York, 1959.

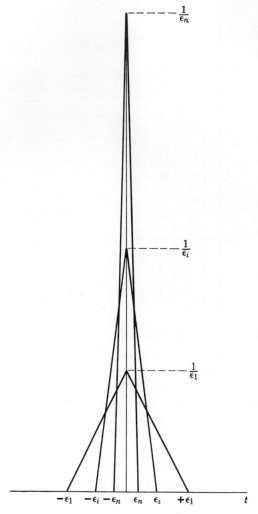

FIG. 2.24. The sequence $\{f_{\epsilon_i}(t)\}$.

From this discussion, we note that the derivative of the unit step function is the unit impulse.

Continuing with this heuristic treatment, we say that the area "under" the impulse is unity, and, since the impulse is zero for $t \neq 0$, we have

$$\int_{-\infty}^{\infty} \delta(t)\, dt = \int_{0-}^{0+} \delta(t)\, dt = 1 \tag{2.41}$$

Thus, the entire area of the impulse is "concentrated" at $t = 0$. Consequently, any integral that does not integrate through $t = 0$ is zero, as seen by

$$\int_{-\infty}^{0-} \delta(t)\, dt = \int_{0+}^{+\infty} \delta(t)\, dt = 0 \qquad (2.42)$$

The change of scale and time shift properties discussed earlier also apply for the impulse function. The derivative of a step function

$$s(t) = A\, u(t - a) \qquad (2.43)$$

yields an impulse function

$$s'(t) = A\, \delta(t - a) \qquad (2.44)$$

which is shown in Fig. 2.25. Graphically, we represent an impulse function by an arrowhead pointing upwards with the constant multiplier A written next to the arrowhead. Note that A is the area under the impulse $A\, \delta(t - a)$.

Consider the implications of Eqs. 2.43 and 2.44. From these equations we see that the derivative of the step at the jump discontinuity of height A yields an impulse of area A at that same point $t = T$. Generalizing on this argument, consider any function $f(t)$ with a jump discontinuity at $t = T$. Then the derivative, $f'(t)$ must have an impulse at $t = T$. As an example, consider $f(t)$ in Fig. 2.26. At $t = T$, $f(t)$ has a discontinuity of height A which is given as

$$A = f(T+) - f(T-) \qquad (2.45)$$

Let us define $f_1(t)$ to be equal to $f(t)$ for $t < T$, and to have the *same shape* as $f(t)$ but without the discontinuity for $t > T$, i.e.,

$$f_1(t) = f(t) - A\, u(t - T) \qquad (2.46)$$

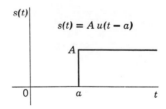

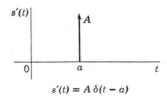

FIG. 2.25

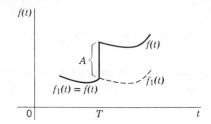

FIG. 2.26. Function with discontinuity at T.

The derivative, $f'(t)$ is then

$$f'(t) = f'_1(t) + A \, \delta(t - T) \qquad (2.47)$$

The following example will illustrate this point more clearly. In Fig. 2.27a, the function $f(t)$ is

$$f(t) = A \, u(t - a) - A \, u(t - b) \qquad (2.48)$$

Its derivative is

$$f'(t) = A \, \delta(t - a) - A \, \delta(t - b) \qquad (2.49)$$

and is shown in Fig. 2.27b. Since $f(t)$ has two discontinuities, at $t = a$ and $t = b$, its derivative must have impulses at those points. The coefficient of the impulse at $t = b$ is negative because

$$f(b+) - f(b-) = -A \qquad (2.50)$$

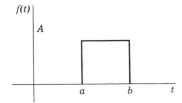

FIG. 2.27a. Square pulse.

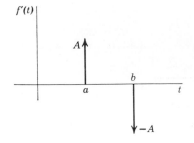

FIG. 2.27b. Derivative of square pulse.

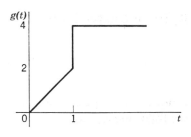

FIG. 2.28a. Signal.

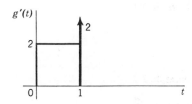

FIG. 2.28b. Derivative.

As a second example, consider the function $g(t)$ shown in Fig. 2.28a. We obtain $g'(t)$ by inspection, and note that the discontinuity at $t = 1$ produces the impulse in $g'(t)$ of area

$$g(1+) - g(1-) = 2, \qquad (2.51)$$

as given in Fig. 2.28b.

Another interesting property of the impulse function is expressed by the integral

$$\int_{-\infty}^{+\infty} f(t)\, \delta(t - T)\, dt = f(T) \qquad (2.52)$$

This integral is easily evaluated if we consider that $\delta(t - T) = 0$ for all $t \neq T$. Therefore, the product

$$f(t)\, \delta(t - T) = 0 \qquad \text{all } t \neq T \qquad (2.53)$$

If $f(t)$ is single-valued at $t = T$, $f(T)$ can be factored from the integral so that we obtain

$$f(T) \int_{-\infty}^{\infty} \delta(t - T)\, dt = f(T) \qquad (2.54)$$

Figure 2.29 shows $f(t)$ and $\delta(t - T)$, where $f(t)$ is continuous at $t = T$.

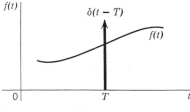

FIG. 2.29

If $f(t)$ has a discontinuity at $t = T$, then the integral

$$\int_{-\infty}^{+\infty} f(t)\,\delta(t - T)\,dt$$

is not defined because the value of $f(T)$ is not uniquely given. Consider the following examples.

Example 2.1

$$f(t) = e^{j\omega t}$$

$$\int_{-\infty}^{+\infty} e^{j\omega t}\,\delta(t - T)\,dt = e^{j\omega T} \tag{2.55}$$

Example 2.2

$$f(t) = \sin t$$

$$\int_{-\infty}^{+\infty} \sin t\,\delta\left(t - \frac{\pi}{4}\right) dt = \frac{1}{\sqrt{2}} \tag{2.56}$$

Consider next the case where $f(t)$ is continuous for $-\infty < t < \infty$. Let us direct our attention to the integral

$$\int_{-\infty}^{\infty} f(t)\,\delta(t - T)\,dt = f(T) \tag{2.57}$$

which holds for all t in this case. Now, if T were varied from $-\infty$ to $+\infty$, then $f(t)$ would be reproduced in its entirety. An operation of this sort corresponds to *scanning* the function $f(t)$ by moving a sheet of paper with a thin slit across a plot of the function, as shown in Fig. 2.30.

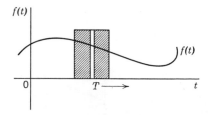

FIG. 2.30. Impulse scanning.

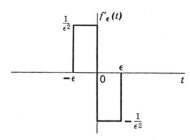

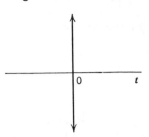

FIG. 2.31. Unit doublet as $\epsilon \to 0$.   **FIG. 2.32.** The doublet $\delta'(t)$.

Let us now examine higher order derivatives of the unit step function. Here we will represent the unit impulse by the function $f_\epsilon(t)$ in Fig. 2.24 which, as $\epsilon \to 0$, becomes the unit impulse. The derivative of $f_\epsilon(t)$ is given in Fig. 2.31. As ϵ approaches zero, $f'_\epsilon(t)$ approaches the derivative of the unit impulse $\delta'(t)$, which consists of a pair of impulses as seen in Fig. 2.32. The area under $\delta'(t)$, which is sometimes called a *doublet*, is equal to zero. Thus

$$\int_{-\infty}^{\infty} \delta'(t)\, dt = 0 \tag{2.58}$$

The other significant property of the doublet is

$$\int_{-\infty}^{\infty} f(t)\, \delta'(t - T)\, dt = -f'(T) \tag{2.59}$$

where $f'(T)$ is the derivative of $f(t)$ evaluated at $t = T$ where, again, we assume that $f(t)$ is continuous. Equation 2.59 can be proved by integration by parts. Thus,

$$\int_{-\infty}^{\infty} f(t)\, \delta'(t - T)\, dt = f(t)\, \delta(t - T)\Big|_{-\infty}^{\infty} - \int_{-\infty}^{\infty} f'(t)\, \delta(t - T)\, dt$$
$$= -f'(T). \tag{2.60}$$

It can be shown in general that

$$\int_{-\infty}^{\infty} f(t)\, \delta^{(n)}(t - T)\, dt = (-1)^n f^{(n)}(T) \tag{2.61}$$

where $\delta^{(n)}$ and $f^{(n)}$ denote nth derivatives. The higher order derivatives of $\delta(t)$ can be evaluated in similar fashion.

2.4 FOURIER SERIES AND ORTHOGONAL FUNCTIONS

One of the most common classes of signals encountered are periodic signals. If T is the period of the signal, then

$$s(t) = s(t \pm nT) \qquad n = 0, 1, 2, \cdots \tag{2.62}$$

In addition to being periodic, if $s(t)$ has only a finite number of discontinuities in any finite period and if the integral

$$\int_{\alpha}^{\alpha + T} |s(t)| \, dt$$

is finite (where α is an arbitrary real number), then $s(t)$ can be expanded into the infinite trigonometric series,

$$
s(t) = \frac{a_0}{2} + a_1 \cos \omega t + a_2 \cos 2\omega t + \cdots
$$
$$
+ b_1 \sin \omega t + b_2 \sin 2\omega t + \cdots \tag{2.63}
$$

where $\omega = 2\pi/T$. This trigonometric series is generally referred to as the *Fourier series*. In compact form, the Fourier series is

$$s(t) = \frac{a_0}{2} + \sum_{n=1}^{\infty} a_n \cos n\omega t + b_n \sin n\omega t \tag{2.64}$$

It is apparent from Eqs. 2.63 and 2.64 that, when $s(t)$ is expanded in a Fourier series, we can describe $s(t)$ completely in terms of the coefficients of its harmonic terms, $a_0, a_1, a_2, \cdots, b_1, b_2, \cdots$. These coefficients constitute a *frequency domain* description of the signal. Our task now is to derive the equations for the coefficients a_i, b_i in terms of the given signal function $s(t)$. Let us first discuss the mathematical basis of Fourier series, the theory of *orthogonal sets*.

Consider any two real functions $f_1(t)$ and $f_2(t)$ which are not identically zero. Then, if

$$\int_{T_1}^{T_2} f_1(t) f_2(t) \, dt = 0 \tag{2.65}$$

we say that $f_1(t)$ and $f_2(t)$ are *orthogonal* over the interval $T_1 \leq t \leq T_2$. For example, the functions $\sin \omega t$ and $\cos \omega t$ are orthogonal over the interval $\alpha \leq t \leq \alpha + T$ (where α is an arbitrary real number and T is the period of both functions). Consider next a set of real functions $\{\phi_1(t), \phi_2(t), \cdots, \phi_n(t)\}$. If the functions obey the condition

$$\int_{T_1}^{T_2} \phi_i(t) \, \phi_j(t) \, dt = 0, \quad i \neq j \tag{2.66}$$

then the set $\{\phi_i(t)\}$ forms an *orthogonal set* over the interval $[T_1, T_2]$. Moreover, if

$$\int_{T_1}^{T_2} \phi_i(t)\, \phi_j(t)\, dt = 0 \qquad i \neq j$$

$$= 1 \qquad i = j \qquad (2.67)$$

the set is *orthonormal* over the interval. For example, the set $\{1, \sin \omega t, \sin 2\omega t, \cdots, \cos \omega t, \cos 2\omega t, \cos 3\omega t, \cdots\}$ is an orthogonal set in the interval $[\alpha, \alpha + T]$ because

$$\int_{\alpha}^{\alpha+T} \cos n\omega t \cos m\omega t\, dt = \frac{T}{2} \qquad n = m$$

$$= 0 \qquad n \neq m \qquad (2.68)$$

$$\int_{\alpha}^{\alpha+T} \sin n\omega t \sin m\omega t\, dt = \frac{T}{2} \qquad n = m$$

$$= 0 \qquad n \neq m \qquad (2.69)$$

All the following cross terms integrate to zero.

$$\int_{\alpha}^{\alpha+T} \cos n\omega t \sin m\omega t\, dt = 0 \qquad \text{all } n, m \qquad (2.70)$$

$$\int_{\alpha}^{\alpha+T} \sin n\omega t\, dt = 0$$

$$\int_{\alpha}^{\alpha+T} \cos n\omega t\, dt = 0 \qquad (2.71)$$

This orthogonal set can be made orthonormal by dividing all sine and cosine terms by $(T/2)^{1/2}$, and dividing the unity term by $(T)^{1/2}$. In general, we can normalize any orthogonal set $\{\phi_1, \phi_2, \cdots, \phi_n\}$ by dividing each term ϕ_i by its norm,

$$\left[\int_{T_1}^{T_2} \phi_i{}^2(t)\, dt \right]^{1/2}$$

For the example just considered, the norm of a term $\cos m\omega t$, is equal to $(T/2)^{1/2}$. The last example also shows that the individual terms of the Fourier series in Eq. 2.63 form an orthogonal set!

With this knowledge of orthogonal sets, we can proceed to derive the equations of the Fourier coefficients in terms of the function $s(t)$. Referring back to the Fourier series in Eq. 2.64, let us multiply both sides of the equation by cos $m\omega t$ and integrate both sides between the limits α and $\alpha + T$ (where α is any real, finite number). Then we obtain

$$\int_\alpha^{\alpha+T} s(t) \cos m\omega t \, dt = \frac{a_0}{2} \int_\alpha^{T+\alpha} \cos m\omega t \, dt$$

$$+ \sum_{n=1}^\infty a_n \int_\alpha^{T+\alpha} \cos n\omega t \cos m\omega t \, dt$$

$$+ \sum_{n=1}^\infty b_n \int_\alpha^{T+\alpha} \sin n\omega t \sin m\omega t \, dt \quad (2.72)$$

Equation 2.72 is simplified by taking note of the orthogonality conditions in the last example, and we obtain,

$$a_n = \frac{2}{T} \int_\alpha^{\alpha+T} s(t) \cos n\omega t \, dt \quad (2.73)$$

When $n = 0$,

$$a_0 = \frac{2}{T} \int_\alpha^{\alpha+T} s(t) \, dt \quad (2.74)$$

Similarly, if we multiply the Fourier series by $\sin m\omega t$ and integrate, we obtain

$$b_n = \frac{2}{T} \int_\alpha^{\alpha+T} s(t) \sin n\omega t \, dt \quad (2.75)$$

As an example, let us determine the Fourier coefficients of the fully rectified sine wave in Fig. 2.33. As we observe, the period is $T = \pi$ so that the fundamental frequency is $\omega = 2$. The signal is given as

$$s(t) = A \, | \sin t | \quad (2.76)$$

Let us take $\alpha = 0$ and evaluate between 0 and π. Using the formula just derived,

$$b_n = \frac{2A}{\pi} \int_0^\pi s(t) \sin 2nt \, dt = 0 \quad (2.77)$$

$$a_0 = \frac{2A}{\pi} \int_0^\pi \sin t \, dt = \frac{4A}{\pi} \quad (2.78)$$

$$a_n = \frac{2A}{\pi} \int_0^\pi s(t) \cos 2nt \, dt$$

$$= \frac{1}{1 - 4n^2} \frac{4A}{\pi} \quad (2.79)$$

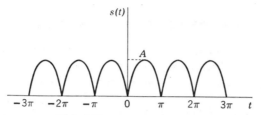

FIG. 2.33. Rectified sine wave.

Thus the Fourier series of the rectified sine wave is

$$s(t) = \frac{4A}{2\pi}\left(1 + \sum_{n=1}^{\infty} \frac{2}{1 - 4n^2} \cos 2nt\right) \tag{2.80}$$

As we have observed, the Fourier series is an infinite series. Since infinite series are cumbersome to use, especially if the coefficients of the higher harmonic terms are very very small, practicability dictates that the series be truncated at a given harmonic $k\omega$. All harmonic terms above $k\omega$ are then discarded. We then have a *finite* series,

$$s_k(t) = \frac{a_0}{2} + \sum_{n=1}^{k} a_n \cos n\omega t + b_n \sin n\omega t \tag{2.81}$$

The question then arises, if only a finite number of terms are used, can the coefficients be chosen more advantageously? Let us consider a criterion for choosing the *optimal* set of coefficients for the finite Fourier series $s_k(t)$. After we truncate at the $k\omega$th harmonic, we are confronted with the following approximation problem. The error between the original signal $s(t)$ and the truncated series $s_k(t)$ is

$$\epsilon(t) = s(t) - s_k(t) \tag{2.82}$$

Let us square this error term to eliminate the change in sign and then integrate this squared error between the limits $[\alpha, \alpha + T]$. We now have a measure of the *total* approximation error

$$\epsilon_k = \int_{\alpha}^{\alpha+T} [s(t) - s_k(t)]^2 \, dt \tag{2.83}$$

where ϵ_k is referred to as the *integral squared error*. Now we must choose the coefficients of the truncated Fourier series to minimize the integral squared error ϵ_k. Without going into the details of the proof,* we can show from our knowledge of orthogonal sets that the optimal set of coefficients for the truncated series are precisely the coefficients of the infinite series! This property of Fourier series is generally known as the *least squares* property which stands for *least integral squared error*.

* For a detailed proof, see E. A. Guillemin, *Mathematics of Circuit Analysis*, John Wiley & Sons, New York, 1949, pp. 482–485.

2.5 EVALUATION OF FOURIER COEFFICIENTS

In this section we will consider two other useful forms of Fourier series. In addition, we will discuss a number of methods to simplify the evaluation of Fourier coefficients. First, let us examine how the evaluation of coefficients is simplified by symmetry considerations. From Eqs. 2.73–2.75, which give the general formulas for the Fourier coefficients, let us take $\alpha = -T/2$ and represent the integrals as the sum of two separate parts, i.e.,

$$a_n = \frac{2}{T}\left[\int_0^{T/2} s(t)\cos n\omega t\,dt + \int_{-T/2}^0 s(t)\cos n\omega t\,dt\right]$$

$$b_n = \frac{2}{T}\left[\int_0^{T/2} s(t)\sin n\omega t\,dt + \int_{-T/2}^0 s(t)\sin n\omega t\,dt\right]$$

$$(2.84)$$

Since the variable (t) in the above integrals is a dummy variable, let us substitute $x = t$ in the integrals with limits $(0;\ T/2)$ and let $x = -t$ in the integrals with limits $(-T/2;\ 0)$. Then we have

$$a_n = \frac{2}{T}\int_0^{T/2}[s(x) + s(-x)]\cos n\omega x\,dx$$

$$b_n = \frac{2}{T}\int_0^{T/2}[s(x) - s(-x)]\sin n\omega x\,dx$$

$$(2.85)$$

Suppose now the function is odd, i.e., $s(x) = -s(-x)$, then we see that $a_n = 0$ for all n, and

$$b_n = \frac{4}{T}\int_0^{T/2} s(x)\sin n\omega x\,dx \qquad (2.86)$$

This implies that, if a function is odd, its Fourier series will contain only sine terms. On the other hand, suppose the function is even, i.e., $s(x) = s(-x)$, then $b_n = 0$ and

$$a_n = \frac{4}{T}\int_0^{T/2} s(x)\cos n\omega x\,dx \qquad (2.87)$$

Consequently, the Fourier series of an even function will contain only cosine terms.

Suppose next, the function $s(t)$ obeys the condition

$$s\left(t \pm \frac{T}{2}\right) = -s(t) \qquad (2.88)$$

as given by the example in Fig. 2.34. Then we can show that $s(t)$ contains only odd harmonic terms, i.e.,

$$a_n = b_n = 0; \qquad n\ \text{even}$$

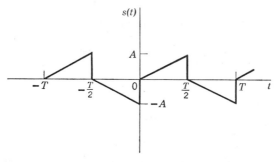

FIG. 2.34

and

$$a_n = \frac{4}{T} \int_0^{T/2} s(t) \cos n\omega t \, dt$$

$$b_n = \frac{4}{T} \int_0^{T/2} s(t) \sin n\omega t \, dt, \qquad n \text{ odd}$$

(2.89)

With this knowledge of symmetry conditions, let us examine how we can approximate an arbitrary time function $s(t)$ by a Fourier series within an interval $[0, T]$. Outside this interval, the Fourier series $s_n(t)$ is not required to fit $s(t)$. Consider the signal $s(t)$ in Fig. 2.35. We can approximate $s(t)$ by any of the periodic functions shown in Fig. 2.36. Observe that each periodic waveform exhibits some sort of symmetry.

Now let us consider two other useful forms of Fourier series. The first is the *Fourier cosine series* which is based upon the trigonometric identity,

$$C_n \cos (n\omega t + \theta_n) = C_n \cos n\omega t \cos \theta_n - C_n \sin n\omega t \sin \theta_n \quad (2.90)$$

We can derive the form of the Fourier cosine series by setting

$$a_n = C_n \cos \theta_n \qquad (2.91)$$

and

$$b_n = -C_n \sin \theta_n \qquad (2.92)$$

FIG. 2.35. Signal to be approximated.

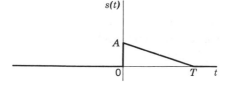

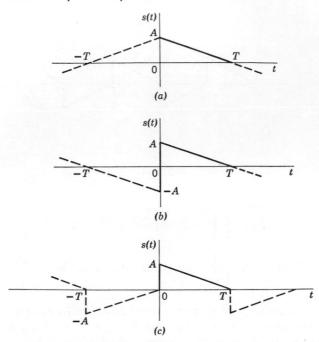

FIG. 2.36. (a) Even function cosine terms only. (b) Odd function sine terms only. (c) Odd harmonics only with both sine and cosine terms.

We then obtain C_n and θ_n in terms of a_n and b_n as

$$C_n = (a_n{}^2 + b_n{}^2)^{1/2}$$
$$C_0 = \frac{a_0}{2} \tag{2.93}$$
$$\theta_n = \tan^{-1}\left(-\frac{b_n}{a_n}\right)$$

If we combine the cosine and sine terms of each harmonic in the original series, we readily obtain from Eqs. 2.90–2.93 the Fourier cosine series

$$f(t) = C_0 + C_1 \cos(\omega t + \theta_1) + C_2 \cos(2\omega t + \theta_2)$$
$$+ C_3 \cos(3\omega t + \theta_3) + \cdots + C_n \cos(n\omega t + \theta_n) + \cdots \tag{2.94}$$

It should be noted that the coefficients C_n are usually taken to be positive. If, however, a term such as $-3 \cos 2\omega t$ carries a negative sign, then we can use the equivalent form

$$-3 \cos 2\omega t = 3 \cos(2\omega t + \pi) \tag{2.95}$$

For example, the Fourier series of the fully rectified sine wave in Fig. 2.33 was shown to be

$$s(t) = \frac{4A}{2\pi} \left(1 + \sum_{n=1}^{\infty} \frac{2}{1 - 4n^2} \cos 2nt \right) \tag{2.96}$$

Expressed as a Fourier cosine series, $s(t)$ is

$$s(t) = \frac{4A}{2\pi} \left[1 + \sum_{n=1}^{\infty} \frac{2}{4n^2 - 1} \cos (2nt + \pi) \right] \tag{2.97}$$

Next we consider the *complex form* of a Fourier series. If we express $\cos n\omega t$ and $\sin n\omega t$ in terms of complex exponentials, then the Fourier series can be written as

$$s(t) = \frac{a_0}{2} + \sum_{n=1}^{\infty} \left[a_n \left(\frac{e^{jn\omega t} + e^{-jn\omega t}}{2} \right) + b_n \left(\frac{e^{jn\omega t} - e^{-jn\omega t}}{2j} \right) \right]$$

$$= \frac{a_0}{2} + \sum_{n=1}^{\infty} \left[\left(\frac{a_n - jb_n}{2} \right) e^{jn\omega t} + \left(\frac{a_n + jb_n}{2} \right) e^{-jn\omega t} \right] \tag{2.98}$$

If we define

$$\beta_n = \frac{a_n - jb_n}{2}, \qquad \beta_{-n} = \frac{a_n + jb_n}{2}, \qquad \beta_0 = \frac{a_0}{2} \tag{2.99}$$

then the complex form of the Fourier series is

$$s(t) = \beta_0 + \sum_{n=1}^{\infty} (\beta_n e^{jn\omega t} + \beta_{-n} e^{-jn\omega t})$$

$$= \sum_{n=-\infty}^{\infty} \beta_n e^{jn\omega t} \tag{2.100}$$

We can readily express the coefficient β_n as a function of $s(t)$, since

$$\beta_n = \frac{a_n - jb_n}{2}$$

$$= \frac{1}{T} \int_0^T s(t)(\cos n\omega t - j \sin n\omega t) \, dt$$

$$= \frac{1}{T} \int_0^T s(t) e^{-jn\omega t} \, dt \tag{2.101}$$

Equation 2.101 is sometimes called the *discrete Fourier transform* of $s(t)$ and Eq. 2.100 is the *inverse transform* of $\beta_n(n\omega) = \beta_n$.

Observe that β_n is usually complex and can be represented as

$$\beta_n = \operatorname{Re} \beta_n + j \operatorname{Im} \beta_n \tag{2.102}$$

The real part of β_n, Re β_n, is obtained from Eq. 2.101 as

$$\text{Re } \beta_n = \frac{1}{T} \int_0^T s(t) \cos n\omega t \, dt \tag{2.103}$$

and the imaginary part of β_n is

$$j \text{ Im } \beta_n = \frac{j}{T} \int_0^T s(t) \sin n\omega t \, dt \tag{2.104}$$

It is clear that Re β_n is an even function in n, whereas Im β_n is an odd function in n. Thus, the *amplitude spectrum* of the Fourier series is defined as

$$|\beta_n| = (\text{Re}^2 \beta_n + \text{Im}^2 \beta_n)^{\frac{1}{2}} \tag{2.105}$$

and the *phase spectrum* is defined as

$$\phi_n = \arctan \left(\frac{\text{Im } \beta_n}{\text{Re } \beta_n} \right) \tag{2.106}$$

It is easily seen that the amplitude spectrum is an even function and the phase spectrum is an odd function in n. The amplitude spectrum provides us with valuable insight as to where to *truncate* the infinite series and still maintain a good approximation to the original waveform. From a plot of the amplitude spectrum, we can almost pick out by inspection the non-trivial terms in the series. For the amplitude spectrum in Fig. 2.37, we see that a good approximation could be obtained if we disregard any harmonic above the third.

As an example, let us obtain the complex Fourier coefficients for the square wave in Fig. 2.38. Let us also find the amplitude and phase spectra of the square wave. From Fig. 2.38, we note that $s(t)$ is an odd function. Moreover, since $s(t - T/2) = -s(t)$, the series has only odd harmonics. From Eq. 2.101 we obtain the coefficients of the complex Fourier series as

$$\beta_n = \frac{1}{T} \int_0^{T/2} A e^{-jn\omega t} \, dt - \frac{1}{T} \int_{T/2}^T A e^{-jn\omega t} \, dt$$

$$= \frac{A}{jn\omega T} (1 - 2e^{-(jn\omega T/2)} + e^{-jn\omega T}) \tag{2.107}$$

Since $n\omega T = n2\pi$, β_n can be simplified to

$$\beta_n = \frac{A}{j2n\pi} (1 - 2e^{-jn\pi} + e^{-j2n\pi}) \tag{2.108}$$

Simplifying β_n one step further, we obtain

$$\beta_n = \frac{2A}{jn\pi} \qquad n \text{ odd}$$

$$= 0 \qquad n \text{ even} \tag{2.109}$$

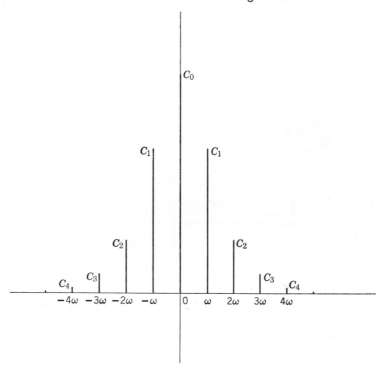

FIG. 2.37. Amplitude spectrum.

The amplitude and phase spectra of the square wave are given in Fig. 2.39. Now we make use of a basic property of impulse functions to simplify the calculation of complex Fourier coefficients. This method is restricted to functions which are made up of *straight-line components* only. We see that the method applies for the square wave in Fig. 2.38 and does not apply for the rectified sine wave in Fig. 2.33. The method is based

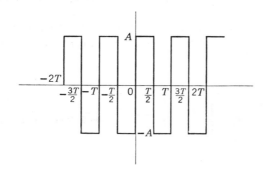

FIG. 2.38. Square wave.

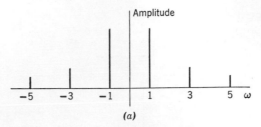

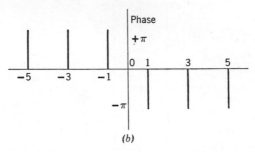

FIG. 2.39. Discrete spectra of square wave. (a) Amplitude. (b) Phase.

upon the relation,

$$\int_{-\infty}^{\infty} f(t)\, \delta(t - T_1)\, dt = f(T_1) \tag{2.110}$$

Let us use this equation to evaluate the complex Fourier coefficients for the impulse train in Fig. 2.40. Using Eq. 2.110 with $f(t) = e^{-jn\omega t}$, we have

$$\beta_n = \frac{A}{T} \int_0^T \delta\left(t - \frac{T}{2}\right) e^{-jn\omega t}\, dt = \frac{A}{T} e^{-(jn\omega T/2)} \tag{2.111}$$

We see that the complex Fourier coefficients for impulse functions are obtained by simply substituting the time at which the impulses occur into the expression, $e^{-jn\omega t}$.

In the evaluation of Fourier coefficients, we must remember that the limits for the β_n integral are taken over *one period* only, i.e., we consider

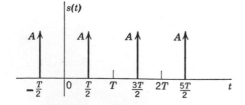

FIG. 2.40. Impulse train.

only a single period of the signal in the analysis. Consider, as an example, the square wave in Fig. 2.38. To evaluate β_n, we consider only a single period of the square wave, say, from $t = 0$ to $t = T$, as shown in Fig. 2.41a. Since the square wave is not made up of impulses, let us differentiate the single period of the square wave to give $s'(t)$ as shown in Fig. 2.41b. We can now evaluate the complex Fourier coefficients for the derivative $s'(t)$, which clearly is made up of impulses alone. Analytically, if $s(t)$ is given as

$$s(t) = \sum_{n=-\infty}^{\infty} \beta_n e^{jn\omega t} \tag{2.112}$$

then the derivative of $s(t)$ is

$$s'(t) = \sum_{n=-\infty}^{\infty} jn\omega \beta_n e^{jn\omega t} \tag{2.113}$$

Here, we define a new complex coefficient

$$\gamma_n = jn\omega \beta_n \tag{2.114}$$

or

$$\beta_n = \frac{\gamma_n}{jn\omega} \tag{2.115}$$

FIG. 2.41a. Square wave over period $[0, T]$.

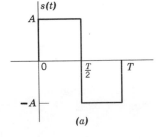

(a)

FIG. 2.41b. Derivative of square wave over period $[0, T]$.

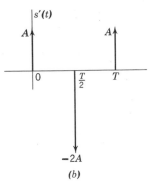

(b)

If the derivative $s'(t)$ is a function which consists of impulse components alone, then we simply evaluate γ_n first and then obtain β_n from Eq. 2.115. For example, the derivative of the square wave yields the impulse train in Fig. 2.41b. In the interval $[0, T]$, the signal $s'(t)$ is given as

$$s'(t) = A\,\delta(t) - 2A\,\delta\left(t - \frac{T}{2}\right) + A\,\delta(t - T) \qquad (2.116)$$

Then the complex coefficients are

$$\gamma_n = \frac{A}{T}\int_0^T s'(t)e^{-jn\omega t}\,dt$$

$$= \frac{A}{T}(1 - 2e^{-(jn\omega T/2)} + e^{-jn\omega T}) \qquad (2.117)$$

The Fourier coefficients of the square wave are

$$\beta_n = \frac{\gamma_n}{jn\omega}$$

$$= \frac{A}{jn\omega T}(1 - 2e^{-(jn\omega T/2)} + e^{-jn\omega T}) \qquad (2.118)$$

which checks with the solution obtained in the standard way in Eq. 2.107.

If the first derivative, $s'(t)$, does not contain impulses, then we must differentiate again to yield

$$s''(t) = \sum_{n=-\infty}^{\infty} \lambda_n e^{jn\omega t} \qquad (2.119)$$

where

$$\lambda_n = jn\omega\gamma_n = (jn\omega)^2\beta_n \qquad (2.120)$$

For the triangular pulse in Fig. 2.42, the second derivative over the period $[0, T]$ is

$$s''(t) = \frac{2A}{T}\left[\delta(t) - 2\delta\left(t - \frac{T}{2}\right) + \delta(t - T)\right] \qquad (2.121)$$

The coefficients λ_n are now obtained as

$$\lambda_n = \frac{1}{T}\int_0^T s''(t)e^{-jn\omega t}\,dt$$

$$= \frac{2A}{T^2}(1 - 2e^{-(jn\omega T/2)} + e^{-jn\omega T}) \qquad (2.122)$$

which simplifies to give

$$\lambda_n = \frac{8A}{T^2} \qquad n \text{ odd}$$

$$= 0 \qquad n \text{ even} \qquad (2.123)$$

From λ_n we obtain

$$\beta_n = \frac{\lambda_n}{(j\omega n)^2}$$

$$= -\frac{2A}{n^2\pi^2} \qquad n \text{ odd}$$

$$= 0 \qquad n \text{ even} \qquad (2.124)$$

A slight difficulty arises if the expression for $s'(t)$ contains an impulse in addition to other straight-line terms. Because of these straight-line terms we must differentiate once more. However, from this additional differentiation, we obtain the derivative of the impulse as well. This presents no difficulty, however, because we know from Eq. 2.59 that

$$\int_{-\infty}^{\infty} s(t)\,\delta'(t - T) = -s'(T) \qquad (2.125)$$

so that

$$\int_{-\infty}^{\infty} \delta'(t - T)e^{-jn\omega t}\,dt = jn\omega e^{-jn\omega T} \qquad (2.126)$$

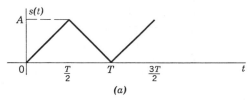

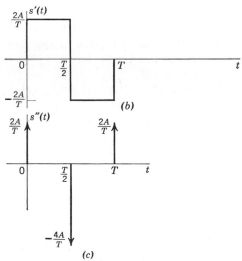

FIG. 2.42. The triangular wave and its derivatives.

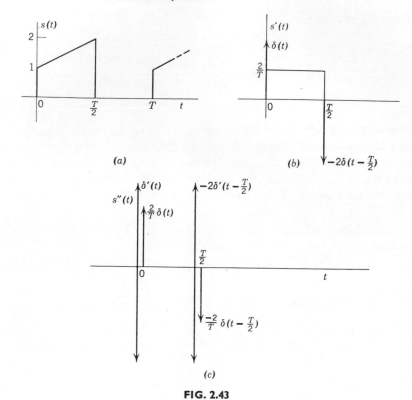

FIG. 2.43

We can therefore tolerate doublets or even higher derivatives of impulses in the analysis. Consider the signal $s(t)$ given in Fig. 2.43a. Its derivative $s'(t)$, shown in Fig. 2.43b, can be expressed as

$$s'(t) = \frac{2}{T}\left[u(t) - u\left(t - \frac{T}{2}\right)\right] + \delta(t) - 2\delta\left(t - \frac{T}{2}\right) \qquad (2.127)$$

The second derivative $s''(t)$ consists of a pair of impulses and a pair of doublets as given by

$$s''(t) = \frac{2}{T}\left[\delta(t) - \delta\left(t - \frac{T}{2}\right)\right] + \delta'(t) - 2\delta'\left(t - \frac{T}{2}\right) \qquad (2.128)$$

as shown in Fig. 2.43c. We therefore evaluate λ_n as

$$\lambda_n = \frac{1}{T}\int_0^T s''(t)e^{-jn\omega t}\, dt$$

$$= \frac{2}{T^2}(1 - e^{-(jn\omega T/2)}) + \frac{j\omega n}{T}(1 - 2e^{-(jn\omega T/2)}) \qquad (2.129)$$

The complex coefficients β_n are now obtained as

$$\beta_n = \frac{\lambda_n}{(j\omega n)^2}$$

$$= \frac{2}{(j\omega n T)^2}(1 - e^{-(jn\omega T/2)}) + \frac{1}{j\omega n T}(1 - 2e^{-(jn\omega T/2)}) \qquad (2.130)$$

Simplifying, we have

$$\beta_n = -\frac{1}{n^2\pi^2} + \frac{3}{j2\pi n} \qquad n \text{ odd}$$

$$= -\frac{1}{j2\pi n} \qquad n \text{ even} \qquad (2.131)$$

In conclusion, it must be pointed out that the method of using impulses to evaluate Fourier coefficients does not give the d-c coefficient, $a_0/2$ or β_0. We obtain this coefficient through standard methods as given by Eq. 2.74.

2.6 THE FOURIER INTEGRAL

In this section we shall extend our analysis of signals to the aperiodic case. We will show through a plausibility argument that, generally, aperiodic signals have continuous amplitude and phase spectra.* In Section 2.5, the complex coefficient β_n for periodic signals was called the discrete Fourier transform,

$$\beta(n\omega) = \frac{1}{T}\int_{-T/2}^{T/2} f(t)e^{-jn\omega t}\, dt \qquad (2.132)$$

and the inverse (discrete) transform was

$$f(t) = \sum_{n=-\infty}^{\infty} \beta_n e^{+jn\omega t} \qquad (2.133)$$

From the discrete Fourier transform $\beta(n\omega)$, we obtain amplitude and phase spectra which consist of discrete lines. The spacing between adjacent lines in the spectrum is given as

$$\Delta\omega = (n + 1)\omega_0 - n\omega_0 = \frac{2\pi}{T} \qquad (2.134)$$

where T is the period of the signal and ω_0 is the fundamental frequency.

---

* The rigorous proof is given in R. V. Churchill, *Fourier Series and Boundary Value Problems*, McGraw-Hill Book Co., New York, 1941, pp. 88–92.

As the period T becomes larger, the spacing between the harmonic lines in the spectrum becomes smaller. For aperiodic signals, we let T approach ∞ in the limit, so that the discrete spectrum becomes *continuous*. We now define the continuous *Fourier transform* to be

$$F(j\omega) = \lim_{\substack{T \to \infty \\ \Delta\omega \to 0}} 2\pi \left[\frac{\beta(n\omega_0)}{\omega_0} \right]$$

$$= \int_{-\infty}^{\infty} f(t)e^{-j\omega t}\, dt \tag{2.135}$$

The inverse transform is

$$f(t) = \frac{1}{2\pi} \int_{-\infty}^{\infty} F(j\omega)e^{j\omega t}\, d\omega \tag{2.136}$$

Equations 2.135 and 2.136 are sometimes called the *Fourier transform pair*. They can be represented in simplified notation as

$$\begin{aligned} F(j\omega) &= \mathscr{F}[f(t)] \\ f(t) &= \mathscr{F}^{-1}[F(j\omega)] \end{aligned} \tag{2.137}$$

where script $\mathscr{F}$ denotes the operation of Fourier transformation and $\mathscr{F}^{-1}$ denotes the operation of Fourier transform inversion.

In general, the Fourier transform $F(j\omega)$ is a complex quantity and is denoted as

$$F(j\omega) = \operatorname{Re} F(j\omega) + j \operatorname{Im} F(j\omega) \tag{2.138}$$

The amplitude spectrum of $F(j\omega)$ is given as

$$A(\omega) = [\operatorname{Re} F(j\omega)^2 + \operatorname{Im} F(j\omega)^2]^{\frac{1}{2}} \tag{2.139}$$

and the phase spectrum is

$$\phi(\omega) = \arctan \left[\frac{\operatorname{Im} F(j\omega)}{\operatorname{Re} F(j\omega)} \right] \tag{2.140}$$

Fourier transforms are invaluable in system analysis because they supply the vital link relating the *time-domain* behavior of a function to its corresponding *frequency-domain* behavior. For a complete understanding of the behavior of the system, both time-domain and frequency-domain information are required. To simplify notational difficulties, we shall henceforth denote by a capital letter a frequency-domain expression, and by a lower-case letter its counterpart in the time-domain.

Now let us discuss certain existence criteria and other properties of Fourier transforms. First, in order for a given function $f(t)$ to possess a

Fourier transform, $f(t)$ must obey the condition that either the integrals

$$\int_{-\infty}^{\infty} |f(t)|\, dt \qquad \text{or} \qquad \int_{-\infty}^{\infty} |f(t)|^2\, dt$$

be finite. It is thus seen that step and ramp functions do not possess Fourier transforms because the area under the curves are infinite. On the other hand the impulse function, $f(t) = A\, \delta(t - T_1)$ does possess a Fourier transform, as shown by

$$F(j\omega) = \int_{-\infty}^{\infty} A\, \delta(t - T_1) e^{-j\omega t}\, dt$$

$$= A e^{-j\omega T_1} \qquad (2.141)$$

In complex notation, the last equation can be written as

$$F(j\omega) = A(\cos \omega T_1 - j \sin \omega T_1) \qquad (2.142)$$

It is readily seen that the amplitude spectrum of the Fourier transform of an impulse function is a constant,

$$A(\omega) = A \qquad (2.143)$$

while the phase spectrum is

$$\phi(\omega) = -\omega T_1 \qquad (2.144)$$

as shown in Fig. 2.44.

Now let us examine some interesting symmetry properties of Fourier transforms of real time functions $f(t)$. We will denote by a subscript e an even function and by a subscript o an odd function. First consider the

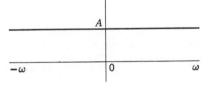

FIG. 2.44. Continuous spectra of impulse function. (*a*) Amplitude spectrum.

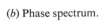

(*b*) Phase spectrum.

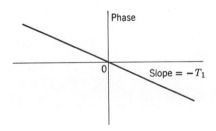

case where the time function, $f(t)$ is even, i.e., $f(t) = f_e(t)$. Then its Fourier transform is

$$F(j\omega) = \int_{-\infty}^{\infty} f_e(t)e^{-j\omega t}\, dt$$

$$= \int_{-\infty}^{\infty} f_e(t)(\cos \omega t - j \sin \omega t)\, dt \qquad (2.145)$$

Observe that $f_e(t) \cos \omega t$ is even and that $f_e(t) \sin \omega t$ is odd. Consequently,

$$\int_{-\infty}^{\infty} f_e(t) \sin \omega t\, dt = 0 \qquad (2.146)$$

and

$$F(j\omega) = F_e(\omega) = 2\int_{0}^{\infty} f_e(t) \cos \omega t\, dt \qquad (2.147)$$

From this analysis we conclude that if $f(t)$ is even its Fourier transform $F(j\omega)$ is also an even function. Moreover, since $f_e(t)$ is real, $F_e(\omega)$ must be also real. Note that the j is deleted from $F_e(\omega)$ to indicate it is real. The inverse transform of an even function $F_e(\omega)$ can, in the same manner, be expressed as

$$f_e(t) = \frac{1}{\pi} \int_{0}^{\infty} F_e(\omega) \cos \omega t\, d\omega \qquad (2.148)$$

On the other hand, if $f(t)$ is odd, its Fourier transform is odd and is a pure imaginary quantity,

$$F_o(j\omega) = -j2\int_{0}^{\infty} f_o(t) \sin \omega t\, dt = jF_o(\omega) \qquad (2.149)$$

Its inverse transform is

$$f_o(t) = -\frac{1}{\pi} \int_{0}^{\infty} F_o(\omega) \sin \omega t\, d\omega \qquad (2.150)$$

Since any function can be decomposed into odd and even parts,

$$f(t) = f_o(t) + f_e(t) \qquad (2.151)$$

we see that the real and imaginary parts of $F(j\omega)$ can be obtained separately by the equation,

$$\mathscr{F}[f_e(t) + f_o(t)] = F_e(\omega) + jF_o(\omega) \qquad (2.152)$$

In many physical applications, we deal with signals which are zero for $t < 0$. From this specification we can obtain a simplified version of the Fourier transform pair. If the signal for t positive is specified as

$$f(-t) = 0 \qquad (2.153)$$

then the inverse transform for the function $f(-t)$ is

$$f(-t) = \frac{1}{2\pi} \int_{-\infty}^{\infty} F(j\omega)e^{-j\omega t} \, d\omega$$

$$= \frac{1}{2\pi} \int_{-\infty}^{\infty} [F_e(\omega) + jF_o(\omega)](\cos \omega t - j \sin \omega t) \, d\omega$$

$$= \frac{1}{\pi} \int_{0}^{\infty} [F_e(\omega) \cos \omega t + F_o(\omega) \sin \omega t] \, d\omega = 0 \qquad (2.154)$$

We then derive

$$\int_{0}^{\infty} F_e(\omega) \cos \omega t \, d\omega = -\int_{0}^{\infty} F_o(\omega) \sin \omega t \, d\omega \qquad (2.155)$$

For t positive the inverse transform $f(t)$ is given as

$$f(t) = \frac{1}{2\pi} \int_{-\infty}^{\infty} F(j\omega)e^{+j\omega t} \, d\omega$$

$$= \frac{1}{2\pi} \int_{-\infty}^{\infty} [F_e(\omega) \cos \omega t - F_o(\omega) \sin \omega t] \, d\omega$$

$$= \frac{2}{\pi} \int_{0}^{\infty} F_e(\omega) \cos \omega t \, d\omega \qquad (2.156)$$

The Fourier transform for the function which is zero for $t < 0$ is

$$F(j\omega) = \int_{0}^{\infty} f(t)e^{-j\omega t} \, dt \qquad (2.157)$$

Let us consider some examples of the above discussion on symmetry. First let us find the time function $f(t)$ which is given by the inverse transform of the discrete amplitude spectrum in Fig. 2.45. The phase spectrum is specified to be identically zero. The line spectrum can be expressed as a sum of two impulses,

$$F(j\omega) = B \, \delta(\omega - \omega_0) + B \, \delta(\omega + \omega_0) \qquad (2.158)$$

Since $F(j\omega)$ is an even function, we obtain the inverse transform as

$$f(t) = \frac{1}{\pi} \int_{0}^{\infty} B \, \delta(\omega - \omega_0) \cos \omega t \, d\omega$$

$$= \frac{B}{\pi} \cos \omega_0 t \qquad (2.159)$$

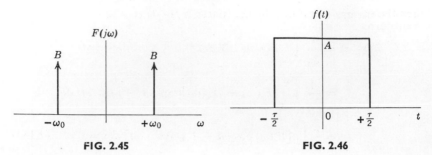

FIG. 2.45   FIG. 2.46

From this example we see that *line spectra in the frequency domain corre-spond to sinusoids in the time domain.*

As a second example, consider the Fourier transform of the square pulse of width τ shown in Fig. 2.46. The Fourier transform of $f(t)$ is

$$F(j\omega) = 2\int_0^{\tau/2} \frac{A}{2} \cos \omega t \, dt$$

$$= \frac{A}{\omega} \sin \frac{\omega\tau}{2} \qquad (2.160)$$

In a slightly different form, $F(j\omega)$ is

$$F(j\omega) = \frac{A\tau}{2} \frac{\sin x}{x} \qquad (2.161)$$

where

$$x = \frac{\omega\tau}{2} \qquad (2.162)$$

A plot of the Fourier transform is given in Fig. 2.47.

We shall have occasion to refer to functions of the form $\sin x/x$ in future analyses.

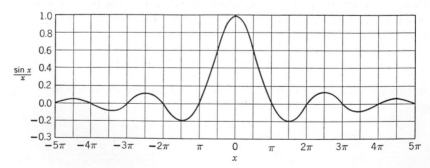

FIG. 2.47. The $\sin x/x$ curve.

Problems

2.1   Resolve the waveforms in the figure into odd and even components.

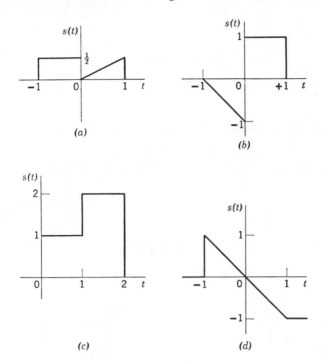

(a)

(b)

(c)

(d)

PROB. 2.1

2.2   Write the equation for the waveforms in the figure on p. 62, using shifted step functions.

2.3   Find the derivatives of the waveforms in Prob. 2.2 and write the equations for the derivatives, using shifted step and/or impulse functions.

2.4   For the waveform $f(t)$ given in the figure on p. 62, plot carefully

$$\int_{-\infty}^{t} f(\tau)\, d\tau$$

for a value of $t > T$.

2.5   For the waveform $f(t)$ shown in the figure on p. 62, determine what value K must be so that

(a)
$$\int_{-\infty}^{\infty} f(t)\, dt = 0$$

(b)
$$\int_{0^{+}}^{\infty} f(t)\, dt = 0$$

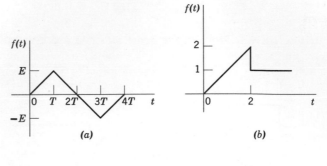

(a)   (b)

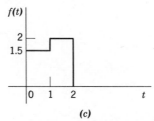

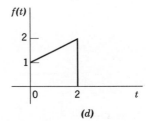

(c)   (d)

PROB 2.2

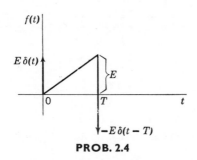

PROB. 2.4

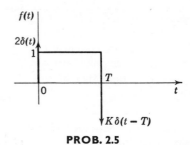

PROB. 2.5

2.6 The waveform $f(t)$ in the figure is defined as

$$f(t) = \frac{3}{\epsilon^3}(t - \epsilon)^2, \qquad 0 \le t \le \epsilon$$

$$= 0, \qquad \text{elsewhere}$$

Show that as $\epsilon \to 0$, $f(t)$ becomes a unit impulse.

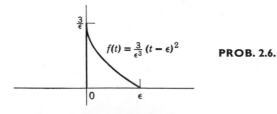

PROB. 2.6.

2.7 Plot

(a) $\qquad\qquad\qquad\qquad \delta(\cos t)$

(b) $\qquad\qquad\qquad\qquad t \operatorname{sgn} (\cos t); \qquad 0 \le t \le 2\pi$

2.8 Evaluate the following integrals

(a) $\qquad\qquad \int_{-\infty}^{\infty} \delta(t - T_1)\, u(t - T_2)\, dt; \qquad T_2 < T_1$

(b) $\qquad\qquad \int_{-\infty}^{\infty} \delta(\omega - \omega_0) \cos \omega t\, d\omega$

(c) $\qquad\qquad \int_{-\infty}^{\infty} [\delta(t) - A\,\delta(t - T_1) + 2A\,\delta(t - T_2)]e^{-jn\omega t}\, dt$

2.9 Evaluate the following integral

$$\int_{-\infty}^{\infty} \sin t \left[\delta\!\left(t - \frac{\pi}{4}\right) + \delta'\!\left(t - \frac{\pi}{2}\right) + \delta''(t - \pi) \right] dt$$

2.10 The response from an impulse sampler is given by the equation

$$r(t) = \int_{-\infty}^{\infty} \sin \frac{\pi t}{T}\, \delta\!\left(t - K\frac{T}{4}\right) dt; \qquad K = 0, 1, 2, 3, \cdots$$

Plot $r(t)$ for $0 \le t \le 2T$.

2.11 If the step response of a linear, time-invariant system is $r_s(t) = 2e^{-t}\, u(t)$, determine the impulse response $h(t)$, and plot.

2.12 For the system in Prob. 2.11, determine the response due to a staircase excitation,

$$s(t) = \sum_{k=0}^{3} u(t - kT)$$

Plot both excitation and response functions.

2.13 If the impulse response of a time-invariant system is $h(t) = e^{-t}\, u(t)$, determine the response due to an excitation,

$$e(t) = 2\delta(t - 1) - 2\delta(t - 2)$$

Plot $e(t)$.

2.14 Show that the set $\{1, \sin n\pi t/T, \cos n\pi t/T\}$, $n = 1, 2, 3, \cdots$, forms an orthogonal set over an interval $[\alpha, \alpha + T]$, where α is any real number. Find the norms for the members of the set and normalize the set.

2.15 Given the functions $f_1(t)$ and $f_2(t)$ expressed in terms of complex Fourier series,

$$f_1(t) = \sum_{n=-\infty}^{\infty} \alpha_n e^{jn\omega t}$$

$$f_2(t) = \sum_{m=-\infty}^{\infty} \beta_m e^{jm\omega t}$$

where both $f_1(t)$ and $f_2(t)$ have the same period T, and

$$\alpha_n = |\alpha_n|\, e^{j\phi_n}, \qquad \beta_m = |\beta_m|\, e^{j\theta_m}$$

show that

$$P = \frac{1}{T} \int_0^T f_1(t) f_2(t)\, dt$$

$$= \alpha_0 \beta_0 + 2 \sum_{n=1}^{\infty} |\alpha_n \beta_n| \cos(\theta_n - \phi_n)$$

Note that

$$\int_0^T e^{j(n+m)\omega t} = \begin{cases} T, & m = -n \\ 0, & m \neq -n \end{cases}$$

2.16   For the periodic signals in the figure, determine the Fourier coefficients a_n, b_n.

2.17   For the waveforms in Prob. 2.16 find the discrete amplitude and phase spectra, and plot.

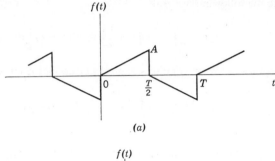

(a)

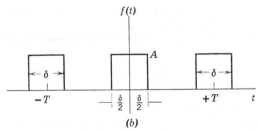

(b)

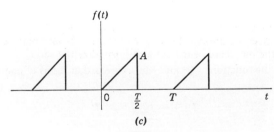

(c)

PROB. 2.16

2.18 For the waveforms in Prob. 2.16 determine the complex Fourier coefficients using the impulse function method.

2.19 Find the complex Fourier coefficients for the function shown in the figure.

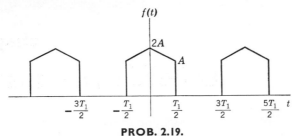

PROB. 2.19.

2.20 Find the Fourier transform for the functions shown in the figure.

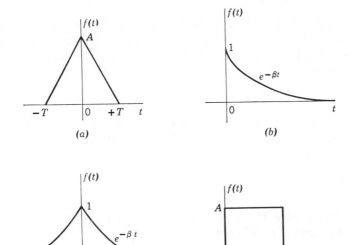

PROB. 2.20.

2.21 Find the Fourier transform for:

(a) $f(t) = A\,\delta(t)$

(b) $f(t) = A \sin \omega_0 t$

chapter 3

Differential equations

3.1 INTRODUCTION

This chapter is devoted to a brief study of ordinary linear differential equations. We will concentrate on the mathematical aspects of differential equations and leave the physical applications for the following chapter. The differential equations considered herein have the general form,

$$F[x(t), x'(t), \cdots, x^{(n)}(t), t] = 0 \qquad (3.1)$$

where t is the independent variable and $x(t)$ is a function dependent upon t. The superscripted terms $x^{(i)}(t)$ indicate the ith derivative of $x(t)$ with respect to t, viz.,

$$x^{(i)}(t) = \frac{d^{(i)}x(t)}{dt^i} \qquad (3.2)$$

The *solution* of $F = 0$ in Eq. 3.1 is $x(t)$ and must be obtained as an explicit function of t. When we substitute the explicit solution $x(t)$ into F, the equation must equal zero. If F in Eq. 3.1 is an ordinary linear differential equation, it is given by the general equation

$$a_n x^{(n)}(t) + a_{n-1}x^{(n-1)}(t) + \cdots + a_1 x'(t) + a_0 x(t) = f(t) \qquad (3.3)$$

The *order* of the equation is n, the order of the highest derivative term. The term $f(t)$ on the right-hand side of the equation is the *forcing function* or *driver*, and is independent of $x(t)$. When $f(t)$ is identically zero, the equation is said to be *homogeneous*; otherwise, the equation is *nonhomogeneous*.

In this chapter we will restrict our study to *ordinary*, *linear* differential equations with *constant coefficients*. Let us now examine the meanings of these terms.

Ordinary. An ordinary differential equation is one in which there is only one independent variable (in our case, t). As a result there is no need for *partial* derivatives.

Constant coefficients. The coefficients a_n, a_{n-1}, $\cdots$, a_2, a_1, a_0 are constant, independent of the variable t.

Linear. A differential equation is linear if it contains only terms of the first degree in $x(t)$ and all its higher derivatives as given by Eq. 3.3. For example, the equation

$$3x'(t) + 2x(t) = \sin t \qquad (3.4)$$

is a linear differential equation. On the other hand,

$$3[x'(t)]^2 + 2x(t)\,x'(t) + 4x(t) = 5t \qquad (3.5)$$

is nonlinear because the terms $[x'(t)]^2$ and $x(t)\,x'(t)$ are nonlinear by the definition just given.

An important implication of the linearity property is the *superposition property*. According to the superposition property, if $x_1(t)$ and $x_2(t)$ are solutions of a given differential equation for forcing functions $f_1(t)$ and $f_2(t)$ respectively, then, if the forcing function were any linear combination of $f_1(t)$ and $f_2(t)$ such as

$$f(t) = a\,f_1(t) + b\,f_2(t) \qquad (3.6)$$

the solution would be

$$x(t) = ax_1(t) + bx_2(t) \qquad (3.7)$$

where a and b are arbitrary constants. It should be emphasized that the superposition property is extremely important and should be kept in mind in any discussion on linear differential equations.

3.2 HOMOGENEOUS LINEAR DIFFERENTIAL EQUATIONS

This section deals with some methods for the solution of homogeneous, linear differential equations with constant coefficients. First, let us find the solution to the equation,

$$x'(t) - 2x(t) = 0 \qquad (3.8)$$

Now, with a little prestidigitation, we *assume* the solution to be of the form

$$x(t) = Ce^{2t} \qquad (3.9)$$

where C is any arbitrary constant. Let us check to see whether $x(t) = Ce^{2t}$ is truly a solution of Eq. 3.8. Substituting the assumed solution in Eq. 3.8, we obtain

$$2Ce^{2t} - 2Ce^{2t} = 0 \qquad (3.10)$$

It can be shown, in general, that the solutions of homogeneous linear differential equations consist of exponential terms of the form $C_i e^{p_i t}$. To obtain the solution of any differential equation, we substitute $C e^{pt}$ for $x(t)$ in the equation and determine those values of p for which the equation is zero. In other words, given the general equation

$$a_n x^{(n)}(t) + \cdots + a_1 x'(t) + a_0 x(t) = 0 \qquad (3.11)$$

we let $x(t) = C e^{pt}$, so that Eq. 3.11 becomes

$$C e^{pt}(a_n p^n + a_{n-1} p^{n-1} + \cdots + a_1 p + a_0) = 0 \qquad (3.12)$$

Since e^{pt} cannot be zero except at $p = -\infty$, then the only nontrivial solutions for Eq. 3.12 occur when the polynomial

$$H(p) \overset{\Delta}{=} a_n p^n + a_{n-1} p^{n-1} + \cdots + a_1 p + a_0 = 0 \qquad (3.13)$$

Equation 3.13 is often referred to as the *characteristic equation* and is denoted symbolically in this discussion as $H(p)$. The characteristic equation is zero only at its roots. Therefore, let us factor $H(p)$ to give

$$H(p) = a_n(p - p_0)(p - p_1) \cdots (p - p_n) \qquad (3.14)$$

From Eq. 3.14, we note that $C_0 e^{p_0 t}$, $C_1 e^{p_1 t}$, $\cdots$, $C_n e^{p_n t}$ are all solutions of Eq. 3.11. By the *superposition principle*, the total solution is a linear combination of all the individual solutions. Therefore, the total solution of the differential equation is

$$x(t) = C_0 e^{p_0 t} + C_1 e^{p_1 t} + \cdots + C_n e^{p_n t} \qquad (3.15)$$

where $C_0, C_1, \cdots, C_n$ are generally complex. The solution $x(t)$ in Eq. 3.15 is not unique unless the constants $C_0, C_1, \cdots, C_n$ are uniquely specified. In order to determine the constants C_1, we need n additional pieces of information about the equation. These pieces of information are usually specified in terms of values of $x(t)$ and its derivatives at $t = 0+$ and are therefore referred to as *initial conditions*. To obtain n coefficients, we must be given the values $x(0+)$, $x'(0+)$, $\cdots$, $x^{(n-1)}(0+)$. In a number of special cases, the values at $t = 0-$ are *not equal* to the values at $t = 0+$. If the initial specifications are given in terms of $x(0-)$, $x'(0-)$, $\cdots$, $x^{(n-1)}(0-)$, we must determine the values at $t = 0+$ in order to solve for the constants C_i. This problem arises when the forcing function $f(t)$ is an impulse function or any of its derivatives. We will discuss this problem in detail in a later section.

For example, in Eq. 3.9 if we are given that $x(0+) = 4$, then we obtain the constant from the equation

$$x(0+) = C e^0 = C \qquad (3.16)$$

so that $x(t)$ is uniquely determined to be

$$x(t) = 4e^{2t}$$

Example 3.1.   Find the solution for

$$x''(t) + 5x'(t) + 4x(t) = 0 \qquad (3.17)$$

given the initial conditions

$$x(0+) = 2 \qquad x'(0+) = -1$$

Solution.   From the given equation, we first obtain the characteristic equation,

$$H(p) = p^2 + 5p + 4 = 0 \qquad (3.18)$$

which factors into

$$(p + 4)(p + 1) = 0 \qquad (3.19)$$

The roots of the characteristic equation (referred to here as *characteristic values*) are $p = -1; \; p = -4$. Then $x(t)$ takes the form

$$x(t) = C_1 e^{-t} + C_2 e^{-4t} \qquad (3.20)$$

From the initial condition $x(0+) = 2$, we obtain the equation

$$x(0+) = 2 = C_1 + C_2 \qquad (3.21)$$

In order to solve for C_1 and C_2 explicitly, we need the additional initial condition $x'(0+) = -1$. Taking the derivative of $x(t)$ in Eq. 3.20, we have

$$x'(t) = -C_1 e^{-t} - 4C_2 e^{-4t} \qquad (3.22)$$

At $t = 0+$, $x'(t)$ is

$$x'(0+) = -1 = -C_1 - 4C_2 \qquad (3.23)$$

Solving Eqs. 3.21 and 3.23 simultaneously, we find that

$$C_1 = \tfrac{7}{3} \qquad C_2 = -\tfrac{1}{3}$$

Thus the final solution is

$$x(t) = \tfrac{7}{3} e^{-t} - \tfrac{1}{3} e^{-4t} \qquad (3.24)$$

Next, let us consider the case when the characteristic equation $H(p)$ has *multiple roots*. Specifically, let us consider the case where $H(p)$ has a root $p = p_0$ of multiplicity k as given by

$$H(p) = a_n(p - p_0)^k(p - p_1) \cdots (p - p_n) \qquad (3.25)$$

It will be left to the reader to show that the solution must then contain k terms involving $e^{p_0 t}$ of the form

$$x(t) = C_{00} e^{p_0 t} + C_{01} t e^{p_0 t} + C_{02} t^2 e^{p_0 t} + \cdots + C_{0k-1} t^{k-1} e^{p_0 t}$$
$$+ C_1 e^{p_1 t} + C_2 e^{p_2 t} + \cdots + C_n e^{p_n t} \qquad (3.26)$$

where the double-scripted terms in Eq. 3.26 denote the terms in the solution due to the multiple root, $(p - p_0)^k$.

Example 3.2.   Solve the equation

$$x''(t) - 8x'(t) + 16x(t) = 0 \qquad (3.27)$$

with

$$x(0+) = 2 \quad \text{and} \quad x'(0+) = 4$$

Solution.   The characteristic equation is

$$H(p) = p^2 - 8p + 16 = (p - 4)^2 \qquad (3.28)$$

Since $H(p)$ has a double root at $p = 4$, the solution must take the form

$$x(t) = C_1 e^{4t} + C_2 t e^{4t} \qquad (3.29)$$

In order to determine C_1 and C_2, we evaluate $x(t)$ and $x'(t)$ at $t = 0+$ to give

$$x(0+) = C_1 = 2$$
$$x'(0+) = 4C_1 + C_2 = 4 \qquad (3.30)$$

Thus the final solution is

$$x(t) = 2e^{4t} - 4te^{4t} \qquad (3.31)$$

Another interesting case arises when $H(p)$ has complex conjugate roots. Consider the equation

$$H(p) = a_2(p - p_1)(p - p_2) \qquad (3.32)$$

where p_1 and p_2 are complex conjugate roots, i.e.,

$$p_1, p_2 = \sigma \pm j\omega \qquad (3.33)$$

The solution $x(t)$ then takes the form

$$x(t) = C_1 e^{(\sigma + j\omega)t} + C_2 e^{(\sigma - j\omega)t} \qquad (3.34)$$

Expanding the term $e^{j\omega t}$ by Euler's equation, $x(t)$ can be expressed as

$$x(t) = C_1 e^{\sigma t}(\cos \omega t + j \sin \omega t) + C_2 e^{\sigma t}(\cos \omega t - j \sin \omega t) \qquad (3.35)$$

which reduces to

$$x(t) = (C_1 + C_2)e^{\sigma t} \cos \omega t + j(C_1 - C_2)e^{\sigma t} \sin \omega t \qquad (3.36)$$

Let us introduce two new constants, M_1 and M_2, so that $x(t)$ might be expressed in the more convenient form,

$$x(t) = M_1 e^{\sigma t} \cos \omega t + M_2 e^{\sigma t} \sin \omega t \qquad (3.37)$$

where M_1 and M_2 are related to the constants C_1 and C_2 by the equations

$$M_1 = C_1 + C_2$$
$$M_2 = j(C_1 - C_2) \qquad (3.38)$$

The constants M_1 and M_2 are determined in the usual manner from initial conditions.

Another convenient form for the solution $x(t)$ can be obtained if we introduce still another pair of constants, M and φ defined by the equations

$$M_1 = M \sin \varphi$$
$$M_2 = M \cos \varphi \qquad (3.39)$$

With the constants M and φ we obtain another form of $x(t)$, *viz.*,

$$x(t) = Me^{\sigma t} \sin(\omega t + \varphi) \qquad (3.40)$$

Example 3.3. Solve the equation

$$x''(t) + 2x'(t) + 5x(t) = 0 \qquad (3.41)$$

with the initial conditions,

$$x(0+) = 1 \qquad x'(0+) = 0$$

Solution. The characteristic equation $H(p)$ is

$$H(p) = p^2 + 2p + 5 = (p + 1 + j2)(p + 1 - j2) \qquad (3.42)$$

so that, assuming the form of solution in Eq. 3.37, we have $\sigma = -1$ and $\omega = 2$. Then $x(t)$ is

$$x(t) = M_1 e^{-t} \cos 2t + M_2 e^{-t} \sin 2t \qquad (3.43)$$

At $t = 0+$,

$$x(0+) = 1 = M_1 \qquad (3.44)$$

The derivative of $x(t)$ is

$$x'(t) = M_1(-e^{-t}\cos 2t - 2e^{-t}\sin 2t) + M_2(-e^{-t}\sin 2t + 2e^{-t}\cos 2t) \quad (3.45)$$

At $t = 0+$, we obtain the following equation

$$x'(0+) = 0 = -M_1 + 2M_2 \qquad (3.46)$$

Solving Eqs. 3.44 and 3.46 simultaneously, we find $M_1 = 1$ and $M_2 = +\frac{1}{2}$. Thus the final solution is

$$x(t) = e^{-t}(\cos 2t + \tfrac{1}{2} \sin 2t) \qquad (3.47)$$

If we had used the form of $x(t)$ given in Eq. 3.40, we would have obtained the solution

$$x(t) = \sqrt{\tfrac{5}{4}} e^{-t} \sin[2t + \tan^{-1}(2)] \qquad (3.48)$$

Now let us consider a differential equation which illustrates everything we have discussed concerning characteristic values.

Example 3.4. The differential equation is

$$x^{(5)}(t) + 9x^{(4)}(t) + 32x^{(3)}(t) + 58x^{(2)}(t) + 56x'(t) + 24x(t) = 0 \quad (3.49)$$

The initial conditions are

$$x^{(4)}(0+) = 0 \qquad x^{(3)}(0+) = 1$$
$$x^{(2)}(0+) = -1 \qquad x'(0+) = 0 \qquad x(0+) = 1$$

Solution. The characteristic equation is

$$H(p) = p^5 + 9p^4 + 32p^3 + 58p^2 + 56p + 24 = 0 \qquad (3.50)$$

which factors into

$$H(p) = (p + 1 + j1)(p + 1 - j1)(p + 2)^2(p + 3) = 0 \qquad (3.51)$$

From $H(p)$ we immediately write $x(t)$ as

$$x(t) = M_1 e^{-t} \cos t + M_2 e^{-t} \sin t + C_0 e^{-2t} + C_1 t e^{-2t} + C_2 e^{-3t} \qquad (3.52)$$

Since there are five coefficients, we need a corresponding number of equations to evaluate the unknowns. These are

$$x(0+) = M_1 + C_0 + C_2 = 1$$
$$x'(0+) = -M_1 + M_2 - 2C_0 - 3C_2 + C_1 = 0$$
$$x''(0+) = -2M_2 + 4C_0 - 4C_1 + 9C_2 = -1 \qquad (3.53)$$
$$x^{(3)}(0+) = 2M_1 + 2M_2 - 8C_0 + 12C_1 - 27C_2 = 1$$
$$x^{(4)}(0+) = -4M_1 + 16C_0 + 81C_2 - 32C_1 = 0$$

Solving these five equations simultaneously, we obtain

$$M_1 = 0 \qquad M_2 = \tfrac{3}{2} \qquad C_0 = 1 \qquad C_1 = \tfrac{1}{2} \qquad C_2 = 0$$

so that the final solution is

$$x(t) = \tfrac{3}{2} e^{-t} \sin t + e^{-2t} + \tfrac{1}{2} t e^{-2t} \qquad (3.54)$$

In conclusion, we have seen that the solution of a homogeneous differential equation may take different forms depending upon the roots of its characteristic equation. The following table should be useful in determining the particular form of solution.

TABLE 3.1

Roots of $H(p)$	Forms of Solution
1. Single real root, $p = p_0$	$e^{p_0 t}$
2. Root of multiplicity, k, $(p - p_1)^k$	$C_0 e^{p_1 t} + C_1 t e^{p_1 t} + \cdots + C_{k-1} t^{k-1} e^{p_1 t}$
3. Complex roots at $p_{2,3} = \sigma + j\omega$	$M_1 e^{\sigma t} \cos \omega t + M_2 e^{\sigma t} \sin \omega t$ or $M e^{\sigma t} \sin (\omega t + \varphi)$
4. Complex roots of multiplicity k at $p_{4,5} = \sigma + j\omega$	$M_0 e^{\sigma t} \cos \omega t + M_1 t e^{\sigma t} \cos \omega t + \cdots$ $+ M_{k-1} t^{k-1} e^{\sigma t} \cos \omega t + N_0 e^{\sigma t} \sin \omega t$ $+ N_1 t e^{\sigma t} \sin \omega t + \cdots$ $+ N_{k-1} t^{k-1} e^{\sigma t} \sin \omega t$

3.3 NONHOMOGENEOUS EQUATIONS

As we had mentioned in the introduction, a nonhomogeneous differential equation is one in which the forcing function $f(t)$ is not identically zero for all t. In this section, we will discuss methods for obtaining the solution $x(t)$ of an equation with constant coefficients,

$$a_n x^{(n)}(t) + a_{n-1} x^{(n-1)}(t) + \cdots + a_0 x(t) = f(t) \qquad (3.55)$$

Let $x_p(t)$ be a particular solution for the above equation, and let $x_c(t)$ be the solution of the homogeneous equation obtained by letting $f(t) = 0$ in Eq. 3.55. It is readily seen that

$$x(t) = x_p(t) + x_c(t) \qquad (3.56)$$

is also a solution of Eq. 3.55. We see that $x_p(t)$ is not unique. According to the *uniqueness theorem*, the solution $x(t)$ in Eq. 3.56 is the unique solution for the nonhomogeneous differential equation *if* it satisfies the specified initial conditions at $t = 0+$.* In Eq. 3.56, $x_p(t)$ is the *particular integral*, $x_c(t)$ is the *complementary function*, and $x(t)$ is the *total solution*.

Since we already know how to find the complementary function $x_c(t)$, we now have to find the particular integral $x_p(t)$. In solving for $x_p(t)$, a very reliable rule of thumb is that $x_p(t)$ usually takes the *same form* as the forcing function if $f(t)$ can be expressed as a sum of exponential functions. Specifically, $x_p(t)$ assumes the form of $f(t)$ plus all of its derivatives. For example, if $f(t) = \alpha \sin \omega t$, then $x_p(t)$ takes the form

$$x_p(t) = A \sin \omega t + B \cos \omega t$$

The only unknowns which must be determined are the coefficients A and B of the terms in $x_p(t)$. The method for obtaining $x_p(t)$ is appropriately called the *method* of *undetermined coefficients*.

In illustrating the method of unknown coefficients, let us take $f(t)$ to be

$$f(t) = \alpha e^{\beta t} \qquad (3.57)$$

where α and β are arbitrary constants. We then assume $x_p(t)$ to have a similar form,

$$x_p(t) = A e^{\beta t} \qquad (3.58)$$

and A is the unknown coefficient. To determine A, we simply substitute the assumed solution $x_p(t)$ into the differential equation. Thus,

$$A e^{\beta t}(a_n \beta^n + a_{n-1}\beta^{n-1} + \cdots + a_1 \beta + a_0) = \alpha e^{\beta t} \qquad (3.59)$$

---

* See, for example, C. R. Wylie, *Advanced Engineering Mathematics* (2nd ed.), McGraw-Hill Book Company, New York, 1960, pp. 83–84.

We see that the polynomial within the parentheses is the characteristic equation $H(p)$ with $p = \beta$. Consequently, the unknown coefficient is obtained as

$$A = \frac{\alpha}{H(\beta)} \tag{3.60}$$

provided $H(\beta) \neq 0$.

Example 3.5.   Determine the solution of the equation

$$x''(t) + 3x'(t) + 2x(t) = 4e^t \tag{3.61}$$

with the initial conditions, $x(0+) = 1$, $x'(0+) = -1$.
   Solution.   The characteristic equation is

$$H(p) = p^2 + 3p + 2 = (p + 2)(p + 1)$$

so that the complementary function is

$$x_c(t) = C_1 e^{-t} + C_2 e^{-2t}$$

For the forcing function $f(t) = 4e^t$, the constants in Eq. 3.60 are $\alpha = 4$, $\beta = 1$. Then,

$$A = \frac{4}{H(1)} = \frac{2}{3}$$

Thus we obtain

$$x_p(t) = \tfrac{2}{3} e^t$$

The total solution is

$$x(t) = x_c(t) + x_p(t) = C_1 e^{-t} + C_2 e^{-2t} + \tfrac{2}{3} e^t \tag{3.62}$$

To evaluate the constants C_1 and C_2, we substitute the given initial conditions, *viz.*,

$$x(0+) = 1 = C_1 + C_2 + \tfrac{2}{3}$$
$$x'(0+) = -1 = -C_1 - 2C_2 + \tfrac{2}{3} \tag{3.63}$$

Solving Eq. 3.63, we find that $C_1 = -1$, $C_2 = \tfrac{4}{3}$. Consequently,

$$x(t) = -e^{-t} + \tfrac{4}{3} e^{-2t} + \tfrac{2}{3} e^t \tag{3.64}$$

   It should be pointed out that we solve for the constants C_1 and C_2 from the initial conditions for the *total solution*. This is because initial conditions are not given for $x_c(t)$ or $x_p(t)$, but for the total solution.
   Next, let us consider an example of a constant forcing function, $f(t) = \alpha$. We may use Eq. 3.60 if we resort to the artifice,

$$f(t) = \alpha = \alpha e^{0t} \tag{3.65}$$

i.e., $\beta = 0$. For the differential equation in Example 5 with $f(t) = 4$, we see that

$$x_p(t) = A = \frac{4}{H(0)} = 2 \tag{3.66}$$

and

$$x(t) = C_1 e^{-t} + C_2 e^{-2t} + 2 \tag{3.67}$$

When the forcing function is a sine or cosine function, we can still consider the forcing function to be of exponential form and make use of the method of undetermined coefficients and Eq. 3.60. Suppose

$$f(t) = \alpha e^{j\omega t} = \alpha(\cos \omega t + j \sin \omega t) \qquad (3.68)$$

then the particular integral $x_{p1}(t)$ can be written as

$$x_{p1}(t) = \text{Re } x_{p1}(t) + j \text{ Im } x_{p1}(t) \qquad (3.69)$$

From the superposition principle, we can show that:

if $\qquad f(t) = \alpha \cos \omega t \qquad$ then $\qquad x_p(t) = \text{Re } x_{p1}(t)$

if $\qquad f(t) = \alpha \sin \omega t \qquad$ then $\qquad x_p(t) = \text{Im } x_{p1}(t)$

Consequently, whether the excitation is a cosine function $\alpha \cos \omega t$ or a sine function $\alpha \sin \omega t$, we can use an exponential driver, $f(t) = \alpha e^{j\omega t}$; then we take the real or imaginary part of the resulting particular integral.

Example 3.6.   Find the particular integral for the equation

$$x''(t) + 5x'(t) + 4x(t) = 2 \sin 3t \qquad (3.70)$$

Solution.   First, let us take the excitation to be

$$f_1(t) = 2e^{j3t} \qquad (3.71)$$

so that the particular integral $x_{p1}(t)$ takes the form

$$x_{p1}(t) = Ae^{j3t} \qquad (3.72)$$

From the characteristic equation,

$$H(p) = p^2 + 5p + 4,$$

we determine the coefficient A to be

$$A = \frac{2}{H(j3)} = \frac{2}{-5 + j15} = \frac{2}{5\sqrt{10}} e^{j[\tan^{-1}(3) - \pi]} \qquad (3.73)$$

Then $x_{p1}(t)$ is

$$x_{p1}(t) = \frac{2}{5\sqrt{10}} e^{j[\tan^{-1}(3) + 3t - \pi]} \qquad (3.74)$$

and the particular integral $x_p(t)$ for the original driver $f(t) = 2 \sin 3t$ is

$$x_p(t) = \text{Im } x_{p1}(t) = \frac{2}{5\sqrt{10}} \sin [3t + \tan^{-1}(3) - \pi] \qquad (3.75)$$

There are certain limitations to the applicability of the method of undetermined coefficients. If $f(t)$ were, for example, a Bessel function $J_0(t)$, we cannot assume $x_p(t)$ to be a Bessel function of the same form (if it is a Bessel function at all). However, we may apply the method to forcing functions of the following types:

1. $f(t) = A$; constant.
2. $f(t) = A(t^n + b_{n-1}t^{n-1} + \cdots + b_1 t + b_0)$; n, integer.
3. $f(t) = e^{pt}$; p real or complex.
4. Any function formed by multiplying terms of type 1, 2, or 3.

For the purposes of linear network analysis, the method is more than adequate.

Suppose the forcing function were

$$f(t) = At^k e^{pt} \qquad p = \sigma + j\omega$$

The particular integral can be written as

$$x_p(t) = (A_k t^k + A_{k-1}t^{k-1} + \cdots + A_1 t + A_0)e^{pt} \qquad (3.76)$$

where the coefficients $A_k, A_{k-1}, \cdots, A_1, A_0$ are to be determined.

3.4 STEP AND IMPULSE RESPONSE

In this section we will discuss solutions of differential equations with step or impulse forcing functions. In physical applications these solutions are called respectively, *step responses* and *impulse responses*. As physical quantities, the step and impulse responses of a linear system are highly significant measures of system performance. It will be shown in a later chapter that a precise mathematical description of a linear system is given by its impulse response. Moreover, a reliable measure of the transient behavior of the system is given by its step and impulse response. In this section, we will be concerned with the mathematical problem of solving for the impulse and step responses, given a linear differential equation with initial conditions at $t = 0-$.

From Chapter 2, recall that the definition of the unit step function was

$$u(t) = 1 \qquad t \geq 0$$
$$= 0 \qquad t < 0$$

and the unit impulse was shown to have the properties:

$$\delta(t) = \infty \qquad t = 0$$
$$= 0 \qquad t \neq 0$$

and

$$\int_{0-}^{0+} \delta(t)\, dt = 1$$

In addition, we have the relationship

$$\delta(t) = \frac{d\,u(t)}{dt}$$

As the definitions of $\delta(t)$ and $u(t)$ indicate, both functions have discontinuities at $t = 0$. In dealing with initial conditions for step and impulse drivers, we must then recognize that the solution $x(t)$ *and its derivatives* $x'(t)$, $x''(t)$, etc., *may not be continuous at* $t = 0$. In other words, it may be that

$$x^{(n)}(0-) \neq x^{(n)}(0+)$$
$$x^{(n-1)}(0-) \neq x^{(n-1)}(0+)$$

$$\cdot$$
$$\cdot$$
$$\cdot$$

$$x(0-) \neq x(0+)$$

In many physical problems, the initial conditions are given at $t = 0-$. However, to evaluate the unknown constants of the total solution, we must have the initial conditions at $t = 0+$. Our task is then to determine the conditions at $t = 0+$, given the initial conditions at $t = 0-$. The method discussed here is borrowed from electromagnetic theory and is often referred to as "integrating through a Green's function."*

Consider the differential equation with an impulse forcing function,

$$a_n x^{(n)}(t) + a_{n-1} x^{(n-1)}(t) + \cdots + a_0 x(t) = A\,\delta(t) \qquad (3.77)$$

To ensure that the right-hand side of Eq. 3.77 will equal the left-hand side, one of the terms $x^{(n)}(t)$, $x^{(n-1)}(t)$, $\cdots$, $x(t)$ must contain an impulse. The question is—which term contains the impulse? A close examination shows that the highest derivative term $x^{(n)}(t)$ *must* contain the impulse. For, if $x^{(n-1)}(t)$ contained the impulse, $x^{(n)}(t)$ would then contain a *doublet*, $C\,\delta'(t)$. This argument holds, similarly, for all lower derivative terms of $x(t)$. If the term $x^{(n)}(t)$ contains the impulse, then $x^{(n-1)}(t)$ would contain a step and $x^{(n-2)}(t)$, a ramp. *We conclude therefore that, for an impulse forcing function, the two highest derivative terms are discontinuous at* $t = 0$. For a step forcing function, only the highest derivative term is discontinuous at $t = 0$.

Since initial conditions are usually given at $t = 0-$, our task is to determine the values $x^{(n)}(0+)$ and $x^{(n-1)}(0+)$ for an impulse forc g

---

* The Green's function is another name for impulse response; see, for example, Morse and Feshbach, *Methods of Theoretical Physics*, McGraw-Hill Book Co., New York, 1952, Chapter 7.

function. Referring to Eq. 3.77, let us integrate the equation between $t = 0-$ and $t = 0+$, $viz.$,

$$a_n \int_{0-}^{0+} x^{(n)}(t) \, dt + a_{n-1} \int_{0-}^{0+} x^{(n-1)}(t) \, dt + \cdots + a_0 \int_{0-}^{0+} x(t) \, dt = A \int_{0-}^{0+} \delta(t) \, dt$$

$$(3.78)$$

After integrating, we obtain

$$a_n[x^{(n-1)}(0+) - x^{(n-1)}(0-)] + a_{n-1}[x^{(n-2)}(0+) - x^{(n-2)}(0-)] + \cdots = A$$

$$(3.79)$$

We know that all derivative terms below $(n - 1)$ are continuous at $t = 0$. Consequently, Eq. 3.79 simplifies to

$$a_n[x^{(n-1)}(0+) - x^{(n-1)}(0-)] = A \qquad (3.80)$$

so that

$$x^{(n-1)}(0+) = \frac{A}{a_n} + x^{(n-1)}(0-) \qquad (3.81)$$

We must next determine $x^{(n)}(0+)$. At $t = 0+$, the differential equation in Eq. 3.77 is

$$a_n x^{(n)}(0+) + a_{n-1} x^{(n-1)}(0+) + \cdots + a_0 x(0+) = 0 \qquad (3.82)$$

Since all derivative terms below $(n - 1)$ are continuous and since we have already solved for $x^{(n-1)}(0+)$, we find that

$$x^{(n)}(0+) = -\frac{1}{a_n} [a_{n-1} x^{(n-1)}(0+) + \cdots + a_1 x'(0+) + a_0 x(0+)]$$

$$(3.83)$$

For a step forcing function $A u(t)$, all derivative terms except $x^{(n)}(t)$ are continuous at $t = 0$. To determine $x^{(n)}(0+)$, we derive in similar manner as Eq. 3.83, the expression

$$x^{(n)}(0+) = \frac{A}{a_n} - \frac{1}{a_n} [a_{n-1} x^{(n-1)}(0+) + \cdots + a_0 x(0+)] \qquad (3.84)$$

The total solution of a differential equation with a step or impulse forcing function can be determined quite straightforwardly once the initial conditions at $t = 0+$ are obtained. For the impulse driver, the forcing function is zero except at $t = 0$. Since the range of our solution is between $t = 0+$ and $t = +\infty$, we solve for the impulse response by considering the differential equation to be *homogeneous* in the range $0+ \leq t < \infty$. The impulse response is the complementary function with constants specified by the initial conditions. We, therefore, obtain the *form* of the impulse response in exactly the same way as the complementary function.

Similarly, the step response is obtained by assuming the forcing function to be a constant in the range $0+ \leq t < \infty$.

Example 3.7.   Find the step and impulse response for the equation

$$2x''(t) + 4x'(t) + 10x(t) = f(t) \tag{3.85}$$

where $f(t) = \delta(t)$ and $f(t) = u(t)$ respectively. The initial conditions at $t = 0-$ are

$$x(0-) = x'(0-) = x''(0-) = 0$$

Solution.   Let us first obtain the impulse response. The initial conditions at $t = 0+$ are:

$$x(0+) = x(0-) = 0$$
$$x'(0+) = \tfrac{1}{2} + x'(0-) = \tfrac{1}{2} \tag{3.86}$$
$$x''(0+) = -\tfrac{1}{2}(4 \times \tfrac{1}{2}) = -1$$

Note that we actually need only $x(0+)$ and $x'(0+)$ to evaluate the constants for the second-order differential equation. Next, we proceed to the complementary function $x_c(t)$. The characteristic equation is

$$H(p) = 2(p^2 + 2p + 5) = 2(p + 1 + j2)(p + 1 - j2) \tag{3.87}$$

Since $H(p)$ has a pair of complex conjugate roots, we use a standard form for $x_c(t)$,

$$x_c(t) = Me^{-t} \sin (2t + \phi) \tag{3.88}$$

Substituting the initial conditions at $t = 0+$, we obtain

$$x(0+) = 0 = M \sin \phi$$
$$x'(0+) = \tfrac{1}{2} = M(2 \cos \phi - M \sin \phi) \tag{3.89}$$

From which we find $\phi = 0$ and $M = \tfrac{1}{4}$. Thus the impulse response, which we will denote here as $x_\delta(t)$, is

$$x_\delta(t) = \tfrac{1}{4}e^{-t} \sin 2t \, u(t) \tag{3.90}$$

Next we must solve for the step response, $x_u(t)$. For convenience, let us write the complementary function as

$$x_c(t) = e^{-t}(A_1 \sin 2t + A_2 \cos 2t) \tag{3.91}$$

The particular integral is evaluated by considering the forcing function to be a constant, $f(t) = 1$, so that

$$x_p(t) = \frac{1}{H(0)} = \frac{1}{10} \tag{3.92}$$

The total solution is then

$$x(t) = (A_1 \sin 2t + A_2 \cos 2t)e^{-t} + \tfrac{1}{10} \tag{3.93}$$

Since $x'(t)$ and $x(t)$ must be continuous for a step forcing function,

$$x(0+) = x(0-) = 0$$
$$x'(0+) = x'(0-) = 0$$

(3.94)

Substituting these initial conditions into $x(t)$ and $x'(t)$, we find that $A_1 = -0.05$, $A_2 = -0.1$. Therefore, the step response is

$$x_u(t) = 0.1[1 - e^{-t}(0.5 \sin 2t + \cos 2t)] u(t)$$

(3.95)

Note that the impulse response and the step response are related by the equation

$$x_\delta(t) = \frac{d}{dt} x_u(t)$$

(3.96)

We can demonstrate Eq. 3.96 by the following procedure. Let us substitute $x_u(t)$ into the original equation, Eq. 3.85,

$$2 \frac{d^2}{dt^2} x_u(t) + 4 \frac{d}{dt} x_u(t) + 10 x_u(t) = u(t)$$

(3.97)

Differentiating both sides, we have

$$2 \frac{d^2}{dt^2} \left[\frac{d}{dt} x_u(t) \right] + 4 \frac{d}{dt} \left[\frac{d}{dt} x_u(t) \right] + 10 \left[\frac{d}{dt} x_u(t) \right] = \delta(t)$$

(3.98)

from which Eq. 3.96 follows.

Generalizing, we see that, if we have the step response for a differential equation, we can obtain the impulse response by differentiating the step response. We can also obtain the response to a ramp function $f(t) = A \rho(t)$ (where A is the height of the step) by integrating the step response. The relationships discussed here can be summarized in Fig. 3.1.

$$x_\rho(t) \xrightarrow{d/dt} x(t) \xrightarrow{d/dt} x_\delta(t)$$

$$x_\delta(t) \xrightarrow{\int_{0-}^{t}} x_u(t) \xrightarrow{\int_{0-}^{t}} x_\rho(t)$$

FIG. 3.1

3.5 INTEGRODIFFERENTIAL EQUATIONS

In this section, we will consider an integrodifferential equation of the form

$$a_n x^n(t) + a_{n-1} x^{n-1}(t) + \cdots + a_0 x(t) + a_{-1} \int_0^t x(\tau)\, d\tau = f(t)$$

(3.99)

where the coefficients $\{a_n, a_{n-1}, \cdots, a_{-1}\}$ are constants. In solving an equation of the form of Eq. 3.99, we use two very similar methods. The first method is to differentiate both sides of Eq. 3.99 to give

$$a_n x^{(n+1)}(t) + a_{n-1} x^{(n)}(t) + \cdots + a_0 x'(t) + a_{-1} x(t) = f'(t) \quad (3.100)$$

The second method consists of a change of variables. We let $y'(t) = x(t)$; Eq. 3.99 then becomes

$$a_n y^{(n+1)}(t) + a_{n-1} y^{(n)}(t) + \cdots + a_0 y'(t) + a_{-1} y(t) = f(t) \quad (3.101)$$

Note that, from Eq. 3.100, we obtain $x(t)$ directly. From Eq. 3.101, we obtain $y(t)$ which we must then differentiate to obtain $x(t)$. An important point to keep in mind is that we might have to derive some additional initial conditions in order to have a sufficient number to evaluate the unknown constants.

Example 3.8. Solve the integrodifferential equation

$$x'(t) + 3x(t) + 2 \int_{0-}^{t} x(\tau)\, d\tau = 5u(t) \quad (3.102)$$

The initial condition is $x(0-) = 1$.

Solution. Since the characteristic equation of Eq. 3.102 is of second degree, we need an additional initial condition $x'(0+)$. We obtain $x'(0+)$ from the given equation at $t = 0+$,

$$x'(0+) + 3x(0+) + 2 \int_{0-}^{0+} x(\tau)\, d\tau = 5 \quad (3.103)$$

Since $x(t)$ is continuous at $t = 0$,

$$\int_{0-}^{0+} x(\tau)\, d\tau = 0 \quad (3.104)$$

and

$$x(0+) = x(0-) = 1 \quad (3.105)$$

Therefore,

$$x'(0+) = 5 - 3x(0+) = 2 \quad (3.106)$$

METHOD 1. Differentiating both sides of Eq. 3.102, we obtain

$$x''(t) + 3x'(t) + 2x(t) = 5\delta(t) \quad (3.107)$$

The complementary function is then

$$x_c(t) = C_1 e^{-t} + C_2 e^{-2t} \quad (3.108)$$

Using the initial conditions for $x(0+)$ and $x'(0+)$, we obtain the total solution,

$$x(t) = 4e^{-t} - 3e^{-2t} \quad (3.109)$$

METHOD 2. Letting $y'(t) = x(t)$, the original differential equation then becomes

$$y''(t) + 3y'(t) + 2y(t) = 5u(t) \quad (3.110)$$

We know that

$$y'(0+) = x(0+) = 1$$
$$y''(0+) = x'(0+) = 2 \tag{3.111}$$

From Eq. 3.110, at $t = 0+$, we obtain

$$y(0+) = \tfrac{1}{2}[5 - y''(0+) - 3y'(0+)] = 0 \tag{3.112}$$

Without going into the details, the total solution can be determined as

$$y(t) = -4e^{-t} + \tfrac{3}{2}e^{-2t} + \tfrac{5}{2} \tag{3.113}$$

Differentiating $y(t)$, we obtain

$$x(t) = y'(t) = 4e^{-t} - 3e^{-2t} \tag{3.114}$$

3.6 SIMULTANEOUS DIFFERENTIAL EQUATIONS

Up to this point, we have considered only differential equations with a single dependent variable $x(t)$. In this section, we will discuss equations with more than one dependent variable. We shall limit our discussion to equations with two unknowns, $x(t)$ and $y(t)$. The methods described herein, however, are applicable to any number of unknowns. Consider first, the system of homogeneous equations

$$\alpha_1 x'(t) + \alpha_0 x(t) + \beta_1 y'(t) + \beta_0 y(t) = 0$$
$$\gamma_1 x'(t) + \gamma_0 x(t) + \delta_1 y'(t) + \delta_0 y(t) = 0 \tag{3.115}$$

where $\alpha_1, \beta_1, \gamma_1, \delta_1$ are arbitrary constants. The complementary function is obtained by assuming that

$$x(t) = C_1 e^{pt}; \qquad y(t) = C_2 e^{pt}$$

so that the characteristic equation is given by the determinant

$$H(p) = \begin{vmatrix} (\alpha_1 p + \alpha_0) & (\beta_1 p + \beta_0) \\ (\gamma_1 p + \gamma_0) & (\delta_1 p + \delta_0) \end{vmatrix} \tag{3.116}$$

The roots of $H(p)$ are found by setting the determinant equal to zero, i.e.,

$$(\alpha_1 p + \alpha_0)(\delta_1 p + \delta_0) - (\beta_1 p + \beta_0)(\gamma_1 p + \gamma_0) = 0 \tag{3.117}$$

It is seen that a nontrivial solution of $H(p) = 0$ exists only if

$$(\alpha_1 p + \alpha_0)(\delta_1 p + \delta_0) \neq (\beta_1 p + \beta_0)(\gamma_1 p + \gamma_0) \tag{3.118}$$

Assuming that the above condition holds, we see that $H(p)$ is a second-degree polynomial in p and can be expressed in factored form as

$$H(p) = C(p - p_0)(p - p_1) \qquad (3.119)$$

where C is a constant multiplier. The complementary functions are

$$\begin{aligned} x(t) &= K_1 e^{p_0 t} + K_2 e^{p_1 t} \\ y(t) &= K_3 e^{p_0 t} + K_4 e^{p_1 t} \end{aligned} \qquad (3.120)$$

and the constants K_1, K_2, K_3, K_4 are determined from initial conditions. As in the case of a single unknown, if $H(p)$ has a pair of double roots; i.e., if $p_0 = p_1$, then

$$\begin{aligned} x(t) &= (K_1 + K_2 t) e^{p_0 t} \\ y(t) &= (K_3 + K_4 t) e^{p_0 t} \end{aligned} \qquad (3.121)$$

If $H(p)$ has a pair of conjugate roots,

$$\left. \begin{aligned} p_1 \\ p_1{}^* \end{aligned} \right\} = \sigma \pm j\omega$$

then

$$\begin{aligned} x(t) &= M_1 e^{\sigma t} \sin(\omega t + \phi) \\ y(t) &= M_2 e^{\sigma t} \sin(\omega t + \phi) \end{aligned} \qquad (3.122)$$

Example 3.9.   Consider the system of equations

$$\begin{aligned} 2x'(t) + 4x(t) + y'(t) - y(t) &= 0 \\ x'(t) + 2x(t) + y'(t) + y(t) &= 0 \end{aligned} \qquad (3.123)$$

with the initial conditions,

$$\begin{aligned} x'(0+) = 1 \qquad y'(0+) = 2 \\ x(0+) = 0 \qquad y(0+) = 1 \end{aligned} \qquad (3.124)$$

Solution.   The characteristic equation is

$$H(p) = \begin{vmatrix} 2p + 4 & p - 1 \\ p + 2 & p + 1 \end{vmatrix} = 0 \qquad (3.125)$$

Evaluating the determinant, we find that

$$H(p) = p^2 + 5p + 6 = (p + 2)(p + 3) \qquad (3.126)$$

so that

$$\begin{aligned} y(t) &= K_1 e^{-2t} + K_2 e^{-3t} \\ x(t) &= K_3 e^{-2t} + K_4 e^{-3t} \end{aligned} \qquad (3.127)$$

With the initial conditions, $x'(0+) = 1$, $x(0+) = 0$, we obtain $K_3 = 1$, $K_4 = -1$. From the conditions $y'(0+) = 2$, $y(0+) = 1$, we obtain $K_1 = 5$, $K_2 = -4$. Thus the final solutions are

$$x(t) = e^{-2t} - e^{-3t}$$

$$y(t) = 5e^{-2t} - 4e^{-3t}$$

(3.128)

Next, let us determine the solutions for a set of nonhomogeneous differential equations. We will use the method of undetermined coefficients here. Consider first, an exponential forcing function given by the set of equations,

$$\alpha_1 x' + \alpha_0 x + \beta_1 y' + \beta_0 y = N e^{\theta t}$$

$$\gamma_1 x' + \gamma_0 x + \delta_1 y' + \delta_0 y = 0$$

(3.129)

We first assume that

$$x_p(t) = A e^{\theta t}$$

$$y_p(t) = B e^{\theta t}$$

(3.130)

Then Eq. 3.129 becomes

$$(\alpha_1 \theta + \alpha_0)A + (\beta_1 \theta + \beta_0)B = N$$

$$(\gamma_1 \theta + \gamma_0)A + (\delta_1 \theta + \delta_0)B = 0$$

(3.131)

The determinant for the set of equations above is

$$H(\theta) = \Delta(\theta) = \begin{vmatrix} \alpha_1 \theta + \alpha_0 & \beta_1 \theta + \beta_0 \\ \gamma_1 \theta + \gamma_0 & \delta_1 \theta + \delta_0 \end{vmatrix}$$

(3.132)

where $H(\theta)$ is the characteristic equation with $p = \theta$. We now determine the undetermined coefficients, A and B from $\Delta(\theta)$ and its cofactors, *viz.*,

$$A = \frac{N\Delta_{11}(\theta)}{\Delta(\theta)}$$

$$B = \frac{N\Delta_{12}(\theta)}{\Delta(\theta)}$$

(3.133)

where Δ_{ij} is the *ij*th cofactor of $\Delta(\theta)$.

Example 3.10. Solve the set of equations,

$$2x' + 4x + y' - y = 3e^{4t}$$

$$x' + 2x + y' + y = 0$$

(3.134)

given the conditions $x'(0+) = 1$, $x(0+) = 0$, $y'(0+) = 2$, $y(0+) = -1$.

Solution.   The complementary functions $x_c(t)$ and $y_c(t)$ as well as the characteristic equation $H(p)$ were determined in Example 9. Now we must find A and B in the equations

$$x_p(t) = Ae^{4t}$$
$$y_p(t) = Be^{4t} \tag{3.135}$$

The characteristic equation with $p = 4$ is

$$H(4) = \begin{vmatrix} 2(4) + 4 & (4) - 1 \\ (4) + 2 & (4) + 1 \end{vmatrix} = 42 \tag{3.136}$$

Then we obtain from Eq. 3.133 the constants

$$A = \tfrac{5}{14} \quad B = -\tfrac{3}{7}$$

The incomplete solutions are

$$x(t) = K_1 e^{-2t} + K_2 e^{-3t} + \tfrac{5}{14}e^{4t}$$
$$y(t) = K_3 e^{-2t} + K_4 e^{-3t} - \tfrac{3}{7}e^{4t} \tag{3.137}$$

Substituting for the initial conditions, we finally obtain

$$y(t) = \tfrac{1}{7}(30e^{-2t} - 34e^{-3t} - 3e^{4t}$$
$$x(t) = \tfrac{1}{14}(-6e^{-2t} + e^{-3t} + 5e^{4t}) \tag{3.138}$$

Example 3.11.   Solve the system of equations,

$$2x' + 4x + y' + 7y = 5u(t)$$
$$x' + x + y' + 3y = 5\delta(t) \tag{3.139}$$

given the initial conditions

$$x(0-) = x'(0-) = y(0-) = y'(0-) = 0$$

Solution.   First we find the characteristic equation

$$H(p) = \Delta(p) = \begin{vmatrix} 2p + 4 & p + 7 \\ p + 1 & p + 3 \end{vmatrix} \tag{3.140}$$

which simplifies to give

$$H(p) = (p^2 + 2p + 5) = (p + 1 + j2)(p + 1 - j2) \tag{3.141}$$

The complementary functions $x_c(t)$ and $y_c(t)$ are then,

$$x_c(t) = A_1 e^{-t} \cos 2t + A_2 e^{-t} \sin 2t$$
$$y_c(t) = B_1 e^{-t} \cos 2t + B_2 e^{-t} \sin 2t \tag{3.142}$$

The particular solutions are obtained for the set of equations with $t > 0$, *viz.*,

$$2x' + 4x + y' + 7y = 5$$
$$x' + x + y' + 3y = 0 \tag{3.143}$$

Using the method of undetermined coefficients, we assume that x_p and y_p are constants:

$$x_p = C_1$$
$$y_p = C_2$$

Since the forcing function 5 can be regarded as an exponential term with zero exponent, i.e.,

$$5 = 5e^{0t}$$

we can solve for C_1 and C_2 with the use of the characteristic equation $H(p)$, with $p = 0$. Thus,

$$H(0) = \Delta(0) = \begin{vmatrix} 4 & 7 \\ 1 & 3 \end{vmatrix} = 5 \qquad (3.144)$$

and

$$C_1 = \frac{5\Delta_{11}(0)}{\Delta(0)} = \frac{5(3)}{5} = 3$$

$$C_2 = -\frac{5(1)}{5} = -1 \qquad (3.145)$$

The general solution is then

$$x(t) = A_1 e^{-t} \cos 2t + A_2 e^{-t} \sin 2t + 3$$
$$y(t) = B_1 e^{-t} \cos 2t + B_2 e^{-t} \sin 2t - 1 \qquad (3.146)$$

In order to find A_1, A_2, B_1, B_2, we need the values $x(0+)$, $x'(0+)$, $y(0+)$, $y'(0+)$. The values for $x(0+)$ and $y(0+)$ are first obtained by integrating the original differential equations between $t = 0-$ and $t = 0+$. Thus,

$$\int_{0-}^{0+} (2x' + 4x + y' + 7y)\, dt = \int_{0-}^{0+} 5u(t)\, dt$$
$$\int_{0-}^{0+} (x' + x + y' + 3y)\, dt = \int_{0-}^{0+} 5\delta(t)\, dt \qquad (3.147)$$

We know that only the highest derivative terms in both equations contain impulses at $t = 0$. Moreover, both $x(t)$ and $y(t)$ contain, at most, step discontinuities at $t = 0$. Therefore, in the integration,

$$\int_{0-}^{0+} (4x + 7y)\, dt = 0$$
$$\int_{0-}^{0+} (x + 3y)\, dt = 0 \qquad (3.148)$$

After integrating, we obtain

$$2x(0+) + y(0+) = 0$$
$$x(0+) + y(0+) = 5 \qquad (3.149)$$

Solving, we find

$$x(0+) = -5 \quad y(0+) = 10 \tag{3.150}$$

To find $x'(0+)$ and $y'(0+)$, we substitute the values for $x(0+)$ and $y(0+)$ into the original equations at $t = 0+$. Thus

$$2x'(0+) - 20 + y'(0+) + 70 = 5$$
$$x'(0+) - 5 + y'(0+) + 30 = 0 \tag{3.151}$$

so that

$$x'(0+) = -20$$
$$y'(0+) = -5 \tag{3.152}$$

Substituting these values into Eq. 3.146, we eventually obtain the final solutions

$$x(t) = (-8e^{-t} \cos 2t - 14e^{-t} \sin 2t + 3) \, u(t),$$
$$y(t) = (11e^{-t} \cos 2t + 3e^{-t} \sin 2t - 1) \, u(t) \tag{3.153}$$

Problems

3.1 Show that
$$x_1(t) = M_1 e^{-t} \cos 2t$$
and
$$x_2(t) = M_2 e^{-t} \sin 2t$$
are solutions for the equation
$$x''(t) + 2x'(t) + 5x(t) = 0$$

Show that $x_1 + x_2$ is also a solution.

3.2 Determine only the *form* of the solution for the equations:

(a) $\qquad\qquad\qquad x''(t) + 4x'(t) + 3x(t) = 0$
(b) $\qquad\qquad\qquad x''(t) + 8x'(t) + 5x(t) = 0$
(c) $\qquad\qquad\qquad\qquad x''(t) - 5x(t) = 0$
(d) $\qquad\qquad\qquad\qquad x''(t) + 5x(t) = 0$
(e) $\qquad\qquad\qquad x''(t) + 6x'(t) + 25x(t) = 0$
(f) $\qquad\qquad\qquad x''(t) + 6x'(t) + 9x(t) = 0$

3.3 Given the initial conditions $x(0+) = 1$, $x'(0+) = -1$, determine the solutions for:

(a) $\qquad\qquad\qquad x''(t) + 6x'(t) + 25x(t) = 0$
(b) $\qquad\qquad\qquad x''(t) + 8x'(t) + 16x(t) = 0$
(c) $\qquad\qquad x''(t) + 4.81x'(t) + 5.76x(t) = 0$

3.4   Find only the particular integrals for the equations:

(a) $x''(t) + 7x'(t) + 12x(t) = e^{-3t}$

(b) $x''(t) + 3x'(t) + 2x(t) = 2 \sin 3t$

(c) $x''(t) + 2x'(t) + 5x(t) = e^{-t} \sin 2t$

(d) $x''(t) + 2x'(t) + 5x(t) = \dfrac{e^{-5t}}{2}$

(e) $x''(t) + 5.0x'(t) + 6.25x(t) = 6$

(f) $x''(t) + 6x'(t) + 5x(t) = 2e^{-t} + 3e^{-3t}$

3.5   Given the initial conditions $x(0+) = 1$, $x'(0+) = 0$, determine the solutions for:

(a) $x''(t) + 4x'(t) + 3x(t) = 5e^{-t} \sin 2t$

(b) $x''(t) + 6x'(t) + 25x(t) = 2 \cos t$

(c) $x''(t) + 8x'(t) + 16x(t) = 2$

3.6   Given the initial conditions, $x(0-) = x'(0-) = 0$, $x''(0-) = 1$, find $x'(0+)$ and $x''(0+)$ for the equations

(a) $6x''(t) + 4x'(t) + 3x(t) = 5\delta(t)$

(b) $4x''(t) + 3x'(t) + 2x(t) = \frac{1}{2}\delta(t)$

3.7   Given the initial conditions $x'(0-) = x''(0-) = x(0-) = 0$, find the solutions for the equations:

(a) $x''(t) + 2x'(t) + 2x(t) = 3\delta(t)$

(b) $x''(t) + 7x'(t) + 12x(t) = 5u(t)$

3.8   Given the initial condition $x(0-) = -2$, solve the integrodifferential equations:

(a) $x'(t) + 5x(t) + 4\displaystyle\int_0^t x(\tau)\, d\tau = 2 \sin t$

(b) $x'(t) + 2x(t) + 2\displaystyle\int_0^t x(\tau)\, d\tau = \dfrac{3}{2} e^{-t}$

(c) $x'(t) + 6x(t) + 9\displaystyle\int_0^t x(\tau)\, d\tau = 2u(t)$

3.9   Solve the system of equations;

$$2x'(t) + 2x(t) + y'(t) - y(t) = 0 = f_1(t)$$
$$x'(t) + x(t) + y'(t) + 2y(t) = 0 = f_2(t)$$

given the initial conditions $y'(0+) = 0$, $y(0+) = 1$, $x'(0+) = 2$, $x(0+) = -1$.

3.10   For the set of equations in Prob. 3.9, let $f_1(t) = 5u(t)$ and $f_2(t) = 3e^{-2t}$. Find the particular integrals for the equations.

3.11   For the set of equations in Prob. 3.9, let $f_1(t) = 2\delta(t)$, and $f_2(t) = 3e^{-t}$. Find $x(t)$ and $y(t)$ for the initial conditions $x(0-) = 1$, $x'(0-) = -1$, $y(0-) = 0$, $y'(0-) = 2$.

3.12   Derive Eq. 3.84.

chapter 4
Network analysis (I)

4.1 INTRODUCTION

In this chapter, we will apply our knowledge of differential equations to the analysis of linear, passive, time-invariant networks. We will assume that the reader is already familiar with Kirchhoff's current and voltage laws, and also methods for writing mesh and node equations for a-c or d-c circuits.* We will, therefore, consider only briefly the problem of writing mesh and node equations when the independent variable is time t. The problems within this chapter have the following format: Given an excitation signal from an energy source and the network, a specified response is to be determined which is a current or voltage in the network. When relating these problems to the mathematics in Chapter 3, we shall see that, physically, the forcing function corresponds to the excitation, the network is described by the differential equation, and the unknown variable $x(t)$ is the response.

The problems encountered will be twofold. First, we must *write* the differential equations of the network using Kirchhoff's current and voltage laws. Next, we must *solve* these equations for a specified current or voltage in the network. Both problems are equally important. It is useless, for example, to solve a differential equation which is set up incorrectly, or whose initial conditions are incorrectly specified.

The usual type of problem to be presented herein might be generally described as follows. A switch is closed at $t = 0$ which connects an energy (voltage or current) source to a network (Fig. 4.1). The analog of a switch closing at $t = 0$ is the energy source whose output is $e(t) u(t)$. Before the

---

* For a comprehensive treatment, see H. H. Skilling, *Electrical Engineering Circuits*, John Wiley and Sons, New York, 1957.

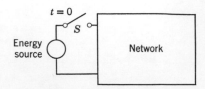

FIG. 4.1. Switching action.

switch is closed, the currents and voltages in the network have known values. These values at $t = 0-$ are the initial conditions. We must then determine the values of the currents and voltages just after the switch closes, at $t = 0+$, to solve the network equations. If the excitation is not an impulse function or any of its derivatives, the current and voltage variables are continuous at $t = 0$. For an impulse driver, the values at $t = 0+$ can be determined from methods given in the previous chapter. Having obtained the initial conditions, we then go on to solve the network differential equations. Unless otherwise stated, all the solutions are valid *only* for $t \geq 0+$.

Since we are dealing only with linear circuits, it is essential that we bear in mind the all-important principle of *superposition*. According to the superposition principle, the current through any element in a linear circuit with n voltage and m current sources is equal to the algebraic sum of currents through the same element resulting from the sources taken one at a time, the other sources having been suppressed. Consider the linear network depicted in Fig. 4.2a with n voltage and m current sources. Suppose

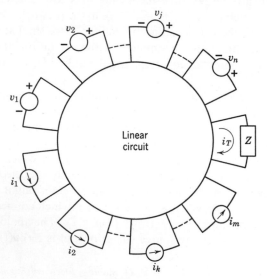

FIG. 4.2*a*

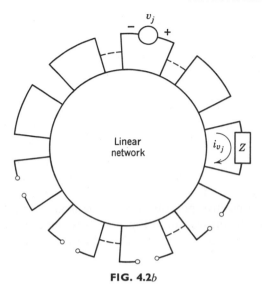

FIG. 4.2*b*

we are interested in the current $i_T(t)$ through a given element Z, as shown. Let us open-circuit all the current sources and short-circuit $n - 1$ voltage sources, leaving only $v_j(t)$ shown in Fig. 4.2*b*. We will denote by $i_{v_j}(t)$ the current through Z due to the voltage source $v_j(t)$ alone. In similar fashion, we will denote by $i_{C_k}(t)$ the current through Z due to the current source $i_k(t)$ alone, as depicted in Fig. 4.2*c*. By the superposition

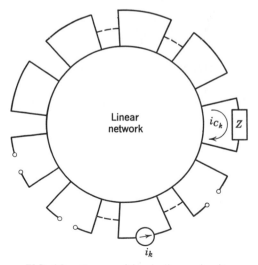

FIG. 4.2*c*. Superposition in linear circuits.

direction, and write the equations for the sum of the voltages around the loops. As the reader might recall from his previous studies, if the number of branches in the network is B, and if the number of nodes is N, then the number of independent loop equations for the network is $B - N + 1$.* We must, in addition, choose the mesh currents such that at least one mesh current passes through every element in the network.

Example 4.1.   In Fig. 4.6, a network is given with seven branches and five nodes. We therefore need $7 - 5 + 1 = 3$ independent mesh equations. The directions of the mesh currents i_1, i_2, i_3 are chosen as indicated. We also note that the capacitors in the circuit have associated initial voltages. These initial voltages are assigned reference polarities, as shown in the figure. Now we proceed to write the mesh equations.

Mesh i_1:

$$v(t) - v_{C_1}(0-) = R_1 i_1(t) + \frac{1}{C_1} \int_{0-}^{t} i_1(\tau)\, d\tau - \frac{1}{C_1} \int_{0-}^{t} i_2(\tau)\, d\tau$$

Mesh i_2:

$$v_{C_1}(0-) - v_{C_2}(0-) = -\frac{1}{C_1} \int_{0-}^{t} i_1(\tau)\, d\tau + L_1 \frac{di_2}{dt}$$

$$+ \left(\frac{1}{C_1} + \frac{1}{C_2} \right) \int_{0-}^{t} i_2(\tau)\, d\tau - \frac{1}{C_2} \int_{0-}^{t} i_3(\tau)\, d\tau$$

Mesh i_3:

$$-v_2(t) + v_{C_2}(0-) = \frac{-1}{C_2} \int_{0-}^{t} i_2(\tau)\, d\tau + \frac{1}{C_2} \int_{0-}^{t} i_3(\tau)\, d\tau + R_2 i_3(t) \quad (4.5)$$

After we find the three unknowns, i_1, i_2, and i_3, we can determine the branch currents and the voltages across the elements. For example, if we were required to find the branch currents i_{C_1} and i_{C_2} through the capacitors, we would use the following relationships

$$i_{C_1} = i_1 - i_2$$

$$\tag{4.6}$$

$$i_{C_2} = i_2 - i_3$$

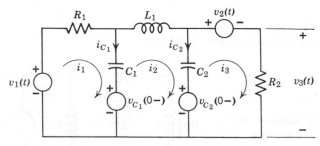

FIG. 4.6

---

* See H. H. Skilling, *op. cit.*

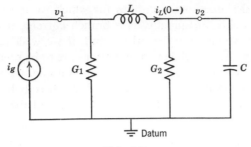

FIG. 4.7

Alternatively, if the voltage $v_3(t)$ in Fig. 4.6 is our objective, we see that

$$v_3(t) = +i_3(t)R_3 \tag{4.7}$$

Network equations can also be written in terms of node equations, which are based upon Kirchhoff's current law. If the number of nodes in the network is N, then the number of independent node equations required for the complete solution of the network is $N - 1$.* We can therefore select one *datum* node in the network. All the node voltages will be positive with respect to this datum node.

Consider the network in Fig. 4.7. Let us write a set of node equations for the network with the datum node shown. Since the number of nodes in the network is $N = 3$, we need $N - 1 = 2$ independent node equations. These are written for nodes v_1 and v_2, as given below.

Node v_1:

$$i_g(t) - i_L(0-) = G_1 v_1(t) + \frac{1}{L} \int_{0-}^{t} v_1(\tau)\, d\tau - \frac{1}{L} \int_{0-}^{t} v_2(\tau)\, d\tau$$

Node v_2:

$$i_L(0-) = -\frac{1}{L} \int_{0-}^{t} v_1(\tau)\, d\tau + \frac{1}{L} \int_{0-}^{t} v_2(\tau)\, d\tau + C \frac{d\, v_2(t)}{dt} + G_2\, v_2(t) \tag{4.8}$$

Further examples are given in the following sections.

4.3 SOLUTION OF NETWORK EQUATIONS

In this section, we will apply our knowledge of differential equations to the analysis of linear networks. There are two important points in network analysis: the *writing* of network equations and the *solution* of these same equations. Network equations can be written on either a mesh or node basis. The choice between mesh and node equations depends

---

* See H. H. Skilling, *op. cit.*

largely upon the unknown quantities for which we must solve. For instance, if the unknown quantity is a branch current, it is preferable to write mesh equations. On the other hand, if we wish to find a voltage across a certain element, then node equations are to be preferred. In many cases, the choice is quite arbitrary. If, for example, we wish to find the voltage v across a resistor R, we can either find v directly by node equations or find the branch current through the resistor and then multiply by R.

Example 4.2. Given the R-L network in Fig. 4.8, find the current $i(t)$, given that the excitation (voltage source) is an impulse, $e(t) = \delta(t)$, and that $i_L(0-) = 0$.

Solution. The differential equation relating the excitation $e(t)$ and the response $i(t)$ is

$$\delta(t) = L\frac{di}{dt} + R\,i(t) \tag{4.9}$$

First we must find $i_L(0+)$. We know that the term $L\,i'(t)$ must contain an impulse at $t = 0$; $R\,i(t)$ must then have a step discontinuity at $t = 0$. If we integrate both sides of Eq. 4.9 between $t = 0-$ and $t = 0+$, we obtain

$$L[i(0+) - i(0-)] = 1 \tag{4.10}$$

Therefore

$$i(0+) = \frac{1}{L} \tag{4.11}$$

From this point on, Eq. 4.9 is solved as though it were a homogeneous equation. The characteristic equation is

$$Lp + R = 0 \tag{4.12}$$

so that the complementary function is

$$i(t) = Ke^{-(R/L)t}\,u(t) \tag{4.13}$$

Substituting the value $i(0+)$, we find the impulse response,

$$i(t) = \frac{1}{L}\,e^{-(R/L)t}\,u(t) \tag{4.14}$$

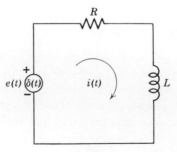

FIG. 4.8

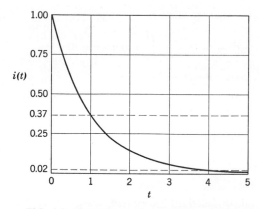

FIG. 4.9. Normalized curve for time constant $T = 1$.

In many physical problems, it is important to know how quickly the response waveform decays. A useful measure of the decay of an exponential is the time constant, T. For the $R\text{-}L$ network just considered, the time constant $T = L/R$. In terms of the time constant, Eq. 4.14 is rewritten as

$$i(t) = \frac{1}{L} e^{-t/T} u(t) \tag{4.15}$$

From a plot of $i(t)$ in Fig. 4.9, with $L = 1$, we see that, when $t = T$,

$$i(T) = 0.37i(0), \qquad i(4T) = 0.02i(0) \tag{4.16, 4.17}$$

Observe that the larger the time constant, the longer it requires for the waveform to reach 37% of its peak value. In circuit design, the time constant T is an important specification—especially in the design of pulse-forming networks.

Example 4.3. Find the current $i(t)$ for the network in Fig. 4.10, when the voltage source is $e(t) = 2e^{-0.5t} u(t)$ and $i(0-) = 0$, $v_C(0-) = 0$.

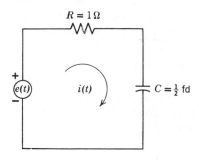

FIG. 4.10

Solution. The differential equation is

$$e(t) = Ri(t) + \frac{1}{C} \int_{0-}^{t} i(\tau) \, d\tau + v_C(0-) \tag{4.18}$$

Or, in terms of the numerical values, we have

$$2e^{-0.5t} u(t) = i(t) + 2 \int_{0-}^{t} i(\tau) \, d\tau \tag{4.19}$$

Differentiating both sides of Eq. 4.19, we obtain

$$2\delta(t) - e^{-0.5t} u(t) = \frac{di(t)}{dt} + 2i(t) \tag{4.20}$$

To obtain the initial condition $i(0+)$, we must integrate Eq. 4.20 between the limits $t = 0-$ and $t = 0+$ to give $i(0+) = 2$. From the characteristic equation

$$H(p) = p + 2 = 0 \tag{4.21}$$

we obtain the complementary function as

$$i_C(t) = Ke^{-2t} \tag{4.22}$$

If we assume the particular integral to be $i_p(t) = Ae^{-0.5t}$, then we obtain

$$A = -\frac{1}{H(-0.5)} = -\frac{2}{3} \tag{4.23}$$

The incomplète solution is

$$i(t) = Ke^{-2t} - \tfrac{2}{3}e^{-0.5t} \tag{4.24}$$

From the initial condition $i(0+) = 2$, we obtain the final solution,

$$i(t) = (\tfrac{8}{3}e^{-2t} - \tfrac{2}{3}e^{-0.5t}) u(t) \tag{4.25}$$

In the solution of network differential equations, the complementary function is called the *free response* whereas the *forced response* is a particular integral. In the case of constant or periodic excitation, the forced response at $t = \infty$ is the *steady-state* solution. Note that the free response is a function of the network elements alone and is independent of excitation. On the other hand, the forced response depends on both the network and the excitation.

It is significant to note that, for networks which have only positive elements, the free response is made up of only damped exponential and/or sinusoids with constant peak amplitudes. In other words, the roots of the characteristic equation, $H(p)$, all have negative or zero real parts. For example, if p_1 is a root of $H(p)$ written as

$$p_1 = \sigma \pm j\omega$$

then $\text{Re}\,(p_1) = \sigma \leq 0$. This fact is intuitively reasonable because, if a bounded excitation produces a response that is exponentially increasing, then conservation of energy is not preserved. This is one of the most important properties of a passive network. If a characteristic equation contains only roots whose real parts are zero or negative and if the $j\omega$ axis roots are simple, then the network which it describes is said to be *stable*; otherwise, the network is *unstable*.* Stability is an important property of passive networks and will be discussed in greater detail later.

In obtaining the steady-state solution for a network with a periodic excitation or a constant (d-c) excitation, we can draw upon knowledge gained from previous circuit courses. For example, for the R-L network in Fig. 4.8, if the excitation were a battery of E volts, then the steady-state current would be

$$i_p(t) = \frac{E}{R}$$

because at $t = \infty$, the inductor L is, in effect, a short circuit. For the R-C circuit in Fig. 4.11, the current generator is

$$i_g(t) = I_0 \sin \omega t \, u(t) \tag{4.26}$$

We can find the steady-state voltage $v_p(t)$ across the capacitor as follows:

$$v_p(t) = \text{Im}\, \frac{I(j\omega)}{Y(j\omega)} \tag{4.27}$$

where $Y(j\omega)$ is the a-c admittance

$$Y(j\omega) = G + j\omega C \tag{4.28}$$

and

$$I(j\omega) = I_0 e^{j\omega t} \tag{4.29}$$

From Eq. 4.27 we obtain

$$v_p(t) = \frac{I_0}{(G^2 + \omega^2 C^2)^{\frac{1}{2}}} \sin\left(\omega t - \tan^{-1} \frac{\omega C}{G}\right) \tag{4.30}$$

Example 4.4. For the R-C network in Fig. 4.11 with the excitation given by Eq. 4.26 as before, find the voltage $v(t)$ across the capacitor; it is given that $v(0-) = v_C(0-) = 0$.

Solution. We have already obtained the particular integral in Eq. 4.30. Now let us find the complementary function. The differential equation on node basis is

$$C\frac{dv}{dt} + Gv = I_0 \sin \omega t \, u(t) \tag{4.31}$$

---

* This is not a formal definition of stability but it suffices for the moment.

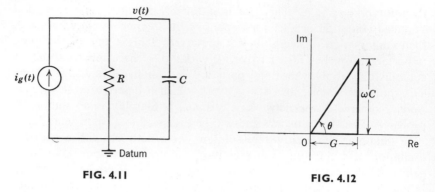

FIG. 4.11   FIG. 4.12

from which we obtain the characteristic equation as

$$H(p) = Cp + G \tag{4.32}$$

so that

$$v_C(t) = Ke^{-G/Ct} u(t) \tag{4.33}$$

and the incomplete solution is

$$v(t) = Ke^{-G/Ct} u(t) + \frac{I_0}{(G^2 + \omega^2 C^2)^{1/2}} \sin\left(\omega t - \tan^{-1}\frac{\omega C}{G}\right) u(t) \tag{4.34}$$

From the initial condition $v(0-) = 0$, we obtain

$$v(0+) = v(0-) = K - \frac{I_0}{(G^2 + \omega^2 C^2)^{1/2}} \sin\left(\tan^{-1}\frac{\omega C}{G}\right) = 0 \tag{4.35}$$

From the argand diagram in Fig. 4.12, we see that

$$\sin\left(\tan^{-1}\frac{\omega C}{G}\right) = \frac{\omega C}{(G^2 + \omega^2 C^2)^{1/2}} \tag{4.36}$$

Consequently,

$$v(t) = \frac{I_0 u(t)}{(G^2 + \omega^2 C^2)^{1/2}}\left[\frac{\omega C e^{-G/Ct}}{(G^2 + \omega^2 C^2)^{1/2}} + \sin\left(\omega t - \tan^{-1}\frac{\omega C}{G}\right)\right] \tag{4.37}$$

From the complementary function in Eq. 4.33, we see that the time constant of the circuit is $T = C/G = RC$.

Next, let us discuss through an example the different kinds of free responses of a second-order network equation that depend on relative values of the network elements. Suppose we are given the network in Fig. 4.13; let us find the free response $v_C(t)$ for the differential equation

$$i_g(t) = C\frac{dv}{dt} + Gv + \frac{1}{L}\int_{0-}^{t} v(\tau)\, d\tau + i_L(0-) \tag{4.38}$$

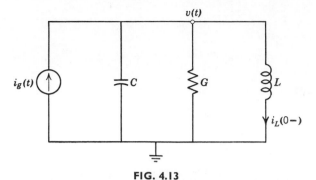

FIG. 4.13

Differentiating both sides of Eq. 4.35, we have

$$i'_g(t) = C\,v''(t) + G\,v'(t) + \frac{1}{L}\,v(t). \tag{4.39}$$

The characteristic equation is then

$$H(p) = Cp^2 + Gp + \frac{1}{L} = C\left(p^2 + \frac{G}{C}p + \frac{1}{LC}\right) \tag{4.40}$$

In factored form, $H(p)$ is

$$H(p) = C(p - p_1)(p - p_2) \tag{4.41}$$

where

$$\left.\begin{array}{c}p_1 \\ p_2\end{array}\right\} = -\frac{G}{2C} \pm \frac{1}{2}\left[\left(\frac{G}{C}\right)^2 - \frac{4}{LC}\right]^{\frac{1}{2}} \triangleq -A \pm B \tag{4.42}$$

There are three different kinds of responses depending upon whether B is real, zero, or imaginary.

CASE 1. B is real, i.e.,

$$\left(\frac{G}{C}\right)^2 > \frac{4}{LC}$$

then the free response is

$$v_C(t) = K_1 e^{-(A - B)t} + K_2 e^{-(A + B)t} \tag{4.43}$$

which is a sum of damped exponentials. In this case, the response is said to be *overdamped*. An example of an overdamped response is shown in Fig. 4.14.

CASE 2. $B = 0$, i.e.,

$$\left(\frac{G}{C}\right)^2 = \frac{4}{LC}$$

then

$$p_1 = p_2 = -A$$

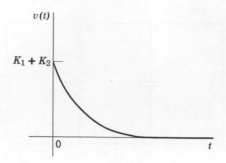

FIG. 4.14. Overdamped response.

so that

$$v_C(t) = (K_1 + K_2 t)e^{-At} \qquad (4.44)$$

When $B = 0$, the response is *critically damped*, as shown in Fig. 4.15.

CASE 3. $B < 0$, i.e.,

$$\left(\frac{G}{C}\right)^2 < \frac{4}{LC}$$

Letting $B = j\beta$, we have

$$v_C(t) = e^{-At}(K_1 \sin \beta t + K_2 \cos \beta t) \qquad (4.45)$$

In this case, the response is said to be *underdamped*, and is shown by the damped oscillatory curve in Fig. 4.16.

Example 4.5. In this example, we will discuss the solution of a set of simultaneous network equations. As in the previous examples, we will rely upon physical reasoning rather than formal mathematical operations to obtain the initial currents and voltages as well as the steady-state solutions. In the network of Fig. 4.17, the switch S is thrown from position 1 to position 2 at $t = 0$. It is known that prior to $t = 0$, the circuit had been in steady state. We will make the idealized assumption that the switch closes instantaneously at $t = 0$ and there is no "sparking" between the contacts of the switch. Our task is to find $i_1(t)$ and $i_2(t)$ after the switch position changes. The values of the batteries V_1 and V_2 are $V_1 = 2$ v, $V_2 = 3$ v; and the element values are given as

$$L = 1 \text{ h}, \qquad R_1 = 0.5 \ \Omega$$
$$C = \tfrac{1}{3} \text{ fd}, \qquad R_2 = 2.0 \ \Omega$$

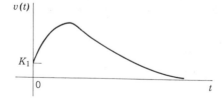

FIG. 4.15. Critically damped response.

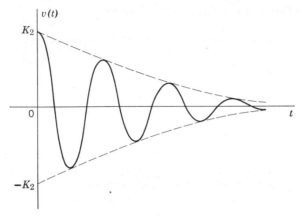

FIG. 4.16. Underdamped response.

The mesh equations for $i_1(t)$ and $i_2(t)$ after $t = 0$ are:

$$V_2 = L\,i'_1(t) + R_1\,i_1(t) - R_1\,i_2(t) \tag{4.46}$$

$$-v_C(0-) = -R_1\,i_1(t) + \frac{1}{C}\int_{0-}^{t} i_2(\tau)\,d\tau + (R_1 + R_2)\,i_2(t) \tag{4.47}$$

Since Eq. 4.47 contains an integral, we differentiate it to give

$$0 = -R_1\,i'_1(t) + \frac{1}{C}\,i_2(t) + (R_1 + R_2)\,i'_2(t) \tag{4.48}$$

Using Eqs. 4.46 and 4.48 as our system of equations, we obtain the characteristic equation,

$$H(p) = \begin{vmatrix} Lp + R_1 & -R_1 \\ -R_1p & \dfrac{1}{C} + (R_1 + R_2)p \end{vmatrix}$$

$$= L(R_1 + R_2)p^2 + \left(\frac{L}{C} + R_1R_2\right)p + \frac{R_1}{C} \tag{4.49}$$

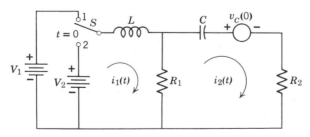

FIG. 4.17

Substituting the element values into $H(p)$, we have

$$H(p) = 2.5p^2 + 4p + 1.5 = 2.5(p + 1)(p + 0.6) \qquad (4.50)$$

The free responses are then

$$i_{1C}(t) = (K_1 e^{-0.6t} + K_2 e^{-t}) u(t)$$
$$i_{2C}(t) = (K_3 e^{-0.6t} + K_4 e^{-t}) u(t) \qquad (4.51)$$

The steady-state solutions for the mesh currents are obtained at $t = \infty$ by considering the circuit from a d-c viewpoint. The inductor is then a short circuit and the capacitor is an open circuit; thus we have

$$i_{1p}(t) = \frac{V_2}{R_1} = 6 \text{ amp}$$
$$i_{2p}(t) = 0 \qquad (4.52)$$

Now let us determine the initial currents and voltages which, incidentally, have the same values at $t = 0-$ and $t = 0+$ because the voltage sources are not impulses. Before the switch is thrown at $t = 0$, the circuit with V_1 as the voltage source was at steady state. Consequently,

$$v_C(0-) = V_1 = 2 \text{ v}$$

$$i_1(0-) = \frac{V_1}{R_1} = 4 \text{ amp} \qquad (4.53)$$

$$i_2(0-) = 0$$

We next find $i'_1(0+)$ from Eq. 4.46 at $t = 0+$:

$$V_2 = L i'_1(0+) + R_1 i_1(0+) - R_2 i_2(0+) \qquad (4.54)$$

Substituting numerical values into Eq. 4.54 we find,

$$i'_1(0+) = 1 \text{ amp}$$

From Eq. 4.48 at $t = 0+$, we obtain similarly,

$$i'_2(0+) = \frac{R_1}{R_1 + R_2} i'_1(0+) = 0.2 \text{ amp} \qquad (4.55)$$

With these initial values of $i_1(t)$ and $i_2(t)$, we can quickly arrive at the final solutions

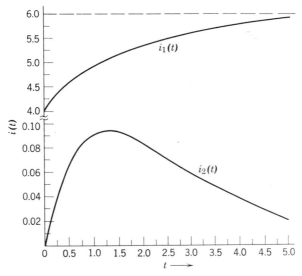

FIG. 4.18

$$i_1(t) = (0.5e^{-t} - 2.5e^{-0.6t} + 6)\, u(t)$$

$$i_2(t) = (-0.5e^{-t} + 0.5e^{-0.6t})\, u(t)$$

(4.56)

which are plotted in Fig. 4.18.

4.4 ANALYSIS OF TRANSFORMERS

According to *Faraday's law of induction*, a current i_1 flowing in a coil L_1 may *induce* a current i_2 in a closed loop containing a second coil L_2. The sufficient conditions for inducing the current i_2 are: (*a*) part of the flux Φ_1 in the coil L_1 must be coupled magnetically to the coil L_2; (*b*) the flux Φ_1 must be changing with time.

In this section, we will analyze circuits containing a device made up of two magnetically coupled coils known as a *transformer*. In Fig. 4.19, the

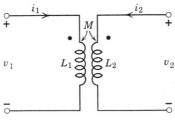

FIG. 4.19. Transformer.

schematic of a transformer is given. The L_1 side of the transformer is usually referred to as the *primary coil* and the L_2 side as the *secondary coil*. The only distinction between primary and secondary is that the energy source is generally at the primary side.

The transformer in Fig. 4.19 is described mathematically by the equations,

$$v_1(t) = L_1 \frac{di_1}{dt} + M \frac{di_2}{dt}$$

$$v_2(t) = M \frac{di_1}{dt} + L_2 \frac{di_2}{dt}$$

(4.57)

where M is the *mutual inductance* which is associated with the flux linking L_1 to L_2, and is related to L_1 and L_2 by the relationship,

$$M = K \sqrt{L_1 L_2}$$

(4.58)

The constant K in Eq. 4.58 is called the *coefficient of coupling*. It is bounded by the limits, $0 \leq |K| \leq 1$. If $|K| = 1$, then all of the flux Φ_1 in coil L_1 is linked magnetically to L_2. In this case, the transformer is a *unity coupled* transformer. If $K = 0$, the coils L_1 and L_2 may be regarded as two separate coils having no effect upon one another.

In the case of circuits with transformers, we must establish reference polarities for the mutually induced voltages $M \, di/dt$. Usually, the references are given by small dots painted on the input and output leads of a transformer, as shown by the dots on the schematic in Fig. 4.20. The reference dots are placed at the time of manufacture according to the procedure to be outlined below. A voltage source v is connected to the primary (L_1) side of the transformer, as shown in Fig. 4.20. On the secondary, a voltmeter is attached. At the primary side, that terminal is assigned the dot reference to which we connect the *positive* lead of the voltage source. The dot reference is placed on the secondary terminal at which the voltmeter indicates a positive voltage. In terms of the primary current i_1, the positive voltage at the secondary dot is due to the current i_1 flowing into the dot on the primary side. Since the positive voltage at the

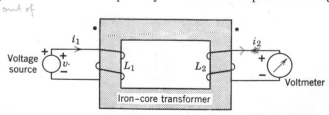

FIG. 4.20. An experiment to determine dot references.

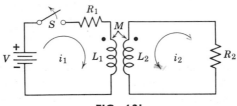

FIG. 4.21

secondary dot corresponds to the current i_2 flowing ~~into~~ out of that dot, we can think of the dot references in the following way. If both currents are flowing into the dots or away from the dots, then the sign of the mutual voltage term $M\, di/dt$ is positive. When one current flows into a dot and the other away from the second dot, then the sign of $M\, di/dt$ is negative.

If N_1 and N_2 are the number of turns of coils L_1 and L_2, then the *flux linkages* of L_1 and L_2 are given by $N_1 i_1$ and $N_2 i_2$ respectively. If both i_1 and i_2 flow into the dots, then the sum of flux linkages of the transformer is

$$\sum \Phi \text{ linkages} = N_1 i_1 + N_2 i_2 \qquad (4.59)$$

If, however, one of the currents, say i_1, flows into a dot, and the other (i_2) flows out of the other dot, then

$$\sum \Phi \text{ linkages} = N_1 i_1 - N_2 i_2 \qquad (4.60)$$

An important rule which governs the behavior of a transformer is that the sum of flux linkages is continuous with time.

Consider the transformer in Fig. 4.21. Let us assume that initially $(t = 0-)$ the switch is closed and the circuit is at steady state. At time $t = 0$, we open the switch. Let us determine the value of $i_2(0+)$. We know that

$$i_1(0-) = \frac{V}{R_1}, \qquad i_1(0+) = 0$$

Moreover, we know that $i_2(0-) = 0$ because the battery does not produce a flux that is changing with time. Because the sum of flux linkages must be continuous, we have

$$N_1 i_1(0+) + N_2 i_2(0+) = N_1 i_1(0-) + N_2 i_2(0-) \qquad (4.61)$$

Therefore,

$$i_2(0+) = \frac{N_1}{N_2} i_1(0-) = \frac{N_1}{N_2} \frac{V}{R_1} \qquad (4.62)$$

From physical considerations, it is known that

$$\frac{N_1{}^2}{N_2{}^2} = \frac{L_1}{L_2} \qquad (4.63)$$

so that

$$i_2(0+) = \sqrt{\frac{L_1}{L_2}} \frac{V}{R_1} \qquad (4.64)$$

We see from this example that currents in a transformer need not be continuous in time; i.e., they may jump instantaneously from one value to another. It is clear that i_1 jumps from V/R_1 to 0 because opening the switch produces an open circuit. Because of the continuity of flux linkages, we see that i_2 also jumps instantaneously at $t = 0$.

Now let us consider some additional problems in determining initial conditions in circuits with transformers. Assume for the circuit in Fig. 4.21 that, prior to $t = 0$, the switch is open and no currents flow in the transformer, so that $i_1(0-) = i_2(0-) = 0$. At $t = 0$, we close the switch. Are the initial conditions $i_1(0+)$ and $i_2(0+)$ equal to $i_1(0-)$ and $i_2(0-)$? Not necessarily, as will be shown in the following.

The differential equations for the transformer are

$$V u(t) = L_1 i'_1(t) + R_1 i_1(t) + M i'_2(t)$$
$$0 = M i'_1(t) + R_2 i_2(t) + L_2 i'_2(t) \qquad (4.65)$$

Integrating this set of equations between $t = 0-$ and $t = 0+$, results in the determinant,

$$\begin{vmatrix} L_1[i_1(0+) - i_1(0-)] & M[i_2(0+) - i_2(0-)] \\ M[i_1(0+) - i_1(0-)] & L_2[i_2(0+) - i_2(0-)] \end{vmatrix} = 0 \qquad (4.66)$$

By evaluating this determinant, we obtain

$$(L_1 L_2 - M^2)[i_1(0+) - i_1(0-)][i_2(0+) - i_2(0-)] = 0 \qquad (4.67)$$

if $L_1 L_2 > M^2$ (i.e., $K < 1$), then the currents must be continuous at $t = 0$ in order for the determinant in Eq. 4.66 to be equal to zero. Thus,

$$i_1(0+) = i_1(0-), \qquad K < 1 \qquad (4.68)$$

and from Eq. 4.61, we have,

$$i_2(0+) = i_2(0-), \qquad K < 1 \qquad (4.69)$$

Suppose, now, $L_1 L_2 = M^2$, i.e., $(K = 1)$, then $i_1(t)$ and $i_2(t)$ need not be continuous at $t = 0$. In fact, we will show that the currents are *discontinuous* at $t = 0$ for a unity-coupled transformer. Assuming that $K = 1$, consider the mesh equation for the secondary at $t = 0+$,

$$R_2 i_2(0+) = -M i'_1(0+) - L_2 i'_2(0+) \qquad (4.70)$$

$$= -\frac{M}{L_1}[L_1 i'_1(0+) + M i'_2(0+)] \qquad (4.71)$$

The mesh equation of the primary side then becomes

$$V = R_1 i_1(0+) + [L_1 i'_1(0+) + M i'_2(0+)] = R_1 i_1(0+) - \frac{L_1}{M} R_2 i_2(0+)$$

(4.72)

We need an additional equation to solve for $i_1(0+)$ and $i_2(0+)$. This is provided by the equation

$$L_1[i_1(0+) - i_1(0-)] + M[i_2(0+) - i_2(0-)] = 0 \qquad (4.73)$$

which we obtained from Eq. 4.66, Since $i_1(0-) = i_2(0-) = 0$, we solve Eq. 4.72 and Eq. 4.73 directly to give

$$i_1(0+) = \frac{V L_2}{R_1 L_2 + R_2 L_1}$$

$$i_2(0+) = \frac{V M}{R_1 L_2 + R_2 L_1}$$

(4.74)

Consider the following example. For the transformer in Fig. 4.21, the element values are

$$L_1 = 4 \text{ h}, \qquad L_2 = 1 \text{ h}$$
$$R_1 = 8 \, \Omega, \qquad R_2 = 3 \, \Omega$$
$$M = 2 \text{ h}, \qquad V = 10 \text{ v}$$

Assuming that the circuit is at steady state before the switch is closed at $t = 0$, let us find $i_1(t)$ and $i_2(t)$. The differential equations written on mesh basis are:

$$10 = 4 \frac{di_1}{dt} + 8i_1 + 2 \frac{di_2}{dt}$$

$$0 = 2 \frac{di_1}{dt} + \frac{di_2}{dt} + 3i_2$$

(4.75)

The characteristic equation is

$$H(p) = \begin{vmatrix} 4(p + 2) & 2p \\ 2p & (p + 3) \end{vmatrix} = 0 \qquad (4.76)$$

which yields

$$H(p) = 20p + 24 = 20(p + \tfrac{6}{5}) \qquad (4.77)$$

so that the complementary functions are

$$i_{1C}(t) = K_1 e^{-1.2t}$$

$$i_{2C}(t) = K_2 e^{-1.2t}$$

(4.78)

The particular integrals which we obtain by inspection are

$$i_{1p}(t) = \frac{V}{R_1} = \frac{10}{8} = \frac{5}{4}$$

$$i_{2p}(t) = 0$$

(4.79)

The initial conditions are

$$i_1(0+) = \frac{VL_2}{R_1L_2 + R_2L_1} = \frac{10}{20} = 0.5$$

$$i_2(0+) = \frac{VM}{R_1L_2 + R_2L_1} = 1.0$$

(4.80)

We then find $K_1 = -0.75$ and $K_2 = 1.0$ so that

$$i_1(t) = (-0.75e^{-1.2t} + 1.25)\, u(t)$$

$$i_2(t) = e^{-1.2t}\, u(t)$$

(4.81)

We see that as t approaches infinity, $i_2(t) \to 0$, while $i_1(t)$ goes to its steady-state value of 1.25.

Problems

4.1   Write the mesh equations for the network shown.

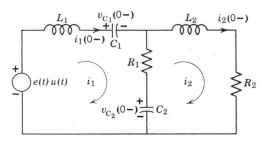

PROB. 4.1

4.2   Write the mesh equations for the network shown. Choose your own reference directions for the mesh currents.

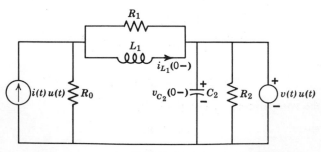

PROB. 4.2

4.3 For the network in Prob. 4.2, write a set of node equations.

4.4 Write a set of network equations to solve for the voltage $v_2(t)$ shown in the figure.

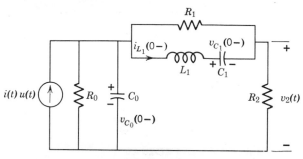

PROB. 4.4

4.5 Find the current $i(t)$ when the voltage source shown in the figure is: (a) $e(t) = u(t)$; (b) $e(t) = \delta(t)$. It is given that $v_C(0-) = i(0-) = 0$.

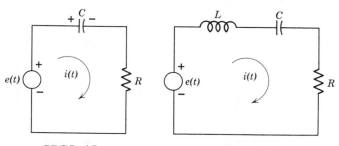

PROB. 4.5   **PROB. 4.6**

4.6 Find the current $i(t)$ in the network shown in the figure, when the voltage source is $e(t) = \delta(t)$. Discuss the three different kinds of impulse response waveforms possible, depending upon the relative values of R, L, and C. It is given that all currents and voltages at $t = 0-$ are zero.

4.7 Find the voltage $v_2(t)$ in the network shown. It is given that $i_L(0-) = i'_L(0-) = 0$, $v_C(0-) = 0$, and $e(t) = (2 + 5e^{-100t})\,u(t)$.

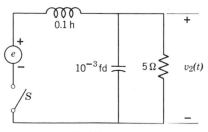

PROB. 4.7

4.8 Solve for the voltage $v_2(t)$ for the network shown in the figure. It is given that $i_L(0-) = i'_L(0-) = 0$ and $v_c(0-) = 0$.

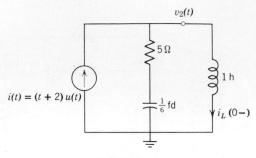

PROB. 4.8

4.9 An R-C differentiator circuit is shown in the figure. Find the requirements for the time constant such that the output voltage $v_0(t)$ is approximately the derivative of the input voltage.

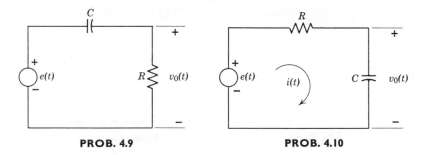

PROB. 4.9   **PROB. 4.10**

4.10 An R-C integrator circuit is shown in the figure. Find the requirements for the time constant such that the output $v_0(t)$ is the integral of the input $e(t)$.

4.11 Find the current $i_2(t)$ in the network shown. It is given that all initial currents and voltages at $t = 0-$ are zero, and that $e(t) = 100 \cos 20t \, u(t)$ volts.

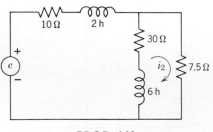

PROB. 4.11

4.12 Determine the expression for $e(t)$ such that $i(t) = 10u(t)$ in the circuit shown.

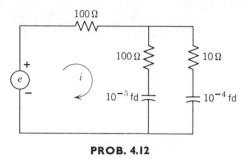

PROB. 4.12

4.13 Find the free response for $i(t)$ in the figure shown for (a) a current source; (b) a voltage source.

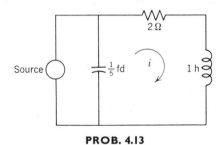

PROB. 4.13

4.14 At $t = 0$, the switch goes from position 1 to position 2. Find $i(t)$ given that $e(t) = e^{-t} \sin 2t$. Assume the circuit had been in steady state for $t < 0$.

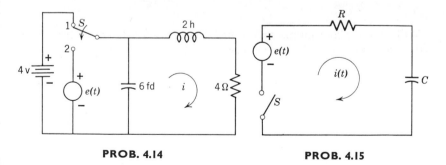

PROB. 4.14   **PROB. 4.15**

4.15 For the circuit shown, solve for $i(t)$ when the initial conditions are $i(0-) = v_C(0-) = 0$, and $e(t) = \sin(\omega t + \theta) u(t)$. What should θ be in terms of R, C, and ω so that the coefficient of the free response term is zero?

4.16 For the circuit shown, find $v_1(t)$ and $v_2(t)$, with $v_1(0-) = v_2(0-) = 0$.

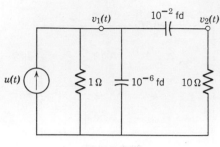

PROB. 4.16

4.17 For the circuit shown, determine $v_2(t)$, given that $v_1(0-) = v_2(0-) = 0$, and that $i_g(t) = 2 \sin 10^5 t \, u(t)$.

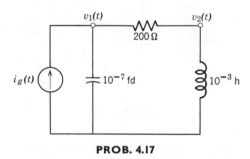

PROB. 4.17

4.18 For the transformer shown, find $i_1(t)$ and $i_2(t)$. It is given that $e(t) = 6u(t)$ and that, prior to the switching action, $i_1(0-) = i_2(0-) = 0$.

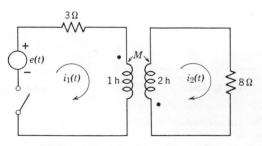

PROB. 4.18. $M = 1 \, \text{h}; e(t) = 6u(t)$.

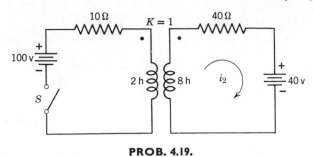

PROB. 4.19.

4.19 For the circuit shown, find $i_2(t)$, given that the circuit had been in steady state prior to the switch closing at $t = 0$.

chapter 5

The Fourier and Laplace transforms

5.1 THE PHILOSOPHY OF TRANSFORM METHODS

In the two previous chapters, we discussed classical methods for solving differential equations. The solutions were obtained directly in the *time domain* since, in the process of solving the differential equation, we deal with functions of time at every step. In this chapter, we will use *Fourier* and *Laplace* transforms to *transform* the differential equation to the *frequency domain*, where the independent variable is angular frequency $j\omega$ for the Fourier transform, and complex frequency s for the Laplace transform. It will be shown that differentiation and integration in the time domain are transformed into *algebraic* operations. Thus, the solution is obtained by simple algebraic operations in the frequency domain.

There is a striking analogy between the use of transform methods to solve differential equations and the use of logarithms for arithmetic operations. Suppose we are given two real numbers, a and b. Let us find the product

$$C = a \times b \tag{5.1}$$

by means of logarithms. Since the logarithm of a product is the sum of the logarithms of the individual terms, we have

$$\log C = \log a \times b = \log a + \log b \tag{5.2}$$

so that

$$C = \log^{-1} (\log a + \log b) \tag{5.3}$$

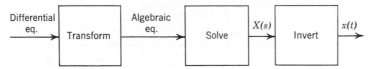

FIG. 5.1. Philosophy of transform methods.

If a and b were two six-digit numbers, using logarithms would probably facilitate the calculations because logarithms transform multiplication into addition.

An analogous process is the use of transform methods to solve integro-differential equations. Consider the linear differential equation,

$$y(x(t)) = f(t) \tag{5.4}$$

where $f(t)$ is the forcing function, $x(t)$ is the unknown, and $y(x(t))$ is the differential equation. Let us denote by $T(\cdot)$ the transformation process, and let s be the frequency variable. When we transform both sides of Eq. 5.4, we have

$$T[y(x(t))] = T[f(t)] \tag{5.5}$$

Since frequency domain functions are given by capital letters, let us write Eq. 5.5 as

$$Y(X(s), s) = F(s) \tag{5.6}$$

where $X(s) = T[x(t)]$, $F(s) = T[f(t)]$ and $Y(X(s), s)$ is an *algebraic* equation in s. The essence of the transformation process is that differential equations in time are changed into algebraic equations in frequency. We can then solve Eq. 5.6 algebraically to obtain $X(s)$. As a final step, we perform an inverse transformation to obtain

$$x(t) = T^{-1}(X(s)) \tag{5.7}$$

In effecting the transition between the time and frequency domains, a table of transform pairs $\{x(t), X(s)\}$ can be very helpful. A diagram outlining the use of transform methods is given in Fig. 5.1.

5.2 APPLICATIONS OF THE FOURIER INTEGRAL

In this section, we will use Fourier transforms to solve differential equations. The Fourier transform pair as given in Chapter 2 is:

$$F(j\omega) = \int_{-\infty}^{\infty} f(t)e^{-j\omega t}\, dt \tag{5.8}$$

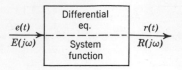

FIG. 5.2. Linear system.

and the inverse transform is

$$f(t) = \frac{1}{2\pi} \int_{-\infty}^{\infty} F(j\omega)e^{j\omega t}\,d\omega \tag{5.9}$$

Consider the derivative of the inverse transform

$$f'(t) = \frac{1}{2\pi} \int_{-\infty}^{\infty} j\omega\, F(j\omega)e^{j\omega t}\,d\omega \tag{5.10}$$

and the second derivative,

$$f''(t) = \frac{1}{2\pi} \int_{-\infty}^{\infty} [-\omega^2\, F(\omega)]e^{j\omega t}\,d\omega \tag{5.11}$$

It is apparent that, if the Fourier transform of $f(t)$ is

$$\mathscr{F}[f(t)] = F(j\omega), \tag{5.12}$$

the transform of its derivative is

$$\mathscr{F}[f'(t)] = j\omega\, F(j\omega) \tag{5.13}$$

and the transform of the second derivative is

$$\mathscr{F}[f''(t)] = (j\omega)^2\, F(j\omega). \tag{5.14}$$

Extending this analysis further, we see that the transform of the nth derivative of $f(t)$ is

$$\mathscr{F}[f^{(n)}(t)] = (j\omega)^n\, F(j\omega) \tag{5.15}$$

Similarly, it is easily shown that the transform for the integral of $f(t)$ is

$$\mathscr{F}\left[\int_{-\infty}^{t} f(\tau)\,d\tau\right] = \frac{1}{j\omega}\, F(j\omega) \tag{5.16}$$

The above discussion forms the basis for the use of Fourier transforms to solve differential equations. As an example, consider the linear system shown in Fig. 5.2. Suppose the system is described by the second-order differential equation,

$$a\,r''(t) + b\,r'(t) + c\,r(t) = k\,e(t) \tag{5.17}$$

where $e(t)$ and $r(t)$ are the system excitation and response. Assuming that the Fourier transforms of $r(t)$ and $e(t)$ exist, let us take the Fourier transform of both sides of Eq. 5.17. We then have

$$(-a\omega^2 + j\omega b + c)\, R(j\omega) = k\, E(j\omega) \tag{5.18}$$

where

$$R(j\omega) = \mathscr{F}[r(t)]; \qquad E(j\omega) = \mathscr{F}[e(t)]$$

$R(j\omega)$ is now obtained algebraically as

$$R(j\omega) = \frac{k}{-a\omega^2 + j\omega b + c}\, E(j\omega) \tag{5.19}$$

The time response $r(t)$ is the inverse transform,

$$r(t) = \mathscr{F}^{-1}[R(j\omega)] = \frac{1}{2\pi} \int_{-\infty}^{\infty} \frac{k\, E(j\omega)}{-a\omega^2 + j\omega b + c}\, e^{j\omega t}\, d\omega \tag{5.20}$$

In Eq. 5.19, the *system function* $H(j\omega)$ is the ratio of the transform of the response to the transform of the excitation, or

$$H(j\omega) = \frac{R(j\omega)}{E(j\omega)} = \frac{k}{-a\omega^2 + j\omega b + c} \tag{5.21}$$

Since the constants a, b, c, and k are functions of the elements of the system alone, we see that $H(j\omega)$ is not dependent upon the excitation $E(j\omega)$. The response $R(j\omega)$, on the other hand, is dependent upon both $E(j\omega)$ and $H(j\omega)$. In fact, Eq. 5.21 might appear more meaningful if it were written as

$$R(j\omega) = E(j\omega)\, H(j\omega) \tag{5.22}$$

If the system function $H(j\omega)$ is known, then we can determine the response due to any arbitrary excitation from Eq. 5.22.

Before discussing an example, let us first determine the Fourier transform of an extremely useful time function, $f(t) = e^{-at}\, u(t)$ where a is real and positive. The Fourier transform of $f(t)$ is

$$F(j\omega) = \int_{-\infty}^{\infty} e^{-at}\, u(t) e^{-j\omega t}\, dt = \int_{0}^{\infty} e^{-at} e^{-j\omega t}\, dt = \frac{1}{a + j\omega} \tag{5.23}$$

Example 5.1.   Given the equation

$$x'(t) + 2x(t) = \delta(t) \tag{5.24}$$

find the impulse response $x_\delta(t)$, given that $x(0-) = 0$.

Solution.   Taking the Fourier transform of both sides of the equation, we obtain

$$(j\omega + 2)\, X(j\omega) = 1 \tag{5.25}$$

The system function is simply,

$$H(j\omega) = X(j\omega) = \frac{1}{j\omega + 2} \tag{5.26}$$

We see now that the *impulse response is the inverse transform of the system function*, i.e.,

$$x_\delta(t) = \mathscr{F}^{-1}[H(j\omega)] = e^{-2t}\, u(t) \tag{5.27}$$

as we had just established. From this example, we see that the impulse response and the system function constitute a transform pair. Specifying either quantity is sufficient because the other is then found via the transform-pair relationship.

Example 5.2.   For the system described in the previous example, find the response due to the excitation,

$$e(t) = 3e^{-t}\, u(t) \tag{5.28}$$

Solution.   The Fourier transform of $e(t)$ is

$$E(j\omega) = \frac{3}{j\omega + 1} \tag{5.29}$$

Since we already have the system function from the previous example, the transform of the response is

$$R(j\omega) = E(j\omega)\, H(j\omega) = \frac{3}{(j\omega + 1)(j\omega + 2)} \tag{5.30}$$

A convenient way to obtain the inverse transform of $R(j\omega)$ is to expand $R(j\omega)$ in partial fractions and then to identify the separate parts of the partial fraction with time functions. As the reader might recall from earlier mathematics courses, the partial fraction expansion of $R(j\omega)$ takes the form

$$R(j\omega) = \frac{3}{(j\omega + 1)(j\omega + 2)} = \frac{K_1}{j\omega + 2} + \frac{K_2}{j\omega + 1} \tag{5.31}$$

Multiplying both sides of the last equation by $(j\omega + 1)(j\omega + 2)$, we have

$$3 = K_1(j\omega + 1) + K_2(j\omega + 2) \tag{5.32}$$

Letting $j\omega = -2$, we obtain $K_1 = -3$; then when $j\omega = -1$, we obtain $K_2 = 3$. Therefore,

$$R(j\omega) = \frac{3}{j\omega + 1} + \frac{(-3)}{j\omega + 2} \tag{5.33}$$

By inspection, we obtain the inverse transform of the system response as

$$r(t) = \mathscr{F}^{-1}[R(j\omega)] = 3u(t)(e^{-t} - e^{-2t}) \tag{5.34}$$

From this example, we see the utility of a partial fraction expansion in obtaining the inverse transform. Instead of integrating, we obtain the inverse transform by *recognizing* the inverse transform of the component parts of the partial fraction expansion. A similar procedure for obtaining the inverse of a Laplace transform function will be discussed in the following section.

5.3 THE LAPLACE TRANSFORM

The Laplace transform of a function of time $f(t)$ is defined as

$$\mathscr{L}[f(t)] = F(s) = \int_{0-}^{\infty} f(t)e^{-st}\, dt \qquad (5.35)$$

where s is the complex frequency variable,

$$s = \sigma + j\omega \qquad (5.36)$$

This definition of the Laplace transform is different from the definition given in most standard texts*, in that the lower limit of integration is $t = 0-$ instead of $t = 0+$. We thus take into account the possibility that $f(t)$ may be an impulse or one of its higher derivatives. It is clear that $\mathscr{L}[\delta(t)] = 0$ for the $0+$ definition; whereas for the $0-$ definition, $\mathscr{L}[\delta(t)] = 1$. In the case when no impulses or higher derivatives of impulses are involved, it was shown in Chapter 3 that $f(0-) = f(0+)$. Therefore, all of the "strong results" resulting from a rigorous treatment of Laplace transforms† obtained by using $t = 0+$ as a lower limit also apply for the $0-$ definition.

In order for a function to possess a Laplace transform, it must obey the condition,

$$\int_{0-}^{\infty} |f(t)|\, e^{-\sigma t}\, dt < \infty \qquad (5.37)$$

for a real, positive σ. Note that, for a function to have a Fourier transform, it must obey the condition,

$$\int_{-\infty}^{\infty} |f(t)|\, dt < \infty \qquad (5.38)$$

As a result, a ramp function or a step function will not possess a Fourier transform‡ but will have a Laplace transform because of the added convergence factor $e^{-\sigma t}$. However, the function e^{t^2} will not even have a Laplace transform. In transient problems, the Laplace transform is preferred to the Fourier transform, not only because a larger class of waveforms have Laplace transforms, but also because the Laplace transform takes directly into account initial conditions at $t = 0-$ due to the

---

* M. E. Van Valkenburg, *Network Analysis*, Prentice-Hall, Englewood Cliffs, N.J., 1956.

† D. V. Widder, *The Laplace Transform*, Princeton University Press, Princeton, 1941.

‡ These functions do not possess Fourier transforms in the strict sense, but may possess a *generalized* Fourier transform containing impulses in frequency; see M. J. Lighthill, *Fourier Analysis and Generalized Functions*, Cambridge University Press, New York, 1959.

lower limit of integration in the Laplace transform. In contrast, the Fourier transform has limits of integration $(-\infty, \infty)$ and, in order to take into account initial conditions due to a switch closing at $t = 0$, the forcing function must take a form as $f(t) u(t) + x(0-) \delta(t)$, where $x(0-)$ represents the initial condition.

The inverse transform, $\mathscr{L}^{-1}[F(s)]$ is

$$f(t) = \frac{1}{2\pi j} \int_{\sigma_1 - j\infty}^{\sigma_1 + j\infty} F(s)e^{st} \, ds \tag{5.39}$$

where σ_1 is a real positive quantity which is greater than the σ convergence factor in Eq. 5.37. Note that the inverse transform as defined involves a complex integration known as a *contour integration*.* Since it is beyond the intended scope of this book to cover contour integration, we will use a partial fraction expansion procedure to obtain the inverse transform. To find inverse transforms by recognition, we must remember certain basic transform pairs and also use a table of Laplace transforms. Two of the most basic transform pairs are now given. Consider first the transform of a unit step function, $u(t)$.

1. $f(t) = u(t)$:

$$F(s) = \int_{0-}^{\infty} u(t)e^{-st} \, dt = -\frac{e^{-st}}{s} \bigg|_{0-}^{\infty} = 0 - \left(-\frac{1}{s}\right) = \frac{1}{s} \tag{5.40}$$

Next, let us find the transform of an exponential function of time.

2. $f(t) = e^{at} u(t)$:

$$F(s) = \int_{0-}^{\infty} e^{at}e^{-st} \, dt = -\frac{e^{-(s-a)t}}{s-a} \bigg|_{0-}^{\infty} = \frac{1}{s-a} \tag{5.41}$$

With these two transform pairs and with the use of the properties of Laplace transforms which we will discuss in the next section, we can build up an extensive table of transform pairs.

5.4 PROPERTIES OF LAPLACE TRANSFORMS

In this section, we will discuss a number of important properties of Laplace transforms. Using these properties we will build up a table of transforms. To facilitate this task, we will illustrate each property by considering the transforms of important signal waveforms. First let us discuss the *linearity* property.

---

* For a lucid treatment, see S. Goldman, *Transformation Calculus and Electrical Transients*, Prentice-Hall, Englewood Cliffs, N.J., 1949, Chapter 7.

Linearity

The transform of a finite sum of time functions is the sum of the transforms of the individual functions, i.e.,

$$\mathscr{L}\left[\sum_i f_i(t)\right] = \sum_i \mathscr{L}[f_i(t)] \tag{5.42}$$

This property follows readily from the definition of the Laplace transform.

Example 5.3. $f(t) = \sin \omega t$. Expanding $\sin \omega t$ by Euler's identity, we have,

$$f(t) = \frac{1}{2j}(e^{j\omega t} - e^{-j\omega t}) \tag{5.43}$$

The Laplace transform of $f(t)$ is the sum of the transforms of the individual cisoidal $e^{\pm j\omega t}$ terms. Thus,

$$\mathscr{L}[\sin \omega t] = \frac{1}{2j}\left(\frac{1}{s - j\omega} - \frac{1}{s + j\omega}\right) = \frac{\omega}{s^2 + \omega^2} \tag{5.44}$$

Real differentiation

Given that $\mathscr{L}[f(t)] = F(s)$, then

$$\mathscr{L}\left[\frac{df}{dt}\right] = s F(s) - f(0-) \tag{5.45}$$

where $f(0-)$ is the value of $f(t)$ at $t = 0-$.

Proof. By definition,

$$\mathscr{L}[f'(t)] = \int_{0-}^{\infty} e^{-st} f'(t)\, dt \tag{5.46}$$

Integrating Eq. 5.46 by parts, we have,

$$\mathscr{L}[f'(t)] = e^{-st} f(t)\Big|_{0-}^{\infty} + s\int_{0-}^{\infty} f(t) e^{-st}\, dt \tag{5.47}$$

Since $e^{-st} \to 0$ as $t \to \infty$, and because the integral on the right-hand side is $\mathscr{L}[f(t)] = F(s)$, we have,

$$\mathscr{L}[f'(t)] = s F(s) - f(0-) \tag{5.48}$$

Similarly, we can show for the nth derivative,

$$\mathscr{L}\left[\frac{d^n f(t)}{dt^n}\right] = s^n F(s) - s^{n-1} f(0-) - s^{n-2} f'(0-) - \cdots - f^{(n-1)}(0-) \tag{5.49}$$

where $f^{(n-1)}(0-)$ is the $(n-1)$st derivative of $f(t)$ at $t = 0-$. We thus see that differentiating by t in the time domain is equivalent to multiplying by s in the complex frequency domain. In addition, the initial conditions are taken into account by the terms $f^{(i)}(0-)$. It is this property that transforms differential equations in the time domain to algebraic equations in the frequency domain.

Example 5.4a. $f(t) = \sin \omega t$. Let us find

$$\mathscr{L}[\cos \omega t] = \mathscr{L}\left[\frac{1}{\omega}\frac{d}{dt}\sin \omega t\right] \tag{5.50}$$

By the real differentiation property, we have

$$\mathscr{L}\left[\frac{d}{dt}\sin \omega t\right] = s\left(\frac{\omega}{s^2 + \omega^2}\right) \tag{5.51}$$

so that

$$\mathscr{L}[\cos \omega t] = \frac{s}{\omega}\left(\frac{\omega}{s^2 + \omega^2}\right) = \frac{s}{s^2 + \omega^2} \tag{5.52}$$

In this example, note that $\sin \omega(0-) = 0$.

Example 5.4b. $f(t) = u(t)$. Let us find $\mathscr{L}[f'(t)]$, which is the transform of the unit impulse. We know that

$$\mathscr{L}[u(t)] = \frac{1}{s} \tag{5.53}$$

Then,

$$\mathscr{L}[\delta(t)] = s\left(\frac{1}{s}\right) = 1 \tag{5.54}$$

since $u(0-) = 0$.

Real integration

If $\mathscr{L}[f(t)] = F(s)$, then the Laplace transform of the integral of $f(t)$ is $F(s)$ divided by s, i.e.,

$$\mathscr{L}\left[\int_{0-}^{t} f(\tau)\,d\tau\right] = \frac{F(s)}{s} \tag{5.55}$$

Proof. By definition,

$$\mathscr{L}\left[\int_{0-}^{t} f(\tau)\,d\tau\right] = \int_{0-}^{\infty} e^{-st}\left[\int_{0-}^{t} f(\tau)\,d\tau\right]dt \tag{5.56}$$

Integrating by parts, we obtain,

$$\mathscr{L}\left[\int_{0-}^{t} f(\tau)\,d\tau\right] = -\frac{e^{-st}}{s}\int_{0-}^{t} f(\tau)\,d\tau\Big|_{0-}^{\infty} + \frac{1}{s}\int_{0-}^{\infty} e^{-st} f(t)\,dt \tag{5.57}$$

Since $e^{-st} \to 0$ as $t \to \infty$, and since

$$\int_{0-}^{t} f(\tau)\,d\tau\Big|_{t=0-} = 0 \tag{5.58}$$

we then have

$$\mathscr{L}\left[\int_{0-}^{t} f(\tau)\, d\tau\right] = \frac{F(s)}{s} \qquad (5.59)$$

Example 5.5.   Let us find the transform of the unit ramp function, $\rho(t) = t\, u(t)$. We know that

$$\int_{0-}^{t} u(\tau)\, d\tau = \rho(t) \qquad (5.60)$$

Since

$$\mathscr{L}[u(t)] = \frac{1}{s} \qquad (5.61)$$

then

$$\mathscr{L}[\rho(t)] = \frac{\mathscr{L}[u(t)]}{s} = \frac{1}{s^2} \qquad (5.62)$$

Differentiation by s

Differentiation by s in the complex frequency domain corresponds to multiplication by t in the time domain, i.e.,

$$\mathscr{L}[t f(t)] = -\frac{d F(s)}{ds} \qquad (5.63)$$

Proof.   From the definition of the Laplace transform, we see that

$$\frac{d F(s)}{ds} = \int_{0-}^{\infty} f(t)\, \frac{d}{ds} e^{-st}\, dt = -\int_{0-}^{\infty} t f(t) e^{-st}\, dt = -\mathscr{L}[t f(t)] \qquad (5.64)$$

Example 5.6.   Given $f(t) = e^{-\alpha t}$, whose transform is

$$F(s) = \frac{1}{s + \alpha} \qquad (5.65)$$

let us find $\mathscr{L}[te^{-\alpha t}]$. By the above theorem,

$$\mathscr{L}[te^{-\alpha t}] = -\frac{d}{ds}\left(\frac{1}{s + \alpha}\right) = \frac{1}{(s + \alpha)^2} \qquad (5.66)$$

Similarly, we can show that

$$\mathscr{L}[t^n e^{-\alpha t}] = \frac{n!}{(s + \alpha)^{n+1}} \qquad (5.67)$$

where n is a positive integer.

Complex Translation

By the complex translation property, if $F(s) = \mathscr{L}[f(t)]$, then,

$$F(s - a) = \mathscr{L}[e^{at} f(t)] \qquad (5.68)$$

where a is a complex number.

Proof. By definition,

$$\mathscr{L}[e^{at} f(t)] = \int_{0-}^{\infty} e^{at} f(t) e^{-st}\, dt = \int_{0-}^{\infty} e^{-(s-a)t} f(t)\, dt = F(s - a) \quad (5.69)$$

Example 5.7.   Given $f(t) = \sin \omega t$, find $\mathscr{L}[e^{-at} \sin \omega t]$. Since

$$\mathscr{L}[\sin \omega t] = \frac{\omega}{s^2 + \omega^2} \quad (5.70)$$

by the above theorem,

$$\mathscr{L}[e^{-at} \sin \omega t] = \frac{\omega}{(s + a)^2 + \omega^2} \quad (5.71)$$

Similarly, we can show that

$$\mathscr{L}[e^{-at} \cos \omega t] = \frac{s + a}{(s + a)^2 + \omega^2} \quad (5.72)$$

Real translation (shifting theorem)

Here we will consider the very important concept of the transform of a shifted or delayed function of time. If $\mathscr{L}[f(t)] = F(s)$, then the transform of the function delayed by time a is

$$\mathscr{L}[f(t - a)\, u(t - a)] = e^{-as} F(s) \quad (5.73)$$

Proof. By definition,

$$\mathscr{L}[f(t - a)\, u(t - a)] = \int_{a}^{\infty} e^{-st} f(t - a)\, dt \quad (5.74)$$

Introducing a new dummy variable, $\tau = t - a$, we have

$$\mathscr{L}[f(\tau)\, u(\tau)] = \int_{0-}^{\infty} e^{-s(\tau + a)} f(\tau)\, d\tau = e^{-as} \int_{0-}^{\infty} f(\tau) e^{-s\tau}\, d\tau = e^{-as} F(s)$$
$$(5.75)$$

In Eq. 5.75, $f(\tau)\, u(\tau)$ is the shifted or delayed time function; therefore, the theorem is proved.

It is important to recognize that the term e^{-as} is a time-delay operator. If we are given the function, $e^{-as} G(s)$, and were required to find $\mathscr{L}^{-1}[e^{-as} G(s)] = g_1(t)$, we can discard, for the moment, e^{-as}, find the inverse transform $\mathscr{L}^{-1}[G(s)] = g(t)$, and then take into account the time delay by setting

$$g(t - a)\, u(t - a) = g_1(t) \quad (5.76)$$

Example 5.8a.   Given the square pulse $f(t)$ in Fig. 5.3, let us first find its transform $F(s)$. Then, let us determine the inverse transform of the square of $F(s)$, i.e., let us find

$$f_1(t) = \mathscr{L}^{-1}[F^2(s)] \quad (5.77)$$

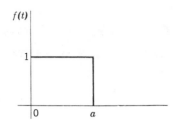

FIG. 5.3. Square pulse.

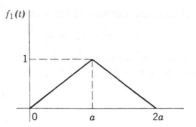

FIG. 5.4. Triangular pulse.

Solution. The square pulse is given in terms of step functions as

$$f(t) = u(t) - u(t - a) \tag{5.78}$$

Its Laplace transform is then

$$F(s) = \frac{1}{s}(1 - e^{-as}) \tag{5.79}$$

Squaring $F(s)$, we obtain

$$F^2(s) = \frac{1}{s^2}(1 - 2e^{-as} + e^{-2as}) \tag{5.80}$$

To find the inverse transform of $F^2(s)$, we need only to determine the inverse transform of the term with zero delay, which is

$$\mathscr{L}^{-1}\left[\frac{1}{s^2}\right] = tu(t) \tag{5.81}$$

Then

$$\mathscr{L}^{-1}[F^2(s)] = tu(t) - 2(t - a)\,u(t - a) + (t - 2a)\,u(t - 2a) \tag{5.82}$$

so that the resulting waveform is shown in Fig. 5.4. From this example, we see that the square of a transformed function *does not* correspond to the square of its inverse transform.

Example 5.8b. In Fig. 5.5, the output of an ideal sampler is shown. It consists of a train of impulses,

$$f(t) = K_0\,\delta(t) + K_1\,\delta(t - T_1) + \cdots + K_n\,\delta(t - nT_1) \tag{5.83}$$

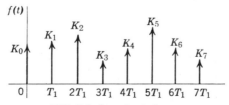

FIG. 5.5. Impulse train.

The Laplace transform of this impulse train is

$$\mathscr{L}[f(t)] = K_0 + K_1 e^{-sT_1} + K_2 e^{-2sT_1} + \cdots + K_n e^{-nsT_1} \quad (5.84)$$

In dealing with sampled signals, the substitution $z = e^{sT_1}$ is often used. Then we can represent the transform of the impulse train as

$$\mathscr{L}[f(t)] = K_0 + \frac{K_1}{z} + \frac{K_2}{z^2} + \cdots + \frac{K_n}{z^n} \quad (5.85)$$

The transform in Eq. 5.85 is called the *z-transform* of $f(t)$. This transform is widely used in connection with sampled-data control systems.

Example 5.8c. Figure 5.6 shows a periodic (for $t \geq 0$) sequence of pulses of height unity and width equal to a. The periodic pulse train can be represented as

$$f(t) = u(t) - u(t - a) + u(t - T) - u[t - (T + a)]$$

$$+ u(t - 2T) - u[t - (2T + a)] + \cdots \quad (5.86)$$

Its Laplace transform is

$$F(s) = \frac{1}{s}(1 - e^{-as} + e^{-sT} - e^{-(T+a)s} + \cdots)$$

$$= \frac{1}{s}[1 - e^{-as} + e^{-sT}(1 - e^{-as}) + e^{-2sT}(1 - e^{-as}) + \cdots] \quad (5.87)$$

which simplifies further to give

$$F(s) = \frac{1}{s}(1 - e^{-as})(1 + e^{-sT} + e^{-2sT} + \cdots) \quad (5.88)$$

We then see that $F(s)$ can be given in the closed form,

$$F(s) = \frac{1}{s}\frac{1 - e^{-as}}{1 - e^{-sT}} \quad (5.89)$$

Other periodic pulse trains can also be given in closed form. The reader is referred to the problems at the end of this chapter.

Also at the end of the chapter is a table of Laplace transforms. Most of the entries are obtained through simple applications of the properties just

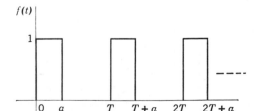

FIG. 5.6. Periodic pulse train.

discussed. It is important to keep these properties in mind, because many transform pairs which are not given in the table can be obtained by using these properties. For example, let us find the inverse transform of

$$F(s) = \frac{\omega s}{(s + \sigma)^2 + \omega^2} \tag{5.90}$$

Since the s in the numerator implies differentiation in the time domain, we can write

$$F(s) = s \frac{\omega}{(s + \sigma)^2 + \omega^2} \tag{5.91}$$

Using the differentiation property, we obtain,

$$\mathscr{L}^{-1}[F(s)] = \frac{d}{dt} (e^{-\sigma t} \sin \omega t)$$

$$= (-\sigma \sin \omega t + \omega \cos \omega t)e^{-\sigma t} \tag{5.92}$$

Note that $e^{-\sigma t} \sin \omega t$ at $t = 0-$ is zero.

5.5 USES OF LAPLACE TRANSFORMS

Evaluation of definite integrals

The Laplace transform is often useful in the evaluation of definite integrals. An obvious example occurs in the evaluation of

$$I = \int_0^\infty e^{-2t} \sin 5t \, dt \tag{5.93}$$

If we replace e^{-2t} by e^{-st}, the integral I then becomes the Laplace transform of $\sin 5t$, which is

$$\mathscr{L}[\sin 5t] = \frac{5}{s^2 + 25} \tag{5.94}$$

Replacing s by 2, we have

$$I = \frac{5}{(2)^2 + 25} = \frac{5}{29} \tag{5.95}$$

Perhaps a more subtle example is the evaluation of

$$I = \int_{-1}^{+1} t^2 e^{-2|t|} \, dt \tag{5.96}$$

First, we note that $t^2 e^{-2|t|}$ is an even function; therefore,

$$I = 2 \int_0^1 t^2 e^{-2t} \, dt \tag{5.97}$$

From the table of Laplace transforms we see that

$$\mathscr{L}[t^2 e^{-2t}] = \frac{2}{(s+2)^3} \tag{5.98}$$

and the transform of

$$f(t) = \int_{0-}^{t} \tau^2 e^{-2\tau}\, d\tau \tag{5.99}$$

is

$$\mathscr{L}[f(t)] = \frac{2}{s(s+2)^3} \tag{5.100}$$

It will be shown later that the partial-fraction expansion of $\mathscr{L}[f(t)]$ in Eq. 5.100 consists of three terms for the multiple root, $(s+2)^3$, as given by

$$\mathscr{L}[f(t)] = \frac{0.25}{s} - \frac{0.25}{s+2} - \frac{0.5}{(s+2)^2} - \frac{1}{(s+2)^3} \tag{5.101}$$

Taking the inverse transform of the last equation, we obtain

$$f(t) = 0.25(1 - e^{-2t} - 2te^{-2t} - 2t^2 e^{-2t})\, u(t) \tag{5.102}$$

Now observe that the definite integral in Eq. 5.97 is equal to $2f(t)$ at $t = 1$, i.e.,

$$I = 2f(1) = -2.5e^{-2} + 0.5 = 0.162 \tag{5.103}$$

Solution of integro-differential equations

From the previous section, we have seen that the real differentiation and real integration properties of the Laplace transform change differential equations in time to algebraic equations in frequency. Let us consider some examples of the use of Laplace transforms in solving differential equations.

Example 5.9.   Let us solve the differential equation,

$$x''(t) + 3x'(t) + 2x(t) = 4e^t \tag{5.104}$$

given the initial conditions, $x(0-) = 1$, $x'(0-) = -1$.

Solution.   We first proceed by taking the Laplace transform of the differential equation which then becomes

$$[s^2 X(s) - sx(0-) - x'(0-)] + 3[sX(s) - x(0-)] + 2X(s) = \frac{4}{s-1} \tag{5.105}$$

Substituting the initial conditions into Eq. 5.105 and simplifying, we have

$$(s^2 + 3s + 2)\, X(s) = \frac{4}{s-1} + s + 2 \tag{5.106}$$

We then obtain $X(s)$ explicitly as

$$X(s) = \frac{s^2 + s + 2}{(s-1)(s+1)(s+2)} \tag{5.107}$$

To find the inverse transform, $x(t) = \mathscr{L}^{-1}[X(s)]$, we expand $X(s)$ into partial fractions,

$$X(s) = \frac{K_{-1}}{s-1} + \frac{K_1}{s+1} + \frac{K_2}{s+2} \qquad (5.108)$$

Solving for K_{-1}, K_1, and K_2 algebraically, we obtain

$$K_{-1} = \tfrac{2}{3} \quad K_1 = -1 \quad K_2 = \tfrac{4}{3}$$

The final solution is the inverse transform of $X(s)$ or

$$x(t) = \tfrac{2}{3}e^t - e^{-t} + \tfrac{4}{3}e^{-2t} \qquad (5.109)$$

In order to compare the Laplace transform method to the classical method of solving differential equations, the reader is referred to the example in Chapter 3, Eq. 3.64, where the differential equation in Eq. 5.104 is solved classically.

Example 5.10.   Given the set of simultaneous differential equations,

$$2x'(t) + 4x(t) + y'(t) + 7y(t) = 5u(t)$$
$$x'(t) + x(t) + y'(t) + 3y(t) = 5\delta(t) \qquad (5.110)$$

with the initial conditions $x(0-) = y(0-) = 0$, let us find $x(t)$ and $y(t)$.
Solution.   Transforming the set of equations, we obtain

$$2(s+2)\,X(s) + (s+7)\,Y(s) = \frac{5}{s}$$
$$(s+1)\,X(s) + (s+3)\,Y(s) = 5 \qquad (5.111)$$

Solving for $X(s)$ and $Y(s)$ simultaneously, we have

$$X(s) = \frac{(5/s)\Delta_{11} + 5\Delta_{21}}{\Delta}$$
$$Y(s) = \frac{(5/s)\Delta_{12} + 5\Delta_{22}}{\Delta} \qquad (5.112)$$

where Δ is the determinant of the set of equations in Eq. 5.111, and Δ_{ij} is the ijth cofactor of Δ. More explicitly, $X(s)$ is

$$X(s) = \frac{-5s^2 - 30s + 15}{s(s^2 + 2s + 5)} \qquad (5.113)$$

Expanding $X(s)$ in partial fractions, we have

$$X(s) = \frac{K_1}{s} + \frac{K_2 s + K_3}{s^2 + 2s + 5} \qquad (5.114)$$

Multiplying both sides of Eq. 5.114 by s and letting $s = 0$, we find

$$K_1 = s\,X(s)\big|_{s=0} = 3$$

K_2 and K_3 are then obtained from the equation

$$X(s) - \frac{3}{s} = \frac{-8s - 36}{s^2 + 2s + 5} \tag{5.115}$$

A further simplification occurs by completing the square of the denominator of $X(s)$, i.e.,

$$s^2 + 2s + 5 = (s + 1)^2 + 4 \tag{5.116}$$

As a result of Eq. 5.116, we can rewrite $X(s)$ as

$$X(s) = \frac{3}{s} - \frac{8(s + 1) + 14(2)}{(s + 1)^2 + (2)^2} \tag{5.117}$$

so that the inverse transform is

$$x(t) = (3 - 8e^{-t} \cos 2t - 14e^{-t} \sin 2t) u(t) \tag{5.118}$$

In similar fashion, we obtain $Y(s)$ to be

$$Y(s) = -\frac{1}{s} + \frac{11s + 17}{s^2 + 2s + 5} = -\frac{1}{s} + \frac{11(s + 1) + 3(2)}{(s + 1)^2 + (2)^2} \tag{5.119}$$

The inverse transform is then seen to be

$$y(t) = (-1 + 11e^{-t} \cos 2t + 3e^{-t} \sin 2t) u(t) \tag{5.120}$$

This example is also solved by classical methods in Chapter 3, Eq. 3.153. We note one sharp point of contrast. While we had to find the initial conditions at $t = 0+$ in order to solve the differential equations directly in the time domain, the Laplace transform method works directly with the initial conditions at $t = 0-$. In addition, we obtain *both* the complementary function and the particular integral in a single operation when we use Laplace transforms. These are the reasons why the Laplace transform method is so effective in the solution of differential equations.

5.6 PARTIAL-FRACTION EXPANSIONS

As we have seen, the ease with which we use transform methods depends upon how quickly we are able to obtain the partial-fraction expansion of a given transform function. In this section, we will elaborate on some simple and effective methods for partial-fraction expansions. We will discuss procedures for (*a*) simple roots; (*b*) complex conjugate roots; and (*c*) multiple roots.

It should be recalled that, if the degree of the numerator is greater or equal to the degree of the denominator, we can divide the numerator by the denominator such that the remainder can be expanded more easily into partial fractions. Consider the following example,

$$F(s) = \frac{N(s)}{D(s)} = \frac{s^3 + 3s^2 + 3s + 2}{s^2 + 2s + 2} \qquad (5.121)$$

Since the degree of $N(s)$ is greater than the degree of $D(s)$, we divide $D(s)$ into $N(s)$ to give

$$F(s) = s + 1 - \frac{s}{s^2 + 2s + 2} \qquad (5.122)$$

Here we see the remainder term can be easily expanded into partial fractions. However, there is no real need at this point because the denominator $s^2 + 2s + 2$ can be written as

$$s^2 + 2s + 2 = (s + 1)^2 + 1 \qquad (5.123)$$

We can then write $F(s)$ as

$$F(s) = s + 1 - \frac{(s + 1) - 1}{(s + 1)^2 + 1} \qquad (5.124)$$

so that the inverse transform can be obtained directly from the transform tables, viz.

$$\mathcal{L}^{-1}[F(s)] = \delta'(t) + \delta(t) + e^{-t}(\sin t - \cos t) \qquad (5.125)$$

From this example, we see that intuition and a knowledge of the transform table can often save considerable work. Consider some further examples in which intuition plays a dominant role.

Example 5.11. Find the partial-fraction expansion of

$$F(s) = \frac{2s + 3}{(s + 1)(s + 2)} \qquad (5.126)$$

If we see that $F(s)$ can also be written as

$$F(s) = \frac{(s + 1) + (s + 2)}{(s + 1)(s + 2)} \qquad (5.127)$$

then the partial-fraction expansion is trivially,

$$F(s) = \frac{1}{s + 1} + \frac{1}{s + 2} \qquad (5.128)$$

Example 5.12. The partial-fraction expansion of

$$F(s) = \frac{s + 5}{(s + 2)^2} \qquad (5.129)$$

We see that $F(s)$ can be rewritten as

$$F(s) = \frac{(s + 2) + 3}{(s + 2)^2} = \frac{1}{(s + 2)} + \frac{3}{(s + 2)^2} \qquad (5.130)$$

Now, let us discuss some formal methods for partial-fraction expansions. First, we will examine a method for simple real roots. Consider the function

$$F(s) = \frac{N(s)}{(s - s_0)(s - s_1)(s - s_2)} \qquad (5.131)$$

where s_0, s_1, and s_2 are distinct, real roots, and the degree of $N(s) < 3$. Expanding $F(s)$ we have,

$$F(s) = \frac{K_0}{s - s_0} + \frac{K_1}{s - s_1} + \frac{K_2}{s - s_2} \qquad (5.132)$$

Let us first obtain the constant K_0. We proceed by multiplying both sides of the equation by $(s - s_0)$ to give

$$(s - s_0)\,F(s) = K_0 + \frac{(s - s_0)K_1}{s - s_1} + \frac{(s - s_0)K_2}{s - s_2} \qquad (5.133)$$

If we let $s = s_0$ in the last equation, we obtain

$$K_0 = (s - s_0)\,F(s)\big|_{s=s_0} \qquad (5.134)$$

Similarly, we see that the other constants can be evaluated through the general relation,

$$K_i = (s - s_i)\,F(s)\big|_{s=s_i} \qquad (5.135)$$

Example 5.13.   Let us find the partial-fraction expansion for

$$F(s) = \frac{s^2 + 2s - 2}{s(s + 2)(s - 3)} = \frac{K_0}{s} + \frac{K_1}{s + 2} + \frac{K_2}{s - 3} \qquad (5.136)$$

Using Eq. 5.135, we find

$$K_0 = s\,F(s)\big|_{s=0}$$

$$= \frac{s^2 + 2s - 2}{(s + 2)(s - 3)}\bigg|_{s=0} = \frac{1}{3}$$

$$K_1 = \frac{s^2 + 2s - 2}{s(s - 3)}\bigg|_{s=-2} = -\frac{1}{5}$$

$$K_2 = \frac{s^2 + 2s - 2}{s(s + 2)}\bigg|_{s=3} = \frac{13}{15} \qquad (5.137)$$

Equation 5.135 is also applicable to a function with complex roots in its denominator. Suppose $F(s)$ is given by

$$F(s) = \frac{N(s)}{D_1(s)(s - \alpha - j\beta)(s - \alpha + j\beta)}$$

$$= \frac{K_1}{s - \alpha - j\beta} + \frac{K_2}{s - \alpha + j\beta} + \frac{N_1(s)}{D_1(s)}$$

(5.138)

where N_1/D_1 is the remainder term. Using Eq. 5.135, we have

$$K_1 = \frac{N(\alpha + j\beta)}{2j\beta D_1(\alpha + j\beta)}$$

$$K_2 = \frac{N(\alpha - j\beta)}{-2j\beta D_1(\alpha - j\beta)}$$

(5.139)

where we assume that $s = \alpha \pm j\beta$ are not zeros of $D_1(s)$.

It can be shown that the constants K_1 and K_2 associated with conjugate roots are themselves conjugate. Therefore, if we denote K_1 as

$$K_1 = A + jB$$

(5.140)

then

$$K_2 = A - jB = K_1{}^*$$

(5.141)

If we denote the inverse transform of the complex conjugate terms as $f_1(t)$, we see that

$$f_1(t) = \mathscr{L}^{-1}\left[\frac{K_1}{s - \alpha - j\beta} + \frac{K_1{}^*}{s - \alpha + j\beta}\right]$$

$$= e^{\alpha t}(K_1 e^{j\beta t} + K_1{}^* e^{-j\beta t})$$

$$= 2e^{\alpha t}(A \cos \beta t - B \sin \beta t)$$

(5.142)

A more convenient way to express the inverse transform $f_1(t)$ is to introduce the variables M and Φ defined by the equations

$$M \sin \Phi = 2A$$

$$M \cos \Phi = -2B$$

(5.143)

where A and B are the real and imaginary parts of K_1 in Eq. 5.140. In terms of M and Φ, the inverse transform is

$$f_1(t) = Me^{\alpha t} \sin (\beta t + \Phi)$$

(5.144)

To obtain M and Φ from K_1, we note that

$$Me^{j\Phi} = M \cos \Phi + jM \sin \Phi = -2B + j2A = 2jK_1$$

(5.145)

When related to the original function $F(s)$, we see from Eq. 5.139 that

$$Me^{j\Phi} = \frac{N(\alpha + j\beta)}{\beta D_1(\alpha + j\beta)}$$

(5.146)

Example 5.14.   Let us find the inverse transform of

$$F(s) = \frac{s^2 + 3}{(s^2 + 2s + 5)(s + 2)} \tag{5.147}$$

For the simple root, $s = -2$, the constant K is

$$K = (s + 2) F(s) \big|_{s=-2} = \tfrac{7}{5} \tag{5.148}$$

For the complex conjugate roots,

$$s^2 + 2s + 5 = (s + 1 + j2)(s + 1 - j2) \tag{5.149}$$

We see that $\alpha = -1$, $\beta = 2$, so

$$Me^{j\Phi} = \frac{s^2 + 3}{2(s + 2)} \bigg|_{s=-1+j2} = \frac{2}{\sqrt{5}} e^{-j(\tan^{-1} 2 + \pi/2)} \tag{5.150}$$

The inverse transform is then

$$\mathscr{L}^{-1}[F(s)] = \frac{7}{5} e^{-2t} + \frac{2}{\sqrt{5}} e^{-t} \sin\left(2t - \frac{\pi}{2} - \tan^{-1} 2\right)$$

$$= \frac{7}{5} e^{-2t} - \frac{2}{\sqrt{5}} e^{-t} \cos(2t - \tan^{-1} 2) \tag{5.151}$$

Now we will study a powerful method for obtaining a partial-fraction expansion with multiple roots.* Other methods require a number of differentiations, and are generally tedious. The method described here requires no differentiation and is very simple to use.

Suppose we are given the function

$$F(s) = \frac{N(s)}{(s - s_0)^n D_1(s)} \tag{5.152}$$

with multiple roots of degree n at $s = s_0$. Let us first *remove* the multiple roots by defining a new function

$$F_1(s) = (s - s_0)^n F(s) = \frac{N(s)}{D_1(s)} \tag{5.153}$$

Next, we introduce a new variable p such that

$$p = s - s_0$$

Then we can write $F_1(s)$ as

$$F_1(p + s_0) = \frac{N(p + s_0)}{D_1(p + s_0)} \tag{5.154}$$

---

* The author is indebted to Professor Leonard O. Goldstone of the Polytechnic Institute of Brooklyn for pointing out this method.

Dividing $N(p + s_0)$ by $D_1(p + s_0)$, with both polynomials written in *ascending* powers of p, we obtain,

$$F_1(p + s_0) = K_0 + K_1 p + K_2 p^2 + \cdots + K_{n-1} p^{n-1} + \frac{K_n p^n}{D_1(p + s_0)}$$

(5.155)

The original function $F(s)$ is related to $F_1(p + s_0)$ by the equation

$$F(p + s_0) = \frac{F_1(p + s_0)}{p^n} = \frac{K_0}{p^n} + \frac{K_1}{p^{n-1}} + \cdots + \frac{K_{n-1}}{p} + \frac{K_n}{D_1(p + s_0)}$$

(5.156)

Substituting $s - s_0 = p$ in the above equation, we obtain

$$F(s) = \frac{K_0}{(s - s_0)^n} + \frac{K_1}{(s - s_0)^{n-1}} + \cdots + \frac{K_{n-1}}{(s - s_0)} + \frac{K_n}{D_1(s)}$$

(5.157)

We have thus found the partial-fraction expansion for the multiple-root terms. The remaining terms $K_n/[D_1(s)]$ still must be expanded into partial fractions. Consider the following example.

Example 5.15.

$$F(s) = \frac{2}{(s + 1)^3(s + 2)}$$

(5.158)

Using the method given above, $F_1(s)$ is

$$F_1(s) = (s + 1)^3 F(s) = \frac{2}{s + 2}$$

(5.159)

Setting $p = s + 1$, we then have

$$F_1(p - 1) = \frac{2}{p + 1}$$

(5.160)

The expansion of $F_1(p - 1)$ into a series as given in Eq. 5.155 requires dividing the numerator 2 by the denominator $1 + p$, with both numerator and denominator arranged in ascending power of p. The division here is

$$
\begin{array}{r}
2 - 2p + 2p^2 \\
\hline
1 + p \overline{)2} \\
\underline{2 + 2p} \\
-2p \\
\underline{-2p - 2p^2} \\
2p^2 \\
\underline{2p^2 + 2p^3} \\
-2p^3
\end{array}
$$

Since the multiplicity of the root is $N = 3$, we terminate the division after we have three terms in the quotient. We then have

$$F_1(p - 1) = 2 - 2p + 2p^2 - \frac{2p^3}{p + 1} \tag{5.161}$$

The original function $F(p - 1)$ is

$$F(p - 1) = \frac{F_1(p - 1)}{p^3} = \frac{2}{p^3} - \frac{2}{p^2} + \frac{2}{p} - \frac{2}{p + 1} \tag{5.162}$$

Substituting $s + 1 = p$, we have

$$F(s) = \frac{2}{(s + 1)^3} - \frac{2}{(s + 1)^2} + \frac{2}{(s + 1)} - \frac{2}{s + 2} \tag{5.163}$$

Example 5.16.   As a second example, consider the function

$$F(s) = \frac{s + 2}{s^2(s + 1)^2} \tag{5.164}$$

Since we have two sets of multiple roots here—at $s = 0$, and $s = -1$—we have a choice of expanding $F_1(s)$ about $s = 0$ or $s = -1$. Let us arbitrarily choose to expand about $s = 0$; since $p = s$ here, we do not have to make any substitutions. $F_1(s)$ is then

$$F_1(s) = \frac{s + 2}{(s + 1)^2} = \frac{2 + s}{1 + 2s + s^2} \tag{5.165}$$

Expanding $F_1(s)$, we obtain

$$F_1(s) = 2 - 3s + \frac{s^2(3s + 4)}{(s + 1)^2} \tag{5.166}$$

$F(s)$ is then

$$F(s) = \frac{2}{s^2} - \frac{3}{s} + \frac{3s + 4}{(s + 1)^2} \tag{5.167}$$

We must now repeat this process for the term

$$\frac{3s + 4}{(s + 1)^2}$$

Fortunately we see that the term can be written as

$$\frac{3s + 4}{(s + 1)^2} = \frac{3(s + 1) + 1}{(s + 1)^2} = \frac{3}{(s + 1)} + \frac{1}{(s + 1)^2} \tag{5.168}$$

The final answer is then

$$F(s) = \frac{2}{s^2} - \frac{3}{s} + \frac{3}{s + 1} + \frac{1}{(s + 1)^2} \tag{5.169}$$

5.7 THE INITIAL AND FINAL VALUE THEOREMS

In this section, we will discuss two very useful theorems of Laplace transforms. The first is the *initial value* theorem. It relates the initial value of $f(t)$ at $t = 0+$ to the limiting value of $s F(s)$ as s approaches infinity, i.e.,

$$\lim_{t \to 0+} f(t) = \lim_{s \to \infty} s F(s) \qquad (5.170)$$

The only restriction is that $f(t)$ must be continuous or contain at most a step discontinuity at $t = 0$. In terms of the transform, $F(s) = \mathscr{L}[f(t)]$, this restriction implies that $F(s)$ must be a *proper fraction*, i.e., the degree of the denominator polynomial of $F(s)$ must be greater than the degree of the numerator of $F(s)$. Now consider the proof of the initial value theorem which we give in two parts.

(*a*) The function $f(t)$ is continuous at $t = 0$, i.e.,

$$f(0-) = f(0+)$$

From the relationship

$$\mathscr{L}[f'(t)] = \int_{0-}^{\infty} f'(t)e^{-st}\, dt = s F(s) - f(0-) \qquad (5.171)$$

we obtain

$$\lim_{s \to \infty} \mathscr{L}[f'(t)] = \lim_{s \to \infty} s F(s) - f(0-) = 0 \qquad (5.172)$$

Therefore,

$$\lim_{s \to \infty} s F(s) = f(0-) = f(0+) \qquad (5.173)$$

(*b*) The function $f(t)$ has a step discontinuity at $t = 0$. Let us represent $f(t)$ in terms of a continuous part $f_1(t)$ and a step discontinuity $D\, u(t)$, as shown in Fig. 5.7. We can then write $f(t)$ as

$$f(t) = f_1(t) + D\, u(t) \qquad (5.174)$$

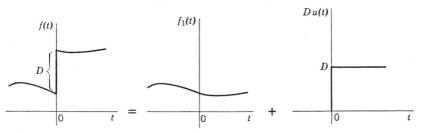

FIG. 5.7. Decomposition of a discontinuous function into a continuous function plus a step function.

where $D = f(0+) - f(0-)$. The derivative of $f(t)$ is

$$f'(t) = f'_1(t) + D\, \delta(t) \tag{5.175}$$

Since $f_1(t)$ is continuous at $t = 0$, we know from part (a) that

$$\lim_{s \to \infty} s\, F_1(s) = f_1(0-) = f(0-) \tag{5.176}$$

Taking the Laplace transform of both sides of Eq. 5.175, we have

$$s\, F(s) - f(0-) = s\, F_1(s) - f_1(0-) + D \tag{5.177}$$

which simplifies to

$$s\, F(s) = s\, F_1(s) + D \tag{5.178}$$

Now, if we take the limit of Eq. 5.178 as $s \to \infty$ and let $f(0+) - f(0-) = D$, we have

$$\lim_{s \to \infty} s\, F(s) = \lim_{s \to \infty} s\, F_1(s) + f(0+) - f(0-) \tag{5.179}$$

By Eq. 5.176, we then obtain

$$\lim_{s \to \infty} s\, F(s) = f(0+) \tag{5.180}$$

Example 5.17.   Given the function

$$F(s) = \frac{2(s + 1)}{s^2 + 2s + 5} \tag{5.181}$$

let us find $f(0+)$. Since the degree of the denominator is greater than the degree of the numerator of $F(s)$, the initial value theorem applies. Thus

$$\lim_{s \to \infty} s\, F(s) = \lim_{s \to \infty} \frac{2(s + 1)s}{s^2 + 2s + 5} = 2 \tag{5.182}$$

Since

$$\mathscr{L}^{-1}[F(s)] = 2e^{-t} \cos 2t \tag{5.183}$$

we see that $f(0+) = 2$.

Example 5.18.   Now let us consider a case where the initial value theorem does not apply. Given the function

$$f(t) = \delta(t) + 3e^{-t} \tag{5.184}$$

we see that $f(0+) = 3$. The transform of $f(t)$ is

$$F(s) = 1 + \frac{3}{s + 1} \tag{5.185}$$

so that

$$\lim_{s \to \infty} s\, F(s) = \lim_{s \to \infty} s\left(1 + \frac{3}{s + 1}\right) = \infty \tag{5.186}$$

Next, we will consider the *final value* theorem which states that

$$\lim_{t \to \infty} f(t) = \lim_{s \to 0} s\, F(s) \qquad (5.187)$$

provided the roots of the denominator of $F(s)$, which we refer to as *poles*, have negative or zero real parts, i.e., the poles of $F(s)$ must not be in the right half of the complex-frequency plane. The proof is quite simple. First,

$$\int_{0-}^{\infty} f'(t) e^{-st}\, dt = s\, F(s) - f(0-) \qquad (5.188)$$

Taking the limit as $s \to 0$ in the last equation, we have

$$\int_{0-}^{\infty} f'(t)\, dt = \lim_{s \to 0} s\, F(s) - f(0-) \qquad (5.189)$$

Evaluating the integral, we obtain

$$f(\infty) - f(0-) = \lim_{s \to 0} s\, F(s) - f(0-) \qquad (5.190)$$

Consequently,

$$f(\infty) = \lim_{s \to 0} s\, F(s) \qquad (5.191)$$

Example 5.19.   Given the function

$$f(t) = 3u(t) + 2e^{-t} \qquad (5.192)$$

which has the transform

$$F(s) = \frac{3}{s} + \frac{2}{s + 1} = \frac{5s + 3}{s(s + 1)} \qquad (5.193)$$

let us find the final value $f(\infty)$. Since the poles of $F(s)$ are at $s = 0$ and $s = -1$, we see the final value theorem applies. We find that

$$\lim_{s \to 0} s\, F(s) = 3 \qquad (5.194)$$

which is the final value of $f(t)$ as seen from Eq. 5.193.

Example 5.20.   Given

$$f(t) = 2e^{t} \qquad (5.195)$$

we see that

$$\lim_{t \to \infty} f(t) = \infty \qquad (5.196)$$

But from

$$s\, F(s) = \frac{2s}{s - 1} \qquad (5.197)$$

we have

$$\lim_{s \to 0} s\, F(s) = 0 \qquad (5.198)$$

We see that the final value theorem does not apply in this case because the pole $s = 1$ is in the right half of the complex-frequency plane.

TABLE 5.1.   LAPLACE TRANSFORMS

$f(t)$	$F(s)$
1. $f(t)$	$F(s) = \displaystyle\int_{0-}^{\infty} f(t) e^{-st}\, dt$
2. $a_1 f_1(t) + a_2 f_2(t)$	$a_1\, F_1(s) + a_2\, F_2(s)$
3. $\dfrac{d}{dt} f(t)$	$s\, F(s) - f(0-)$
4. $\dfrac{d^n}{dt^n} f(t)$	$s^n\, F(s) - \displaystyle\sum_{j=1}^{n} s^{n-j} f^{j-1}(0-)$
5. $\displaystyle\int_{0-}^{t} f(\tau)\, d\tau$	$\dfrac{1}{s} F(s)$
6. $\displaystyle\int_{0-}^{t} \int_{0-}^{t} f(\tau)\, d\tau$	$\dfrac{1}{s^2} F(s)$
7. $(-t)^n f(t)$	$\dfrac{d^n}{ds^n} F(s)$
8. $f(t-a)\, u(t-a)$	$e^{-as}\, F(s)$
9. $e^{at} f(t)$	$F(s-a)$
10. $\delta(t)$	1
11. $\dfrac{d^n}{dt^n} \delta(t)$	s^n
12. $u(t)$	$\dfrac{1}{s}$
13. t	$\dfrac{1}{s^2}$
14. $\dfrac{t^n}{n!}$	$\dfrac{1}{s^{n+1}}$
15. $e^{-\alpha t}$	$\dfrac{1}{s+\alpha}$
16. $\dfrac{1}{\beta - \alpha}(e^{-\alpha t} - e^{-\beta t})$	$\dfrac{1}{(s+\alpha)(s+\beta)}$
17. $\sin \omega t$	$\dfrac{\omega}{s^2 + \omega^2}$

TABLE 5.1.   LAPLACE TRANSFORMS (cont'd)

$f(t)$	$F(s)$
18. $\cos \omega t$	$\dfrac{s}{s^2 + \omega^2}$
19. $\sinh at$	$\dfrac{a}{s^2 - a^2}$
20. $\cosh at$	$\dfrac{s}{s^2 - a^2}$
21. $e^{-\alpha t} \sin \omega t$	$\dfrac{\omega}{(s + a)^2 + \omega^2}$
22. $e^{-\alpha t} \cos \omega t$	$\dfrac{(s + \alpha)}{(s + \alpha)^2 + \omega^2}$
23. $\dfrac{e^{-\alpha t} t^n}{n!}$	$\dfrac{1}{(s + \alpha)^{n+1}}$
24. $\dfrac{s}{(s^2 + \omega^2)^2}$	$\dfrac{t}{2\omega} \sin \omega t$
25. $\dfrac{1}{\alpha^n} J_n(\alpha t); n = 0, 1, 2, 3, \cdots$ (Bessel function of first kind, nth order)	$\dfrac{1}{(s^2 + \alpha^2)^{\frac{1}{2}}[(s^2 + \alpha^2)^{\frac{1}{2}} - s]^{-n}}$
26. $(\pi t)^{-\frac{1}{2}}$	$s^{-\frac{1}{2}}$
27. t^k (k need not be an integer)	$\dfrac{\Gamma(k + 1)}{s^{k+1}}$

Problems

5.1   The system function of a network is given as

$$H(j\omega) = \frac{3}{(j\omega + 2)(j\omega + 3)}$$

(a) Find the impulse response of the network.
(b) Find the response to an excitation $e(t) = 2e^{-t} u(t)$.

5.2   Find the Laplace transforms of

(a) $\qquad\qquad\qquad f(t) = \sin (\omega t + \theta)$
(b) $\qquad\qquad\qquad f(t) = e^{-(t+a)} \cos (\omega t + \theta)$

(c) $\qquad f(t) = (a + be^{-ct})\,u(t)$

(d) $\qquad f(t) = t\sin at$

(e) $\qquad f(t) = te^{-at}\cos bt$

5.3 Find the Laplace transforms for the waveforms shown.

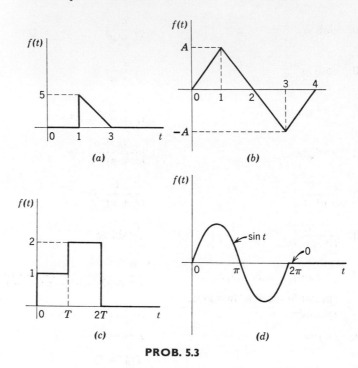

PROB. 5.3

5.4 Find the Laplace transforms for the derivatives of the waveforms in Prob. 5.3.

5.5 Find the inverse transforms for

(a) $$F(s) = \frac{2s + 9}{(s + 3)(s + 4)}$$

(b) $$F(s) = \frac{5s - 12}{s^2 + 4s + 13}$$

(c) $$F(s) = \frac{4s + 13}{s^2 + 4s - 5}$$

Note that all the inverse transforms may be obtained without resorting to *normal* partial-fraction expansions.

5.6   Find the Laplace transforms of the periodic waveforms shown. All of the transforms are to be given in closed form.

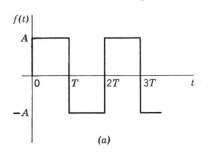

(a)

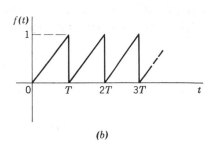

(b)

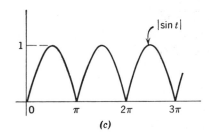

(c)

PROB. 5.6

5.7   Evaluate the definite integrals

(a) $$\int_0^\infty x^{(n-1)} \cos bx \, dx \qquad b > 0; \qquad n \text{ integer}$$

(b) $$\int_0^\pi t \sin 2t \, dt$$

(c) $$\int_0^{\pi/2} t^2 \cos 3t \, dt$$

5.8   Find the system function $H(s)$ for a system described by the differential equation,

$$x''(t) + 3x'(t) + 2x(t) = \delta(t)$$

with $x'(0-) = x(0-) = 0$. Next determine the response for an excitation $2e^{-t}$. Use only Laplace *not* Fourier transforms.

5.9   Find the step response for a system described by the equation

$$x''(t) + 2x'(t) + 5x(t) = u(t)$$

with $x(0-) = -2, x'(0-) = 1$.

5.10   Solve the following differential equations using Laplace transforms

(a) $$x''(t) + 6x'(t) + 9x(t) = \cos 2t$$

(b) $$x''(t) + 5x'(t) + 4x(t) = e^{-t} + e^{-4t}$$
(c) $$x''(t) + 2x'(t) = 4u(t).$$

It is given that $x(0-) = x'(0-) = 0$ for all three equations.

5.11 Find the inverse transforms for

(a) $$F(s) = \frac{(s + 2)(s + 3)}{s(s + 4)}$$

(b) $$F(s) = \frac{(s + 1)^3}{s^4}$$

(c) $$F(s) = \frac{s + 1}{s^2 + 2s + 2}$$

(d) $$F(s) = \frac{s^2 + 3s + 1}{s^2 + s}$$

(e) $$F(s) = \frac{s^2 + 4}{s(s^2 + 2s + 10)}$$

(f) $$F(s) = \frac{s + 5}{(s + 2)^2(s + 1)^2}$$

(g) $$F(s) = \frac{s^3}{(s + 1)(s + 2)^4}$$

(h) $$F(s) = \frac{s + 5}{s^3(s^2 + 2s + 10)}$$

(i) $$F(s) = \frac{e^{-2s}}{s^2 + 2s + 5}$$

5.12 Using Laplace transforms, solve the set of simultaneous equations,

$$2x'(t) + x(t) + y'(t) + 4y(t) = 2e^{-t}$$
$$x'(t) + y'(t) + 8y(t) = \delta(t)$$

The initial conditions are $x(0-) = y(0-) = 0$.

5.13 Using the initial value theorem, find the initial value of the square pulse in the figure shown.

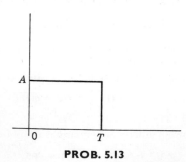

PROB. 5.13

5.14   Using the initial and final value theorems *where they apply*, find $f(0+)$ and $f(\infty)$ for

(a)
$$F(s) = \frac{(s + 1)(s + 2)}{(s + 3)(s + 4)}$$

(b)
$$F(s) = \frac{s}{(s + 1)(s - 2)}$$

(c)
$$F(s) = \frac{s^2 + 3s + 2}{s^3 + 3s^2 + 3s + 1}$$

(d)
$$F(s) = \frac{s(s + 4)(s + 8)}{(s + 1)(s + 6)}$$

chapter 6

Transform methods in network analysis

6.1 THE TRANSFORMED CIRCUIT

In Chapter 4, we discussed the voltage-current relationships of network elements in the time domain. These basic relationships may also be represented in the complex frequency domain. Ideal energy sources, for example, which were given in time domain as $v(t)$ and $i(t)$, may now be represented by their transforms, $V(s) = \mathscr{L}[v(t)]$ and $I(s) = \mathscr{L}[i(t)]$. The resistor, defined by the v-i relationship,

$$v(t) = R\,i(t) \qquad (6.1)$$

is defined in the frequency domain by the transform of Eq. 6.1, or

$$V(s) = R\,I(s) \qquad (6.2)$$

For an inductor, the defining v-i relationships are

$$v(t) = L\frac{di}{dt}$$
$$i(t) = \frac{1}{L}\int_{0-}^{t} v(\tau)\,d\tau + i(0-) \qquad (6.3)$$

Transforming both equations, we obtain

$$V(s) = sL - L\,i(0-)$$
$$I(s) = \frac{1}{sL}V(s) + \frac{i(0-)}{s} \qquad (6.4)$$

The transformed circuit representation for an inductor is depicted in Fig. 6.1.

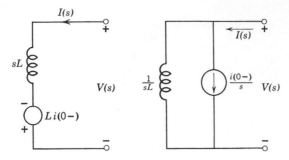

FIG. 6.1. Inductor.

For a capacitor, the defining equations are

$$v(t) = \frac{1}{C} \int_{0-}^{t} i(\tau)\, d\tau + v(0-)$$

$$i(t) = C \frac{dv}{dt}$$

(6.5)

The frequency domain counterpart of these equations are, then,

$$V(s) = \frac{1}{sC} I(s) + \frac{v(0-)}{s}$$

$$I(s) = sC\, V(s) - C\, v(0-)$$

(6.6)

as depicted in Fig. 6.2.

From this analysis, we see that, in the complex frequency representation, the network elements can be represented as *impedances* and *admittances* in series or parallel with energy sources. For example, from Eq. 6.4, we see that the complex frequency impedance representation of an inductor is sL, and its associated admittance is $1/sL$. Similarly, the impedance of a capacitor is $1/sC$ and its admittance is sC. This fact is very useful in circuit analysis. Working from a transformed circuit diagram, we can write mesh and node equations on an impedance or admittance basis directly.

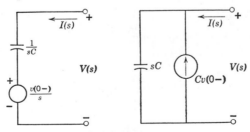

FIG. 6.2. Capacitor.

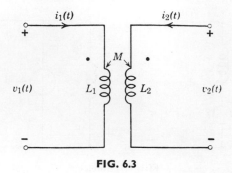

FIG. 6.3

The process of solving network differential equations with the use of transform methods has been given in the previous chapter. To analyze the circuit on a transform basis, the only additional step required is to represent all the network elements in terms of complex impedances or admittances with associated initial energy sources.

Consider the example of the transformer in Fig. 6.3. If we write the defining equations of the transformer directly in the time domain, we have,

$$v_1(t) = L_1 \frac{di_1}{dt} + M \frac{di_2}{dt}$$

$$v_2(t) = M \frac{di_1}{dt} + L_2 \frac{di_2}{dt}$$

(6.7)

Transforming this set of equations, we obtain

$$V_1(s) = sL_1 I_1(s) - L_1 i_1(0-) + sM I_2(s) - M i_2(0-)$$
$$V_2(s) = sM I_1(s) - M i_1(0-) + sL_2 I_2(s) - L_2 i_2(0-)$$

(6.8)

This set of transform equations could have been obtained also by representing the circuit in Fig. 6.3 by its transformed equivalent given in Fig. 6.4.

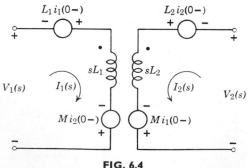

FIG. 6.4

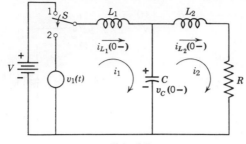

FIG. 6.5

In general, the use of transformed equivalent circuits is considered an easier way to solve the problem.

Example 6.1. In Fig. 6.5, the switch is thrown from position 1 to 2 at $t = 0$. Assuming there is no coupling between L_1 and L_2, let us write the mesh equations from the transformed equivalent circuit in Fig. 6.6. The mesh equations are:

$$V_1(s) + L_1\, i_{L_1}(0-) - \frac{v_C(0-)}{s} = \left(sL_1 + \frac{1}{sC}\right) I_1(s) - \frac{1}{sC} I_2(s)$$

$$\frac{v_C(0-)}{s} + L_2\, i_{L_2}(0-) = -\frac{1}{sC} I_1(s) + \left(\frac{1}{sC} + sL_2 + R\right) I_2(s)$$

$$(6.9)$$

Example 6.2. In Fig. 6.7, the switch is thrown from position 1 to 2 at time $t = 0$. Just before the switch is thrown, the initial conditions are $i_L(0-) = 2$ amp, $v_C(0-) = 2$ v. Let us find the current $i(t)$ after the switching action.

Since the switch is closed at $t = 0$, we can regard the 5-v battery as an equivalent transformed source, $5/s$. The circuit is now redrawn in Fig. 6.8 as a transformed circuit. The mesh equation for the circuit in Fig. 6.8 is

$$\frac{5}{s} - \frac{2}{s} + 2 = \left(3 + s + \frac{2}{s}\right) I(s) \qquad (6.10)$$

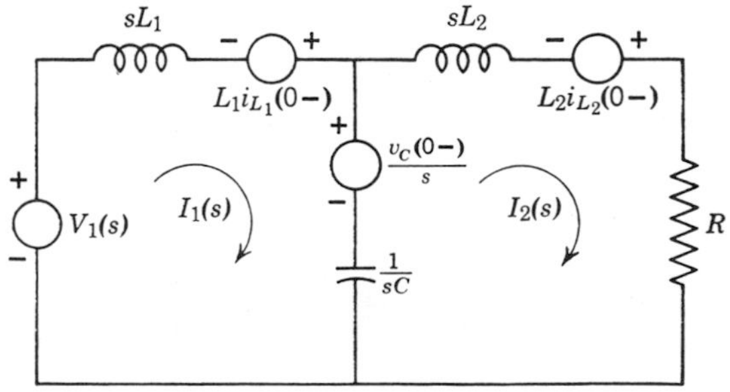

FIG. 6.6

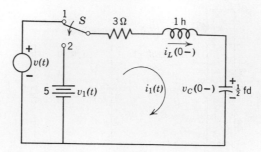

FIG. 6.7

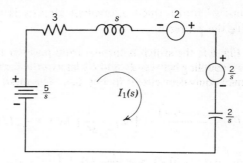

FIG. 6.8

Solving for $I(s)$, we have

$$I(s) = \frac{2s + 3}{(s + 1)(s + 2)} = \frac{1}{s + 1} + \frac{1}{s + 2} \tag{6.11}$$

Therefore,

$$i(t) = \mathscr{L}^{-1}[I(s)] = e^{-t} + e^{-2t} \tag{6.12}$$

Example 6.3. Consider the network in Fig. 6.9. At $t = 0$, the switch is opened. Let us find the node voltages $v_1(t)$ and $v_2(t)$ for the circuit. It is given that

$$L = \tfrac{1}{2}\,\text{h} \qquad C = 1\,\text{fd}$$

$$G = 1\,\text{mho} \qquad V = 1\,\text{v}$$

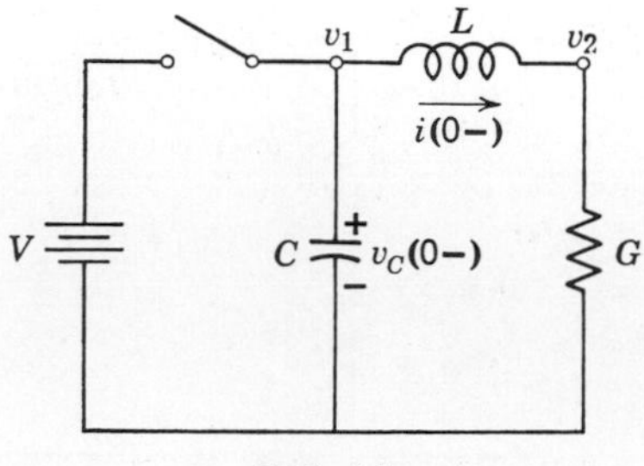

FIG. 6.9

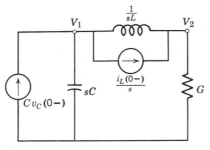

FIG. 6.10

Before we substitute element values, let us write the node equations for the transformed circuit in Fig. 6.10. These are:

Node V_1:

$$-\frac{i_L(0-)}{s} + C\,v_C(0-) = \left(sC + \frac{1}{sL}\right) V_1(s) - \frac{1}{sL} V_2(s) \qquad (6.13)$$

Node V_2:

$$\frac{i_L(0-)}{s} = -\frac{1}{sL} V_1(s) + \left(\frac{1}{sL} + G\right) V_2(s)$$

If we assume that, prior to the switch opening, the circuit had been in steady state, then we have $v_C(0-) = 1$ v, $i_L(0-) = 1$ amp. Substituting numerical values into the set of node equations, we have

$$1 - \frac{1}{s} = \left(s + \frac{2}{s}\right) V_1(s) - \frac{2}{s} V_2(s)$$

$$\frac{1}{s} = -\frac{2}{s} V_1(s) + \left(\frac{2}{s} + 1\right) V_2(s) \qquad (6.14)$$

Simplifying these equations, we obtain

$$s - 1 = (s^2 + 2)\,V_1(s) - 2V_2(s)$$

$$1 = -2V_1(s) + (s + 2)\,V_2(s) \qquad (6.15)$$

Solving these equations simultaneously, we get,

$$V_1(s) = \frac{s + 1}{s^2 + 2s + 2} = \frac{s + 1}{(s + 1)^2 + 1}$$

$$V_2(s) = \frac{s + 2}{s^2 + 2s + 2} = \frac{s + 2}{(s + 1)^2 + 1} \qquad (6.16)$$

so that the inverse transforms are

$$v_1(t) = e^{-t} \cos t, \qquad v_2(t) = e^{-t}(\cos t + \sin t) \qquad (6.17)$$

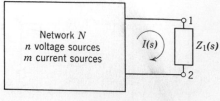

FIG. 6.11

6.2 THÉVENIN'S AND NORTON'S THEOREMS

In network analysis, the objective of a problem is often to determine a *single* branch current through a given element or a *single* voltage across an element. In problems of this kind, it is generally not practicable to write a complete set of mesh or node equations and to solve a system of equations for this one current or voltage. It is then convenient to use two very important theorems on equivalent circuits, known as Thévenin's and Norton's theorems.

Thévenin's theorem

From the standpoint of determining the current $I(s)$ through an element of impedance $Z_1(s)$, shown in Fig. 6.11, the rest of the network N can be replaced by an equivalent impedance $Z_e(s)$ in series with an equivalent voltage source $V_e(s)$, as depicted in Fig. 6.12. The equivalent impedance $Z_e(s)$ is the impedance "looking into" N from the terminals of $Z_1(s)$ when all voltage sources in N are short-circuited and all current sources are open-circuited. The equivalent voltage source $V_e(s)$ is the voltage which appears between the terminals 1 and 2 in Fig. 6.11, when the element $Z_1(s)$ is removed or open-circuited. The only requirement for Thévenin's theorem is that the elements in Z_1 must not be magnetically coupled to any element in N.

The proof follows. The network in Fig. 6.11 contains n voltage and m current sources. We are to find the current $I(s)$ through an element which is not magnetically coupled to the rest of the circuit and whose impedance

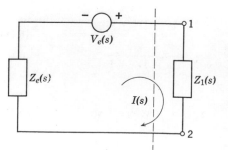

FIG. 6.12. Thévenin's equivalent circuit.

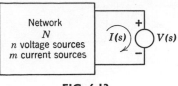

FIG. 6.13

is $Z_1(s)$. According to the compensation theorem,* we can replace $Z_1(s)$ by a voltage source $V(s)$ as shown in Fig. 6.13. Then by the superposition principle, we can think of the current $I(s)$ as the sum of two separate parts,

$$I(s) = I_1(s) + I_2(s) \qquad (6.18)$$

Let the current $I_1(s)$ be the current due to the n voltage and m current sources alone; i.e., we short-circuit the source $V(s)$, as shown in Fig. 6.14a. Therefore, $I_1(s)$ is equal to the short-circuit current, I_{sc}. Let $I_2(s)$ be the current due to the voltage source $V(s)$ alone, with all the rest of the voltage sources short-circuited and current sources open-circuited (Fig. 6.14b). With the m current and n voltage sources removed in Fig. 6.14b, we see that the network N is passive so that $I_2(s)$ is related to the source $V(s)$ by the relation,

$$I_2(s) = - \frac{V(s)}{Z_{in}(s)} \qquad (6.19)$$

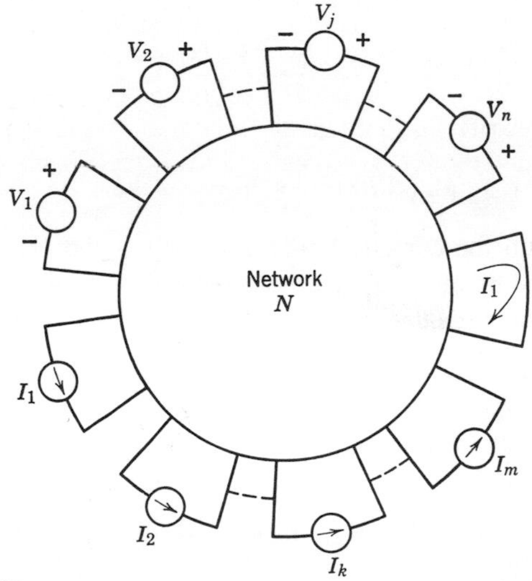

FIG. 6.14a

---

* See H. H. Skilling, *Electrical Engineering Circuits*, John Wiley & Sons, New York, 1957.

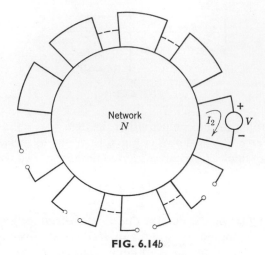

FIG. 6.14b

where $Z_{in}(s)$ is the input impedance of the circuit at the terminals of the source $V(s)$. We can now write $I(s)$ in Eq. 6.18 as

$$I(s) = I_{sc}(s) - \frac{V(s)}{Z_{in}(s)} \qquad (6.20)$$

Since Eq. 6.20 must be satisfied in all cases, consider the particular case when we open-circuit the branch containing $Z_1(s)$. Then $I(s) = 0$ and $V(s)$ is the open-circuit voltage $V_{oc}(s)$. From Eq. 6.20 we have

$$I_{sc}(s) = \frac{V_{oc}(s)}{Z_{in}(s)} \qquad (6.21)$$

so that we can rewrite Eq. 6.20 as

$$Z_{in}(s) \, I(s) - V_{oc}(s) = -V(s) \qquad (6.22)$$

In order to obtain the current $I(s)$ through $Z_1(s)$, the rest of the network N can be replaced by an equivalent voltage source $V_e(s) = V_{oc}(s)$ in series with an equivalent impedance $Z_e(s) = Z_{in}(s)$, as shown in Fig. 6.12.

Example 6.4. Let us determine by Thévenin's theorem the current $I_1(s)$ flowing through the capacitor in the network shown in Fig. 6.15. First, let us obtain $Z_e(s)$ by opening all current sources and short-circuiting all voltage sources. Then, we have the network in Fig. 6.16, where

$$Z_e(s) = R + sL \qquad (6.23)$$

Next, we find $V_e(s)$ by removing the capacitor so that the open-circuit voltage between the terminals 1 and 2 is $V_e(s)$, as shown in Fig. 6.17. We readily

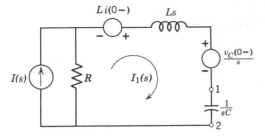

FIG. 6.15

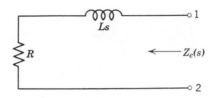

FIG. 6.16

determine from Fig. 6.17 that

$$V_e(s) = I(s)R + L\,i(0-) - \frac{v_C(0-)}{s} \qquad (6.24)$$

By Thévenin's theorem we then have

$$I_1(s) = \frac{V_e(s)}{Z_e(s) + Z(s)} = \frac{I(s)R + L\,i(0-) - v_C(0-)/s}{R + sL + 1/sC} \qquad (6.25)$$

Example 6.5.   For the network in Fig. 6.18, let us determine the voltage $v_0(t)$ across the resistor by Thévenin's theorem. The switch closes at $t = 0$, and we assume that all initial conditions are zero at $t = 0$.

First let us redraw the circuit in terms of its transformed representation given in Fig. 6.19. We can almost determine by inspection that the Thévenin equivalent voltage source of the network to the left of N in Fig. 6.19 is

$$V_e(s) = \frac{V(s)(1/sC)}{L_1 s + 1/sC} \qquad (6.26)$$

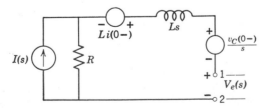

FIG. 6.17

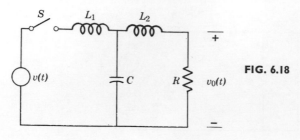

FIG. 6.18

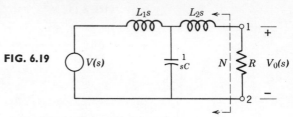

FIG. 6.19

and the input impedance to the left of N is

$$Z_e(s) = sL_2 + \frac{sL_1(1/sC)}{sL_1 + 1/sC} \tag{6.27}$$

We know that

$$V_0(s) = \frac{R\, V_e(s)}{Z_e(s) + R} \tag{6.28}$$

Therefore,

$$V_0(s) = \frac{R\, V(s)(1/sC)}{(R + sL_2)(sL_1 + 1/sC) + L_1/C} \tag{6.29}$$

Finally,

$$v_0(t) = \mathscr{L}^{-1}[V_0(s)] \tag{6.30}$$

Norton's theorem

When it is required to find the voltage across an element whose admittance is $Y_1(s)$, the rest of the network can be represented as an equivalent admittance $Y_e(s)$ in parallel with an equivalent current source $I_e(s)$, as shown in Fig. 6.20. The admittance $Y_e(s)$ is the reciprocal of the Thévenin impedance. The current $I_e(s)$ is that current which flows through a short circuit across $Y_1(s)$. From Fig. 6.20,

$$V_1(s) = \frac{I_e(s)}{Y_e(s) + Y_1(s)} \tag{6.31}$$

The element whose admittance is Y_1 must not be magnetically coupled to any element in the rest of the network.

Consider the network in Fig. 6.21. Let us find the voltage across the capacitor by Norton's theorem. First, the short-circuit current source

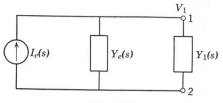

FIG. 6.20

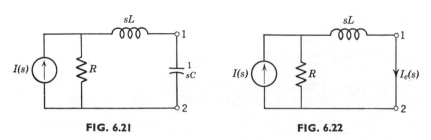

FIG. 6.21   FIG. 6.22

$I_e(s)$ is found by placing a short circuit across the terminals 1 and 2 of the capacitor, as shown in Fig. 6.22. From Fig. 6.22, $I_e(s)$ is

$$I_e(s) = \frac{I(s)R}{sL + R} \tag{6.32}$$

The admittance $Y_e(s)$ is the reciprocal of the Thévenin admittance, or

$$Y_e(s) = \frac{1}{sL + R} \tag{6.33}$$

Then the voltage across the capacitor can be given as

$$V(s) = \frac{I_e(s)}{Y_e(s) + Y_C(s)} = \frac{I(s)R}{(sL + R)sC + 1} \tag{6.34}$$

Example 6.6. In the network in Fig. 6.23, the switch closes at $t = 0$. It is given that $v(t) = 0.1e^{-5t}$ and all initial currents and voltages are zero. Let us find the current $i_2(t)$ by Norton's theorem.

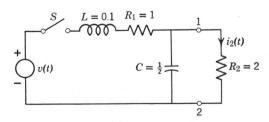

FIG. 6.23

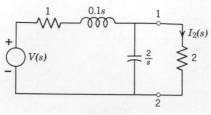

FIG. 6.24

The transformed circuit is given in Fig. 6.24. To find the Norton equivalent current source, we short-circuit points 1 and 2 in the network shown. Then $I_e(s)$ is the current flowing in the short circuit, or

$$I_e(s) = \frac{V(s)}{R_1 + sL} = \frac{0.1}{L(s + R/L)(s + 5)} = \frac{1}{(s + 5)(s + 10)} \qquad (6.35)$$

The equivalent admittance of the circuit as viewed from points 1 and 2 is

$$Y_e(s) = sC + \frac{1}{R_1 + sL} = \frac{s^2LC + sR_1C + 1}{R_1 + sL} = \frac{0.5s^2 + 5s + 10}{s + 10} \qquad (6.36)$$

$I_2(s)$ is then

$$I_2(s) = \frac{I_e(s)}{R_2[Y_e(s) + G_2]} \qquad (6.37)$$

$$= \frac{1}{(s + 5)^2(s + 6)} \qquad (6.38)$$

By inspection, we see that $I_2(s)$ can be written as

$$I_2(s) = \frac{(s + 6) - (s + 5)}{(s + 5)^2(s + 6)} = \frac{1}{(s + 5)^2} - \frac{1}{(s + 6)(s + 5)} \qquad (6.39)$$

Repeating this procedure, we then obtain

$$I_2(s) = \frac{1}{(s + 5)^2} - \frac{1}{s + 5} + \frac{1}{s + 6} \qquad (6.40)$$

Taking the inverse transform of $I_2(s)$, we finally obtain

$$i_2(t) = (te^{-5t} - e^{-5t} + e^{-6t}) u(t) \qquad (6.41)$$

6.3 THE SYSTEM FUNCTION

As we discussed earlier, a linear system is one in which the excitation $e(t)$ is related to the response $r(t)$ by a linear differential equation. When the Laplace transform is used in describing the system, the relation between the excitation $E(s)$ and the response $R(s)$ is an algebraic one. In particular,

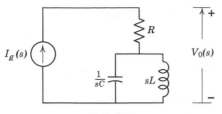

FIG. 6.25

when we discuss initially inert systems, the excitation and response are related by the system function $H(s)$ as given by the relation,

$$R(s) = E(s)\,H(s) \tag{6.42}$$

We will discuss how a system function is obtained for a given network, and how this function can be used in determining the system response.

As mentioned in Chapter 1, the system function may assume many forms and may have special names such as *driving-point admittance, transfer impedance, voltage* or *current ratio transfer function.* This is because the form of the system function depends on whether the excitation is a voltage or current source, and whether the response is a specified current or voltage. We now discuss some specific forms of system functions.

Impedance

When the excitation is a current source and the response is a voltage, then the system function is an impedance. When both excitation and response are measured between the same pair of terminals, then we have a driving-point impedance. An example of a driving-point impedance is given in Fig. 6.25, where

$$H(s) = \frac{V_0(s)}{I_g(s)} = R + \frac{(1/sC)sL}{sL + 1/sC} \tag{6.43}$$

Admittance

When the excitation is a voltage source and the response is a current, then $H(s)$ is an admittance. In Fig. 6.26, the transfer admittance I_2/V_g is

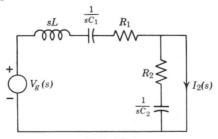

FIG. 6.26

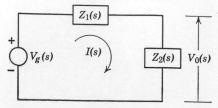

FIG. 6.27

obtained from the network as

$$H(s) = \frac{I_2(s)}{V_g(s)} = \frac{1}{R_1 + sL + 1/sC_1} \tag{6.44}$$

Voltage-ratio transfer function

When the excitation is a voltage source and the response is also a voltage, then $H(s)$ is a voltage-ratio transfer function. In Fig. 6.27, the voltage-ratio transfer function $V_0(s)/V_g(s)$ is obtained as follows: We first find the current

$$I(s) = \frac{V_g(s)}{Z_1(s) + Z_2(s)} \tag{6.45}$$

Since

$$V_0(s) = Z_2(s)\, I(s) \tag{6.46}$$

then

$$\frac{V_0(s)}{V_g(s)} = \frac{Z_2(s)}{Z_1(s) + Z_2(s)} \tag{6.47}$$

Current-ratio transfer function

When the excitation is a current source and the response is another current in the network, then $H(s)$ is called a current-ratio transfer function. As an example, let us find the ratio I_0/I_g for the network given in Fig. 6.28. Referring to the depicted network, we know that

$$I_g(s) = I_1(s) + I_0(s), \qquad I_1(s)\frac{1}{sC} = I_0(s)(R + sL) \tag{6.48,6.49}$$

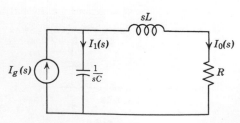

FIG. 6.28

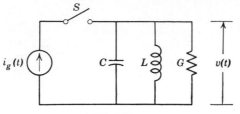

FIG. 6.29

Eliminating the variable I_1, we find

$$I_g(s) = I_0(s)\left(1 + \frac{R + sL}{1/sC}\right) \tag{6.50}$$

so that the current-ratio transfer function is

$$\frac{I_0(s)}{I_g(s)} = \frac{1/sC}{R + sL + 1/sC} \tag{6.51}$$

From the preceding examples, we have seen that the system function is a function of the elements of the network alone, and is obtained from the network by a straightforward application of Kirchhoff's laws. Now, let us obtain the response transform $R(s)$, given the excitation and the system function. Consider the network in Fig. 6.29, where the excitation is the current source $i_g(t)$ and the response is the voltage $v(t)$. We assume that the network is initially inert when the switch is closed at $t = 0$. Let us find the response $V(s)$ for the excitations:

1. $i_g(t) = (\sin \omega_0 t)\, u(t)$.
2. $i_g(t)$ is the square pulse in Fig. 6.30.
3. $i_g(t)$ has the waveform in Fig. 6.31.

First, we obtain the system function as

$$H(s) = \frac{1}{sC + 1/sL + G} = \frac{s}{C[s^2 + s(G/C) + 1/LC]} \tag{6.52}$$

1. $i_g(t) = (\sin \omega_0 t)\, u(t)$. The transform of $i_g(t)$ is

$$I_g(s) = \frac{\omega_0}{s^2 + \omega_0^2} \tag{6.53}$$

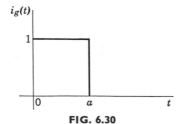

FIG. 6.30

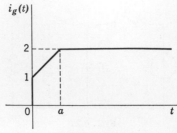

FIG. 6.31

so that

$$V(s) = I_g(s)\, H(s) = \frac{\omega_0}{s^2 + \omega_0^2} \cdot \frac{s}{C[s^2 + s(G/C) + 1/LC]} \tag{6.54}$$

2.   For the square pulse in Fig. 6.30, $i_g(t)$ can be written as

$$i_g(t) = u(t) - u(t - a) \tag{6.55}$$

Its transform is

$$I_g(s) = \frac{1}{s}(1 - e^{-as}) \tag{6.56}$$

The response $V(s)$ is, therefore, given as

$$V(s) = \frac{1 - e^{-as}}{C[s^2 + s(G/C) + 1/LC]} \tag{6.57}$$

Note that in obtaining the inverse transform, $\mathscr{L}^{-1}[V(s)]$, the factor e^{-as} must be regarded as only a delay factor in the time domain. Suppose we rewrite $V(s)$ in Eq. 6.57 as

$$V(s) = \frac{H(s)}{s}(1 - e^{-as}) \tag{6.58}$$

Then, if we denote by $v_1(t)$, the inverse transform,

$$v_1(t) = \mathscr{L}^{-1}\left[\frac{H(s)}{s}\right] \tag{6.59}$$

we obtain the time response,

$$v(t) = v_1(t) - v_1(t - a)\, u(t - a) \tag{6.60}$$

Observe that $v_1(t)$ in Eq. 6.59 is the response of the system to a unit step excitation.

3.   The waveform in Fig. 6.31 can be represented as

$$i_g(t) = u(t) + t\, u(t) - (t - a)\, u(t - a) \tag{6.61}$$

and its transform is

$$I_g(s) = \frac{1}{s}\left(1 + \frac{1}{s} - \frac{e^{-as}}{s}\right) \tag{6.62}$$

$V(s)$ is then

$$V(s) = \left(1 + \frac{1}{s} - \frac{e^{-as}}{s}\right)\frac{1}{C[s^2 + s(G/C) + 1/LC]} \tag{6.63}$$

If we denote by $v_2(t)$ the response of the system to a unit ramp excitation, we see that

$$\mathscr{L}^{-1}[V(s)] = v_1(t) + v_2(t) - v_2(t - a)\,u(t - a) \tag{6.64}$$

where $v_1(t)$ is the step response in Eq. 6.59.

Let us now discuss some further ramifications of the equation for the response,

$$R(s) = H(s)\,E(s)$$

Consider the partial-fraction expansion of $R(s)$,

$$R(s) = \sum_i \frac{A_i}{s - s_i} + \sum_j \frac{B_j}{s - s_j} \tag{6.65}$$

where s_i represents poles of $H(s)$, and s_j represents poles of $E(s)$. Taking the inverse transform of $R(s)$, we obtain

$$r(t) = \sum_i A_i e^{s_i t} + \sum_j B_j e^{s_j t} \tag{6.66}$$

. The terms $A_i e^{s_i t}$ are associated with the system $H(s)$ and are called *free response* terms. The terms $B_j e^{s_j t}$ are due to the excitation and are known as *forced response* terms. The frequencies s_i are the *natural frequencies* of the system and s_j are the *forced frequencies*. It is seen from our discussion of system stability in Chapter 4 that the natural frequencies of a passive network have real parts which are zero or negative. In other words, if we denote s_i as $s_i = \sigma_i + j\omega_i$, then $\sigma_i \leq 0$.

Example 6.7. For the initially inert network in Fig. 6.32, the excitation is

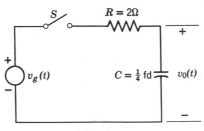

FIG. 6.32

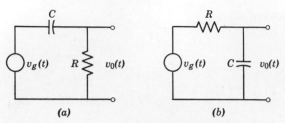

FIG. 6.33. (*a*) *R-C* differentiator. (*b*) *R-C* integrator.

$v_g(t) = \frac{1}{2}\cos t\, u(t)$. Let us find the response $v_0(t)$ and determine the free and forced response parts of $v_0(t)$. The system function is

$$\frac{V_0(s)}{V_g(s)} = \frac{1/sC}{R + 1/sC} = \frac{2}{s+2} \tag{6.67}$$

Since $V_g(s)$ is

$$V_g(s) = \frac{1}{2}\left(\frac{s}{s^2 + 1}\right) \tag{6.68}$$

the response is then

$$V_0(s) = V_g(s)\, H(s) = \frac{s}{(s^2 + 1)(s + 2)} = -\frac{0.4}{s+2} + \frac{0.4s + 0.2}{s^2 + 1} \tag{6.69}$$

We next obtain the inverse transform,

$$v_0(t) = -0.4e^{-2t} + 0.4\cos t + 0.2\sin t \tag{6.70}$$

It is apparent that the free response is

$$-0.4e^{-2t}$$

and the forced response is

$$0.4\cos t + 0.2\sin t$$

As a final topic in our discussion, let us consider the basis of operation for the *R-C* differentiator and integrator shown in Figs. 6.33*a* and 6.33*b*. We will use the Fourier transform in our analysis here so that the system function is given as $H(j\omega)$, where ω is the ordinary radian frequency variable. Consider first the system function of the differentiator in Fig. 6.33*a*,

$$\frac{V_0(j\omega)}{V_g(j\omega)} = \frac{R}{R + 1/j\omega C} = \frac{j\omega RC}{j\omega RC + 1} \tag{6.71}$$

Let us impose the condition that the *R-C* time constant is small as compared to unity, i.e.,

$$RC \ll 1 \tag{6.72}$$

In the frequency range

$$0 \le \omega < \frac{1}{RC}$$

we have, approximately,

$$\frac{V_0(j\omega)}{V_g(j\omega)} \simeq j\omega RC \tag{6.73}$$

Then the response $V_0(j\omega)$ can be expressed as

$$V_0(j\omega) \simeq RC[j\omega V_g(j\omega)] \tag{6.74}$$

Taking the inverse transform of $V_0(j\omega)$, we obtain

$$v_0(t) \simeq RC \frac{d}{dt} v_g(t) \tag{6.75}$$

Note that the derivation of Eq. 6.75 depends upon the assumption that the R-C time constant is much less than unity. This is a necessary condition.

Next, for the R-C integrator in Fig. 6.33b, the voltage-ratio transfer function is

$$\frac{V_0(j\omega)}{V_g(j\omega)} = \frac{1/j\omega C}{1/j\omega C + R} = \frac{1}{j\omega CR + 1} \tag{6.76}$$

If we assume that the R-C time constant is much greater than unity, i.e.,

$$RC \gg 1$$

when the frequency is in the vicinity of

$$\omega > \frac{1}{RC}$$

then

$$V_0(j\omega) \simeq \frac{1}{j\omega RC} V_g(j\omega) \tag{6.77}$$

Under these conditions, the inverse transform is,

$$v_0(t) \simeq \frac{1}{RC} \int_0^t v_g(\tau) \, d\tau \tag{6.78}$$

so that the R-C circuit in Fig. 6.33b is approximately an integrating circuit.

6.4 THE STEP AND IMPULSE RESPONSE

In this section ,we will show that the impulse response $h(t)$ and the system function $H(s)$ constitute a transform pair, so that we can obtain step and impulse responses directly from the system function.

We know, first of all, that the transform of a unit impulse $\delta(t)$ is unity, i.e., $\mathscr{L}[\delta(t)] = 1$. Suppose the system excitation were a unit impulse, then the response $R(s)$ would be

$$R(s) = E(s) \, H(s) = H(s) \tag{6.79}$$

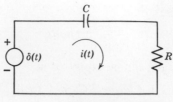

FIG. 6.34

We thus see that the impulse response $h(t)$ and the system function $H(s)$ constitute a transform pair, i.e.,

$$\mathcal{L}[h(t)] = H(s)$$
$$\mathcal{L}^{-1}[H(s)] = h(t) \tag{6.80}$$

Since the system function is usually easy to obtain, it is apparent that we can find the impulse response of a system by taking the inverse transform of $H(s)$.

Example 6.8. Let us find the impulse response of the current $i(t)$ in the R-C circuit in Fig. 6.34. The system function is

$$H(s) = \frac{I(s)}{V_g(s)} = \frac{1}{R + 1/sC} = \frac{s}{R(s + 1/RC)} \tag{6.81}$$

Simplifying $H(s)$ further, we have

$$H(s) = \frac{1}{R}\left(1 - \frac{1/RC}{s + 1/RC}\right) \tag{6.82}$$

The impulse response is then

$$h(t) = \mathcal{L}^{-1}[H(s)] = \frac{1}{R}\left[\delta(t) - \frac{1}{RC}e^{-t/RC}\right]u(t) \tag{6.83}$$

which is shown in Fig. 6.35.

Since the step response is the integral of the impulse response, we can use the integral property of Laplace transforms to obtain the step response as

$$\alpha(t) = \mathcal{L}^{-1}\left[\frac{H(s)}{s}\right] \tag{6.84}$$

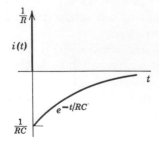

FIG. 6.35. Current impulse response of R-C network in Fig. 6.34.

where $\alpha(t)$ denotes the step response. Similarly, we obtain the unit ramp response from the equation

$$\gamma(t) = \mathscr{L}^{-1}\left[\frac{H(s)}{s^2}\right] \tag{6.85}$$

where $\gamma(t)$ denotes the ramp response. From this discussion, it is clear that a knowledge of the system function provides sufficient information to obtain all the transient response data which are needed to characterize the system.

Example 6.9. Let us find the current step response of the R-L circuit in Fig. 6.36. Since $I(s)$ is the response and $V_g(s)$ is the excitation, the system function is as follows:

$$H(s) = \frac{I(s)}{V_g(s)} = \frac{1}{R + sL} \tag{6.86}$$

Therefore $H(s)/s$ is

$$\frac{H(s)}{s} = \frac{1}{s(R + sL)} = \frac{1}{R}\left(\frac{1}{s} - \frac{1}{s + R/L}\right) \tag{6.87}$$

The step response $\alpha(t)$ is now obtained as:

$$\alpha(t) = \frac{1}{R}(1 - e^{-(R/L)t})\, u(t) \tag{6.88}$$

To check this result, let us consider the impulse response of the R-L circuit which we found in Chapter 4,

$$h(t) = \frac{1}{L}\, e^{-(R/L)t}\, u(t) \tag{6.89}$$

The step response is the integral of the impulse response, or,

$$\alpha(t) = \int_0^t h(\tau)\, d\tau = \frac{1}{R}(1 - e^{-(R/L)t})\, u(t) \tag{6.90}$$

It is readily seen that, if we know the impulse response of an initially inert linear system, we can determine the response of the system due to any other excitation. In other words, the impulse response alone is sufficient to characterize the system from the standpoint of excitation and response.

Example 6.10. In Fig. 6.37, the only information we possess about the system in the black box is: (1) it is an initially inert linear system; (2) when $v_i(t) = \delta(t)$, then

$$v_0(t) = (e^{-2t} + e^{-3t})\, u(t) \tag{6.91}$$

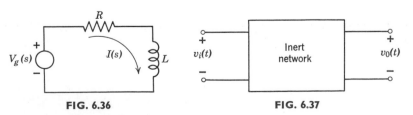

FIG. 6.36   **FIG. 6.37**

With this information, let us determine what the excitation $v_i(t)$ must be in order to produce a response $v_0(t) = te^{-2t} u(t)$. First, we determine the system function to be

$$H(s) = \frac{V_0(s)}{V_i(s)} = \frac{1}{s+2} + \frac{1}{s+3} = \frac{2s+5}{(s+2)(s+3)} \tag{6.92}$$

We next find the transform of $te^{-2t} u(t)$.

$$V_0(s) = \mathcal{L}[te^{-2t}] = \frac{1}{(s+2)^2} \tag{6.93}$$

The unknown excitation is then found from the equation,

$$V_i(s) = \frac{V_0(s)}{H(s)} = \frac{(s+2)(s+3)}{2(s+2.5)(s+2)^2} \tag{6.94}$$

Simplifying and expanding $V_i(s)$ into partial fractions, we have

$$V_i(s) = \frac{(s+3)}{2(s+2.5)(s+2)} = \frac{1}{s+2} - \frac{0.5}{s+2.5} \tag{6.95}$$

The system excitation is then

$$v_i(t) = (e^{-2t} - 0.5e^{-2.5t}) u(t) \tag{6.96}$$

6.5 THE CONVOLUTION INTEGRAL

In this section, we will explore some further ramifications of the use of the impulse response $h(t)$ to determine the system response $r(t)$. Our discussion is based upon the important *convolution theorem* of Laplace (or Fourier) transforms. Given two functions $f_1(t)$ and $f_2(t)$ which are zero for $t < 0$, the convolution theorem states that, if the transform of $f_1(t)$ is $F_1(s)$ and if the transform of $f_2(t)$ is $F_2(s)$, the transform of the *convolution* of $f_1(t)$ and $f_2(t)$ is the product of the individual transforms, $F_1(s) F_2(s)$, i.e.,

$$\mathcal{L}\left[\int_0^t f_1(t-\tau) f_2(\tau)\, d\tau\right] = F_1(s) F_2(s) \tag{6.97}$$

where the integral

$$\int_0^t f_1(t-\tau) f_2(\tau)\, d\tau$$

is the *convolution integral* or *folding integral*, and is denoted operationally as

$$\int_0^t f_1(t-\tau) f_2(\tau)\, d\tau = f_1(t)^* f_2(t) \tag{6.98}$$

Proof.   Let us prove that $\mathscr{L}[f_1 * f_2] = F_1 F_2$. We begin by writing

$$\mathscr{L}[f_1(t) * f_2(t)] = \int_0^\infty e^{-st} \left[\int_0^t f_1(t - \tau) f_2(\tau) \, d\tau \right] dt \qquad (6.99)$$

From the definition of the shifted step function,

$$u(t - \tau) = 1 \qquad \tau \leq t$$
$$= 0 \qquad \tau > t \qquad (6.100)$$

we have the identity,

$$\int_0^t f_1(t - \tau) f_2(\tau) \, d\tau = \int_0^\infty f_1(t - \tau) u(t - \tau) f_2(\tau) \, d\tau \qquad (6.101)$$

Then Eq. 6.99 can be written as

$$\mathscr{L}[f_1(t) * f_2(t)] = \int_0^\infty e^{-st} \int_0^\infty f_1(t - \tau) u(t - \tau) f_2(\tau) \, d\tau \, dt \qquad (6.102)$$

If we let $x = t - \tau$ so that

$$e^{-st} = e^{-s(x + \tau)} \qquad (6.103)$$

then Eq. 6.102 becomes

$$\mathscr{L}[f_1(t) * f_2(t)] = \int_0^\infty \int_0^\infty f_1(x) \, u(x) f_2(\tau) e^{-s\tau} e^{-sx} \, d\tau \, dx$$

$$= \int_0^\infty f_1(x) \, u(x) e^{-sx} \, dx \int_0^\infty f_2(\tau) e^{-s\tau} \, d\tau$$

$$= F_1(s) \, F_2(s). \qquad (6.104)$$

The separation of the double integral in Eq. 6.104 into a product of two integrals is based upon a property of integrals known as the *separability property.**

Example 6.11.   Let us evaluate the convolution of the functions $f_1(t) = e^{-2t} u(t)$ and $f_2(t) = t \, u(t)$, and then compare the result with the inverse transform of $F_1(s) \, F_2(s)$, where

$$F_1(s) = \mathscr{L}[f_1(t)] = \frac{1}{s + 2}$$
$$F_2(s) = \frac{1}{s^2} \qquad (6.105)$$

The convolution of $f_1(t)$ and $f_2(t)$ is obtained by first substituting the dummy variable $t - \tau$ for t in $f_1(t)$, so that

$$f_1(t - \tau) = e^{-2(t - \tau)} u(t - \tau) \qquad (6.106)$$

---

* See, for example, P. Franklin, *Advanced Calculus*, John Wiley & Sons, New York, 1940.

Then $f_1(t) * f_2(t)$ is

$$\int_0^t f_1(t - \tau) f_2(\tau)\, d\tau = \int_0^t \tau e^{-2(t-\tau)}\, d\tau = e^{-2t} \int_0^t \tau e^{2\tau}\, d\tau \qquad (6.107)$$

Integrating by parts, we obtain

$$f_1(t) * f_2(t) = \left(\frac{t}{2} - \frac{1}{4} + \frac{1}{4} e^{-2t}\right) u(t) \qquad (6.108)$$

Next, let us evaluate the inverse transform of $F_1(s)\, F_2(s)$. From Eq. 6.105, we have

$$F_1(s)\, F_2(s) = \frac{1}{s^2(s + 2)} = \frac{\frac{1}{2}}{s^2} - \frac{\frac{1}{4}}{s} + \frac{\frac{1}{4}}{s + 2} \qquad (6.109)$$

so that

$$\mathscr{L}^{-1}[F_1(s)\, F_2(s)] = \left(\frac{t}{2} - \frac{1}{4} + \frac{1}{4} e^{-2t}\right) u(t) \qquad (6.110)$$

An important property of the convolution integral is expressed by the equation,

$$\int_0^t f_1(t - \tau) f_2(\tau)\, d\tau = \int_0^t f_1(\tau) f_2(t - \tau)\, d\tau \qquad (6.111)$$

This is readily seen from the relationships,

$$\mathscr{L}[f_1(t) * f_2(t)] = F_1(s)\, F_2(s) \qquad (6.112)$$

and

$$\mathscr{L}[f_2(t) * f_1(t)] = F_2(s)\, F_1(s) \qquad (6.113)$$

To give the convolution integral a more intuitive meaning, let us examine the convolution or *folding* process from a graphical standpoint. Suppose we take the functions,

$$f_1(\tau) = u(\tau)$$
$$f_2(\tau) = \tau\, u(\tau) \qquad (6.114)$$

as shown in Figs. 6.38a and 6.39a. In Fig. 6.38, the various steps for obtaining the integral

$$\int_0^t f_1(t - \tau) f_2(\tau)\, d\tau$$

are depicted. Part (b) of the figure shows $f_1(-\tau) = u(-\tau)$. The function

$$f_1(t - \tau) = u(t - \tau) \qquad (6.115)$$

in part (c) merely advances $f_1(-\tau)$ by a variable amount t. Next, the product,

$$f_1(t - \tau) f_2(\tau) = u(t - \tau)\tau\, u(\tau) \qquad (6.116)$$

is shown in part (d). We see that the convolution integral is the area under the curve, as indicated by the cross-hatched area in part (d). Since the convolution integral has a variable upper limit, we must obtain the area under the curve of $f_1(t - \tau) f_2(\tau)$ for all t. With t considered a variable in Fig. 6.38d, the area under the curve is

$$f_1{}^* f_2 = f(t) = \frac{t^2}{2} u(t) \tag{6.117}$$

as plotted in part (e) of the figure.

In Fig. 6.39, we see that by folding $f_2(\tau)$ about a point t, we obtain the same result as in Fig. 6.38. The result in Eq. 6.117 can be checked by taking the inverse transform of $F_1(s) F_2(s)$, which is seen to be

$$\mathscr{L}^{-1}[F_1(s)\, F_2(s)] = \mathscr{L}^{-1}\left[\frac{1}{s^3}\right] = \frac{t^2}{2} u(t) \tag{6.118}$$

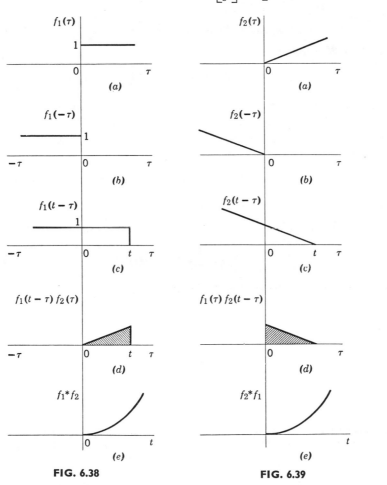

FIG. 6.38   FIG. 6.39

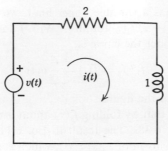

FIG. 6.40

Let us next proceed to examine the role of the convolution integral in system analysis. From the familiar equation

$$R(s) = E(s)\,H(s) \tag{6.119}$$

we obtain the time response as

$$r(t) = \mathscr{L}^{-1}[E(s)\,H(s)] = \int_0^t e(\tau)\,h(t-\tau)\,d\tau \tag{6.120}$$

where $e(\tau)$ is the excitation and $h(\tau)$ is the impulse response of the system. Using Eq. 6.120, we obtain the response of a system directly in the time domain. The only information we need about the system is its impulse response.

Example 6.12a. Let us find the response $i(t)$ of the R-L network in Fig. 6.40 due to the excitation,

$$v(t) = 2e^{-t}\,u(t) \tag{6.121}$$

From Chapter 4, we know that the impulse response for the current is

$$h(t) = \frac{1}{L}\,e^{-(R/L)t}\,u(t) \tag{6.122}$$

Therefore, for the R-L circuit under discussion,

$$h(t) = e^{-2t}\,u(t) \tag{6.123}$$

Using the convolution integral, we obtain the response $i(t)$ as

$$i(t) = \int_0^t v(t-\tau)\,h(\tau)\,d\tau = 2\int_0^t e^{-(t-\tau)}e^{-2\tau}\,d\tau$$

$$= 2e^{-t}\int_0^t e^{-\tau}\,d\tau = 2(e^{-t} - e^{-2t})\,u(t) \tag{6.124}$$

Example 6.12b. The ideal amplifier in Fig. 6.41 has a system function $H(s) = K$, where K is a constant. The impulse response of the ideal amplifier is then

$$h(t) = K\,\delta(t) \tag{6.125}$$

Let us show by means of the convolution integral that the response $r(t)$ is related

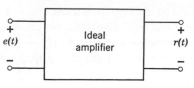

FIG. 6.41

to the excitation $e(t)$ by the equation,

$$r(t) = K\,e(t) \tag{6.126}$$

Using the convolution integral, we have

$$r(t) = \int_0^t e(\tau)\,h(t-\tau)\,d\tau = K\int_0^t e(\tau)\,\delta(t-\tau)\,d\tau = K\,e(t) \tag{6.127}$$

Since t is a variable in the expression for $r(t)$, we see that the ideal amplifier in the time domain is an *impulse-scanning* device which scans the input $e(t)$ from $t = 0$ to $t = \infty$. Thus, the response of an ideal amplifier is a replica of the input $e(t)$ multiplied by the *gain K* of the amplifier.

6.6 THE DUHAMEL SUPERPOSITION INTEGRAL

In the previous section, we have seen the role that the impulse response plays in determining the response of a system to an arbitrary excitation. In this section, we will study the *Duhamel superposition integral* which also describes an input-output relationship for a system. The superposition integral requires the step response $\alpha(t)$ to characterize the system behavior.

We can derive the superposition integral from the convolution integral by integration by parts. The following derivation is perhaps more intuitively satisfying. Consider the excitation $e(t)$ shown by the dotted curve in Fig. 6.42. Let us approximate $e(t)$ by a series of step functions, as indicated in the figure. We can write the staircase approximation of $e(t)$ as

$$e(t) = e(0+)\,u(t) + \Delta E_1\,u(t-\Delta\tau)$$
$$+ \Delta E_2\,u(t-2\Delta\tau) + \cdots + \Delta E_n\,u(t-n\Delta\tau) \tag{6.128}$$

FIG. 6.42. Staircase approximation to a signal.

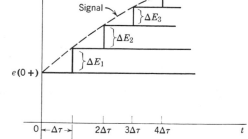

where ΔE_k is the height of the step increment at $t = k \, \Delta \tau$. Since we assume the system to be linear and time invariant, we know that, if the response to a unit step is $\alpha(t)$, the response to a step $K_i \, u(t - \lambda)$ is $K_i \, \alpha(t - \lambda)$. Therefore, we can write the response to the step approximation in Fig. 6.42 as

$$r(t) = e(0+) \, \alpha(t) + \Delta E_1 \, \alpha(t - \Delta \tau)$$
$$+ \Delta E_2 \, \alpha(t - 2 \, \Delta \tau) + \cdots + \Delta E_n \, \alpha(t - n \, \Delta \tau) \tag{6.129}$$

If $\Delta \tau$ is small, $r(t)$ can be given as

$$r(t) = e(0+) \, \alpha(t) + \frac{\Delta E_1}{\Delta \tau} \, \alpha(t - \Delta \tau) \, \Delta \tau + \frac{\Delta E_2}{\Delta \tau}$$
$$\times \, \alpha(t - 2 \, \Delta \tau) \, \Delta \tau + \cdots + \frac{\Delta E_n}{\Delta \tau} \, \alpha(t - n \, \Delta \tau) \, d\tau \tag{6.130}$$

which, in the limit, becomes

$$r(t) = e(0+) \, \alpha(t) + \lim_{\substack{\Delta \tau \to 0 \\ n \to \infty}} \sum_{i=0}^{n} \frac{\Delta E_i}{\Delta \tau} \, \alpha(t - i \, \Delta \tau) \, \Delta \tau$$
$$= e(0+) \, \alpha(t) + \int_0^t e'(\tau) \, \alpha(t - \tau) \, d\tau \tag{6.131}$$

where $e'(\tau)$ is the derivative of $e(\tau)$, $e(0+)$ is the value of $e(t)$ at $t = 0+$, and $\alpha(t)$ is the step response of the system. Equation 6.131 is usually referred to as the *Duhamel superposition integral*.

Another form of the step superposition integral can be derived by integrating

$$r(t) = \int_0^t e(\tau) \, h(t - \tau) \, d\tau$$

by parts with $u = e(\tau)$ and $dv = h(t - \tau) \, d\tau$. We then obtain

$$r(t) = \alpha(0+) \, e(t) + \int_0^t e'(\tau) \, \alpha(t - \tau) \, d\tau \tag{6.132}$$

It can be shown that

$$\int_0^t e'(\tau) \, \alpha(t - \tau) \, d\tau = \int_0^t \alpha'(\tau) \, e(t - \tau) \, d\tau \tag{6.133}$$

so that a number of other forms of the superposition integral are possible.

Example 6.13. Let us find the current $i(t)$ in the R-C circuit in Fig. 6.43 when the voltage source is

$$v_g(t) = (A_1 + A_2 t) \, u(t) \tag{6.134}$$

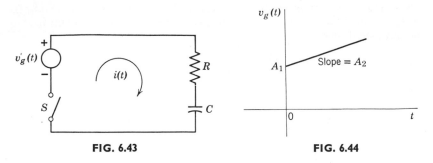

FIG. 6.43   **FIG. 6.44**

as shown in Fig. 6.44. The system function of the R-C circuit is

$$H(s) = \frac{I(s)}{V_g(s)} = \frac{s}{R(s + 1/RC)} \tag{6.135}$$

Therefore, the transform of the step response is

$$\frac{H(s)}{s} = \frac{1}{R(s + 1/RC)} \tag{6.136}$$

Taking the inverse transform of $H(s)/s$, we obtain the step response,

$$\alpha(t) = \frac{1}{R} e^{-t/RC} u(t) \tag{6.137}$$

Let us use the following form of the superposition integral,

$$i(t) = v_g(0+) \alpha(t) + \int_0^t v'_g(\tau) \alpha(t - \tau)\, d\tau \tag{6.138}$$

From Fig. 6.44, we find that $v_g(0+) = A_1$ and $v'_g(\tau) = A_2$ for $t \geq 0+$. Consequently,

$$i(t) = \frac{A_1}{R} e^{-t/RC} + \int_{0+}^t \frac{A_2}{R} e^{-(t-\tau)/RC}\, d\tau$$

$$= \frac{A_1}{R} e^{-t/RC} + \frac{A_2}{R} e^{-t/RC} \int_{0+}^t e^{\tau/RC}\, d\tau \tag{6.139}$$

$$= \frac{A_1}{R} e^{-t/RC} + A_2 C(1 - e^{-t/RC})$$

Problems

6.1 Redraw the circuit in Prob. 4.1 as a transformed circuit and write the mesh equations for the circuit.

6.2 Draw the circuit in Prob. 4.2 as a transformed circuit and write the node equations.

6.3 Use transform methods to determine the expressions for $i_1(t)$ and $i_2(t)$ in the circuit shown. When the switch S is closed at $t = 0$, the circuit has no initially stored energy.

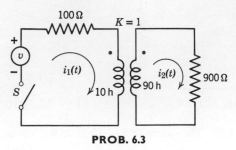

PROB. 6.3

6.4 Determine the expression for $v_0(t)$ when $i(t) = \delta(t)$, assuming the circuit has zero stored energy. Use transform methods.

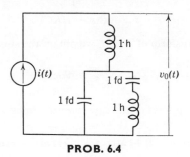

PROB. 6.4

6.5 The circuit shown has zero initial energy. At $t = 0$, the switch S is opened. Find the value of the resistor X such that the response is $v(t) = \frac{1}{2} \sin \sqrt{2}t \, u(t)$. The excitation $i(t)$ is $i(t) = te^{-\sqrt{2}t} u(t)$.

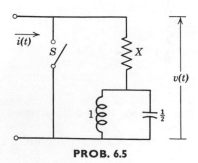

PROB. 6.5

6.6 Use Thévenin's theorem to find the current $i(t)$ shown in the circuit. It is given that $e(t) = te^{-t} u(t)$.

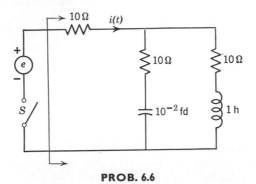

PROB. 6.6

6.7 When the switch S is closed at $t = 0$, the network contains no initial energy. Determine the transform of the Norton equivalent of the circuit to the left of the arrows in the circuit shown. Determine the expression for $i(t)$ using the Norton equivalent circuit.

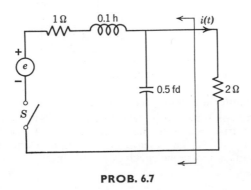

PROB. 6.7

6.8 Find the current $i(t)$ for the circuit in Prob. 4.11, using Thévenin's theorem.

6.9 The response $v_0(t)$ for a unit step input is given as

$$v_0(t) = u(t) + 2e^{-t} u(t) - 2e^{-t}(t + 1) u(t)$$

(a) Find the response $v_0(t)$ when the input $v_i(t)$ is a unit impulse.
(b) Find the system function in terms of R, L, and C from the circuit shown, i.e., find $H(s) = V_0(s)/V_i(s)$.
(c) If $R = 1 \, \Omega$, find the values of C and L.
(d) If $v_i(t) = \sin t$, find $v_0(t)$.

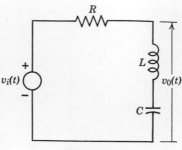

PROB. 6.9

6.10   Using transform methods, solve Prob. 4.18.

6.11   In the circuit shown, when $e(t) = \delta(t)$, $v_2(t) = 2\delta(t) + \frac{1}{2}u(t) + 3e^{-2t}$. Find the values of R_1, R_2, C_1, C_2 from the system function.

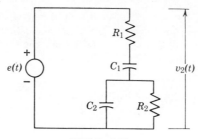

PROB. 6.11

6.12   Using transform methods, solve Prob. 4.14.

6.13   The circuit is subjected to two different excitations as shown in the figure. If the step driver is applied, the current is $i(t) = (1 - e^{-100t})\,u(t)$. Using notions of linearity, obtain the waveform for the current when the input is the ramp driver shown, assuming the circuit is initially inert.

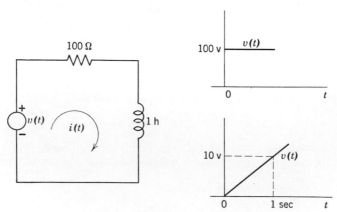

PROB. 6.13

6.14 The *R-L* circuit shown is to be used as: (*a*) an integrator; (*b*) a differentiator. Draw the terminals for the output voltage in each case, and determine the time constant and frequency limitations for the two cases.

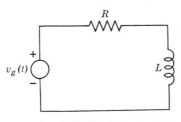

PROB. 6.14

6.15 For the *R-C* circuit shown, determine the current $i(t)$ for the excitation $e(t)$ shown. Use the convolution integral.

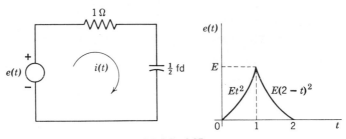

PROB. 6.15

6.16 For the network shown, the excitation is a voltage $e(t)$ and the response is the voltage $v(t)$ across the capacitor.

(*a*) Find $v(t)$ when $e(t)$ is a unit impulse.
(*b*) Find $v(t)$ using the convolution integral when $e(t)$ is as shown.

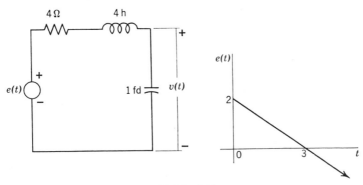

PROB. 6.16

6.17 By graphical means, determine the convolution of $f(t)$, shown in the figure, with itself, i.e., determine $f(t)*f(t)$.

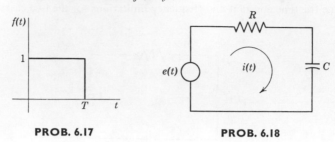

PROB. 6.17   **PROB. 6.18**

6.18 For the initially inert R-C network shown, find $i(t)$ when $e(t)$ is

$$e(t) = \sin^2 \frac{t}{2} \quad 0 \le t \le 2\pi$$

$$= 0 \qquad \text{elsewhere.}$$

Use the step superposition integral.

6.19 (a) Find the Thévenin impedance $Z_{ab}(s)$ looking into the circuit at points a–b.

(b) Determine the Thévenin impedance $Z_{a'b'}(s)$ for the circuit shown in the figure. Find the values of R and C such that $Z_{a'b'}(s) = Z_{ab}(s)$. (*Hint:* Expand $Z_{ab}(s)$ and $Z_{a'b'}(s)$ into partial fractions and match terms.)

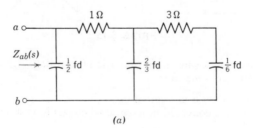

(a)

PROB. 6.19a

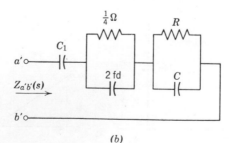

(b)

PROB. 6.19b

chapter 7

Poles and zeros

7.1 POLES AND ZEROS

In this chapter, we will discuss the many implications of a *pole-zero* description of a given rational function with real coefficients, $F(s)$. We have already defined the poles of $F(s)$ as being the roots of the denominator of $F(s)$. The zeros of $F(s)$ are now defined as the roots of the numerator. In the complex s plane, a pole is denoted by a small cross and the zero by a small circle. Thus, for the function,

$$F(s) = \frac{s(s - 1 + j1)(s - 1 - j1)}{(s + 1)^2(s + j2)(s - j2)} \tag{7.1}$$

the poles are at

$$s = -1 \quad \text{(double)}$$
$$s = -j2$$
$$s = +j2$$

and the zeros are at

$$s = 0$$
$$s = 1 + j1$$
$$s = 1 - j1$$
$$s = \infty$$

The poles and zeros of $F(s)$ are shown in Fig. 7.1.

Now let us consider some pole-zero diagrams corresponding to standard signals. For example, the unit step function is given in the complex frequency domain as

$$\mathscr{L}[u(t)] = \frac{1}{s} \tag{7.2}$$

and has a pole at the origin, as shown in Fig. 7.2a. The exponential

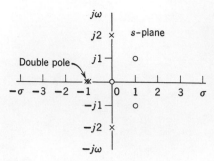

FIG. 7.1. Pole-zero diagram of $F(s)$.

signal $e^{-\sigma_0 t}$, where $\sigma_0 > 0$, has a transform

$$\mathscr{L}[e^{-\sigma_0 t}] = \frac{1}{s + \sigma_0} \tag{7.3}$$

which has a single pole at $s = -\sigma_0$, as indicated in Fig. 7.2b. The cosine function $\cos \omega_0 t$, whose transform is

$$\mathscr{L}[\cos \omega_0 t] = \frac{s}{s^2 + \omega_0^2} \tag{7.4}$$

has a zero at the origin and a pair of conjugate poles at $s = \pm j\omega_0$, as depicted in Fig. 7.2c. Figure 7.2d shows the pole-zero diagram corresponding to a damped cosine wave whose transform is

$$\mathscr{L}[e^{-\sigma_0 t} \cos \omega_0 t] = \frac{s + \sigma_0}{(s + \sigma_0)^2 + \omega_0^2} \tag{7.5}$$

From these four pole-zero diagrams, we note that the poles corresponding to decaying exponential waves are on the $-\sigma$ axis and have zero

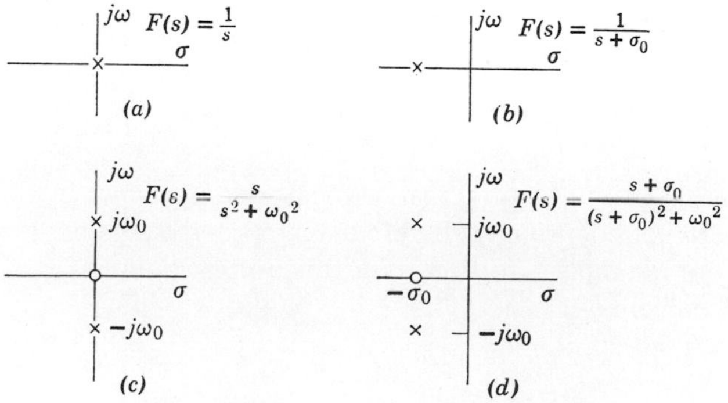

$jω$ $F(s) = \frac{1}{s}$
$σ$

(a)

$jω$ $F(s) = \frac{1}{s + \sigma_0}$
$σ$

(b)

$jω$ $F(s) = \frac{s}{s^2 + \omega_0^2}$
$j\omega_0$
$σ$
$-j\omega_0$

(c)

$jω$ $F(s) = \frac{s + \sigma_0}{(s + \sigma_0)^2 + \omega_0^2}$
$j\omega_0$
$-\sigma_0$ $σ$
$-j\omega_0$

(d)

FIG. 7.2. Poles and zeros of various functions.

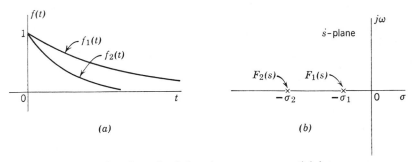

FIG. 7.3. Effect of pole location upon exponential decay.

imaginary parts. The poles and zeros corresponding to undamped sinusoids are on the $j\omega$ axis, and have zero real parts. Consequently, the poles and zeros for damped sinusoids must have real and imaginary parts which are both nonzero.

Now let us consider two exponential waves, $f_1(t) = e^{-\sigma_1 t}$ and $f_2(t) = e^{-\sigma_2 t}$ where $\sigma_2 > \sigma_1 > 0$, so that $f_2(t)$ decays faster than $f_1(t)$, as shown in Fig. 7.3a. The transforms of the two functions are

$$F_1(s) = \frac{1}{s + \sigma_1}$$

$$F_2(s) = \frac{1}{s + \sigma_2}$$

(7.6)

as depicted by the pole-zero diagram in Fig. 7.3b. Note that the further the pole is from the origin on the $-\sigma$ axis, the more rapid the exponential decay. Now consider two sine waves, $\sin \omega_1 t$ and $\sin \omega_2 t$, where $\omega_2 > \omega_1 > 0$. Their corresponding poles are shown in Fig. 7.4. We note here that the

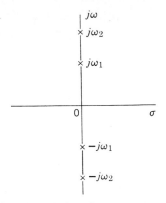

FIG. 7.4. Pole locations corresponding to $\sin \omega_2 t$ and $\sin \omega_1 t$.

FIG. 7.5

distance from the origin on the $j\omega$ axis represents frequency of oscillation; the greater the distance, the higher the frequency.

Using these rules of thumb, let us compare the time responses $f_1(t)$ and $f_2(t)$ corresponding to the pole pairs $\{s_1, s_1^*\}$ and $\{s_2, s_2^*\}$ shown in Fig. 7.5. We see that both pairs of poles corresponds to damped sinusoids. The damped sinusoid $f_1(t)$ has a smaller frequency of oscillation than $f_2(t)$ because the imaginary part of s_1 is less than the imaginary part of s_2. Also, $f_2(t)$ decays more rapidly than $f_1(t)$ because $\text{Re } s_1 > \text{Re } s_2$. The time responses $f_1(t)$ and $f_2(t)$ are shown in Fig. 7.6.

Let us examine more closely the effect of the positions of the poles in the complex frequency plane upon transient response. We will denote a pole p_i as a complex number, $p_i = \sigma_i + j\omega_i$. For a given function $F(s)$ with only first-order poles, consider the partial-fraction expansion,

$$F(s) = \frac{K_0}{s - p_0} + \frac{K_1}{s - p_1} + \cdots + \frac{K_n}{s - p_n} \tag{7.7}$$

The inverse transform of $F(s)$ is

$$
\begin{aligned}
f(t) &= K_0 e^{p_0 t} + K_1 e^{p_1 t} + \cdots + K_n e^{p_n t} \\
&= K_0 e^{\sigma_0 t} e^{j\omega_0 t} + K_1 e^{\sigma_1 t} e^{j\omega_1 t} + \cdots + K_n e^{\sigma_n t} e^{j\omega_n t}
\end{aligned}
\tag{7.8}
$$

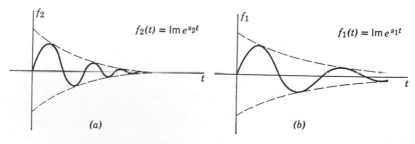

FIG. 7.6. Time responses for poles in Fig. 7.5.

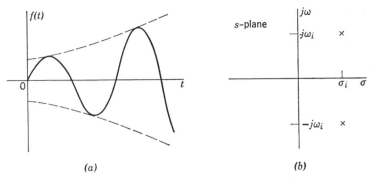

FIG. 7.7. Effect of right-half plane poles upon time response.

In $f(t)$, we see that, if the real part of a pole is positive, i.e., $\sigma_1 > 0$, then the corresponding term in the partial-fraction expansion

$$K_1 e^{\sigma_i t} e^{j\omega_i t}$$

is an exponentially increasing sinusoid, as shown in Fig. 7.7a. We thus see that poles in the right half of the s-plane (Fig. 7.7b) give rise to exponentially increasing transient responses. A system function which has poles in the right-half plane is, therefore, unstable. Another unstable situation arises if there is a pair of *double poles* on the $j\omega$ axis, such as for the function

$$F(s) = \frac{s}{(s^2 + \omega_0^2)^2} \tag{7.9}$$

whose pole-zero diagram is shown in Fig. 7.8a. The inverse transform of $F(s)$ is

$$f(t) = \frac{t}{2\omega_0} \sin \omega_0 t \tag{7.10}$$

which is shown in Fig. 7.8b. It is apparent that a stable system function cannot have multiple poles on the $j\omega$ axis also.

Consider the system function $H(s) = N(s)/D(s)$. If we factor the numerator and denominator polynomials, we obtain

$$H(s) = \frac{H_0(s - z_0)(s - z_1) \cdots (s - z_n)}{(s - p_0)(s - p_1) \cdots (s - p_m)} \tag{7.11}$$

It is clear that $H(s)$ is completely specified in terms of its poles and zeros and an additional constant multiplier H_0. From the pole-zero plot of $H(s)$, we can obtain a substantial amount of information concerning the

this question, consider the partial fraction expansion,

$$F(s) = \sum_i^N \frac{K_i}{s - s_i} \tag{7.16}$$

where we shall assume that $F(s)$ has only simple poles and no poles at $s = \infty$.

The inverse transform is

$$f(t) = \sum_i^N K_i e^{s_i t} \tag{7.17}$$

It is clear that the time response $f(t)$ not only depends on the complex frequencies s_i but also on the constant multipliers K_i. These constants K_i are called *residues* when they are associated with first-order poles. We will show that the zeros as well as the poles play an important part in the determination of the residues K_i.

From Chapter 5, we know a number of different methods for obtaining the residues by partial-fraction expansion. Now we will consider a graphical method whereby the residues are obtained directly from a pole-zero diagram. Suppose we are given

$$F(s) = \frac{A_0(s - z_0)(s - z_1) \cdots (s - z_n)}{(s - p_0)(s - p_1) \cdots (s - p_m)} \tag{7.18}$$

where $m > n$ and all the poles are simple. Let us expand $F(s)$ as

$$F(s) = \frac{K_0}{s - p_0} + \frac{K_1}{s - p_1} + \cdots + \frac{K_m}{s - p_m} \tag{7.19}$$

Our task is to determine the residues K_i. We know that

$$K_i = (s - p_i) F(s)\Big|_{s = p_i} = \frac{A_0(p_i - z_0)(p_i - z_1) \cdots (p_i - z_n)}{(p_i - p_0) \cdots (p_i - p_{i-1})(p_i - p_{i+1}) \cdots (p_i - p_m)} \tag{7.20}$$

When we interpret the above equation from a complex-plane viewpoint, we see that each one of the terms $(p_i - z_j)$ represents a vector drawn from a zero, z_j, to the pole in question, p_i. Similarly, the terms $(p_i - p_k)$, where $i \neq k$, represent vectors from the other poles to the pole p_i. In other words, the residue K_i of any pole p_i is equal to the ratio of the product of the vectors from the zeros to p_i, to the product of the vectors from the other poles to p_i. To illustrate this idea, let us consider the pole-zero plot of

$$F(s) = \frac{A_0(s - z_0)(s - z_1)}{(s - p_0)(s - p_1)(s - p_1{}^*)} \tag{7.21}$$

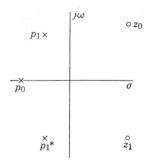

FIG. 7.10. Poles and zeros of $F(s)$.

given in Fig. 7.10. The partial-fraction expansion of $F(s)$ is

$$F(s) = \frac{K_0}{s - p_0} + \frac{K_1}{s - p_1} + \frac{K_1^*}{s - p_1^*} \qquad (7.22)$$

where (*) denotes *complex conjugate*. Let us find the residues K_0 and K_1 by means of the graphical method described. First, we will evaluate K_1 by drawing vectors from the poles and zeros to p_1, as shown in Fig. 7.11*a*. The residue K_1 is then

$$K_1 = \frac{A_0 \mathbf{AB}}{\mathbf{CD}} \qquad (7.23)$$

eg. $A = re^{i\theta}$ $B = Re^{i\varphi}$ *etc.*

where symbols in boldface represent vectors. We know that the residue of the conjugate pole p_1^* is simply the conjugate of K_1 in Eq. 7.23. Next, to evaluate K_0, we draw vectors from the poles and zeros to p_0, as indicated in Fig. 7.11*b*. We see that

$$K_0 = \frac{A_0 \mathbf{RL}}{\mathbf{MN}} \qquad (7.24)$$

With the use of a ruler and a protractor, we determine the lengths and the

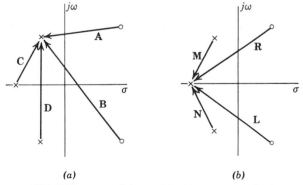

(a)   (b)

FIG. 7.11. Determining residues by vector method.

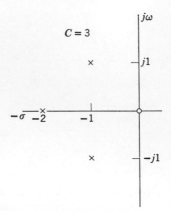

FIG. 7.12. Pole-zero diagram of $F(s)$.

angles of the vectors so that the residues can be determined quickly and easily. Consider the following example. The pole-zero plot of

$$F(s) = \frac{3s}{(s+2)(s+1-j1)(s+1+j1)} \quad (7.25)$$

is shown in Fig. 7.12. The partial-fraction expansion of $F(s)$ is

$$F(s) = \frac{K_1}{s+1-j1} + \frac{K_1^*}{s+1+j1} + \frac{K_2}{s+2} \quad (7.26)$$

First let us evaluate K_1. The phasors from the poles and zeros to the pole at $-1 + j1$ are shown in Fig. 7.13a. We see that K_1 is

$$K_1 = 3 \times \frac{\sqrt{2}\,\underline{/135°}}{\sqrt{2}\,\underline{/45°} \times 2\,\underline{/90°}} = \frac{3}{2}$$

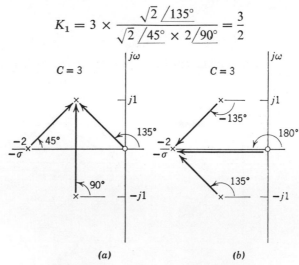

(a)   *(b)*

FIG. 7.13. Evaluation of residues of $F(s)$.

From Fig. 7.13b we find the value of the residue K_2 to be

$$K_2 = - \frac{3 \times 2}{\sqrt{2}\,\underline{/-135°} \times \sqrt{2}\,\underline{/+135°}} = -3$$

Therefore, the partial-fraction expansion of $F(s)$ is

$$F(s) = \frac{\frac{3}{2}}{s + 1 - j1} + \frac{\frac{3}{2}}{s + 1 + j1} - \frac{3}{s + 2} \qquad (7.27)$$

7.3 AMPLITUDE AND PHASE RESPONSE

In this section, we will study the relationship between the poles and zeros of a system function and its steady-state sinusoidal response. In other words, we will investigate the effect of pole and zero positions upon the behavior of $H(s)$ along the $j\omega$ axis. The steady-state response of a system function is given by the equation

$$H(j\omega) = M(\omega)e^{j\phi(\omega)} \qquad (7.28)$$

where $M(\omega)$ is the *amplitude* or *magnitude response* function, and is an even function in ω. $\phi(\omega)$ represents the *phase response*, and is an odd function of ω.

The amplitude and phase response of a system provides valuable information in the analysis and design of transmission circuits. Consider the amplitude and phase characteristics of a low-pass filter shown in Figs. 7.14a and 7.14b. The *cutoff* frequency of the filter is indicated on the

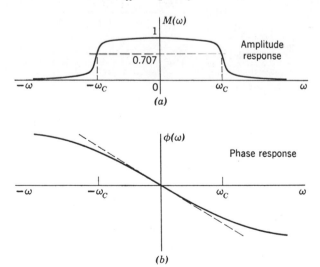

FIG. 7.14. Amplitude and phase response of low-pass filter.

amplitude response curves as ω_C. It is generally taken to be the "half-power" frequency at which the system function $|H(j\omega_C)|$ is equal to 0.707 of the maximum amplitude $|H(j\omega_{max})|$. In terms of decibels, the half-power point is that frequency at which $20 \log |H(j\omega_C)|$ is down 3 db from $20 \log |H(j\omega_{max})|$. The system described by the amplitude and phase characteristics in Fig. 7.14 shows that the system will not "pass" frequencies that are greater than ω_C. Suppose we consider a pulse train whose amplitude spectrum contains significant harmonics above ω_C. We know that the system will pass the harmonics below ω_C, but will block all harmonics above ω_C. Therefore, the output pulse train will be distorted when compared to the original pulse train because many higher harmonic terms will be missing. It will be shown in a later chapter that, if the phase response $\phi(\omega)$ is *linear*, then minimum pulse distortion will result. We see from the phase response $\phi(\omega)$ in Fig. 7.14 that the phase response is approximately linear over the range $-\omega_C \leq \omega \leq +\omega_C$. If all of the significant harmonic terms are less than ω_C, then the system will produce minimum *phase distortion*. With this example, we see the importance of an amplitude-phase description of a system. In the remaining part of this chapter, we will concentrate on methods to obtain amplitude and phase response curves, both analytically and graphically.

To obtain amplitude and phase curves, we let $s = j\omega$ in the system function and express $H(j\omega)$ in polar form. For example, for the amplitude and phase response of the voltage ratio V_2/V_1 of the R-C network shown in Fig. 7.15, the system function is,

$$H(s) = \frac{V_2(s)}{V_1(s)} = \frac{1/RC}{s + 1/RC} \tag{7.29}$$

Letting $s = j\omega$, $H(j\omega)$ is

$$H(j\omega) = \frac{1/RC}{j\omega + 1/RC} \tag{7.30}$$

In polar form $H(j\omega)$ becomes

$$H(j\omega) = \frac{1/RC}{(\omega^2 + 1/R^2C^2)^{\frac{1}{2}}} e^{-j \tan^{-1} \omega RC} = M(\omega)e^{j\phi(\omega)} \tag{7.31}$$

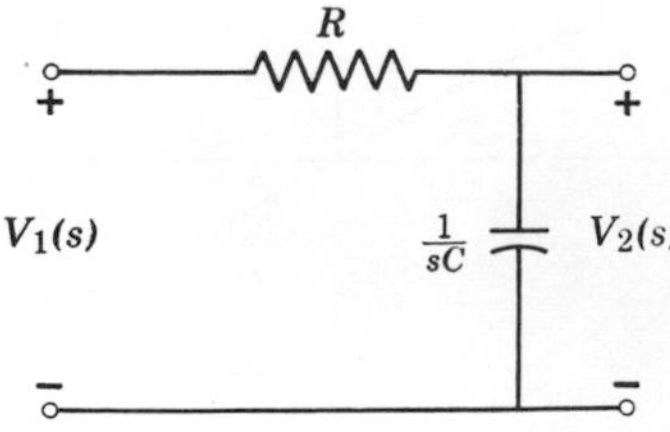

FIG. 7.15

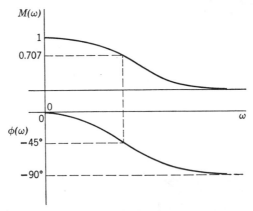

FIG. 7.16. Amplitude and phase response of R-C network.

The amplitude and phase curves are plotted on Fig. 7.16. At the point $\omega = 0$, the amplitude is unity and the phase is zero degrees. As ω increases, the amplitude and phase decrease monotonically. When $\omega = 1/RC$, the amplitude is 0.707 and the phase is $-45°$. This point is the half-power point of the amplitude response. Finally as $\omega \to \infty$, $M(\omega)$ approaches zero and $\phi(\omega)$ approaches $-90°$.

Now let us turn to a method to obtain the amplitude and phase response from the pole-zero diagram of a system function. Suppose we have the system function,

$$H(s) = \frac{A_0(s - z_0)(s - z_1)}{(s - p_0)(s - p_1)(s - p_2)} \tag{7.32}$$

$H(j\omega)$ can be written as

$$H(j\omega) = \frac{A_0(j\omega - z_0)(j\omega - z_1)}{(j\omega - p_0)(j\omega - p_1)(j\omega - p_2)} \tag{7.33}$$

Each one of the factors $(j\omega - z_i)$ or $(j\omega - p_j)$ corresponds to a vector from the zero z_i or pole p_j directed to any point $j\omega$ on the imaginary axis. Therefore, if we express the factors in polar form,

$$(j\omega - z_i) = N_i e^{j\psi_i}, \qquad (j\omega - p_j) = M_j e^{j\theta_j} \tag{7.34}$$

then $H(j\omega)$ can be given as

$$H(j\omega) = \frac{A_0 N_0 N_1}{M_0 M_1 M_2} e^{j(\psi_0 + \psi_1 - \theta_0 - \theta_1 - \theta_2)} \tag{7.35}$$

as shown in Fig. 7.17, where we note that θ_1 is negative.

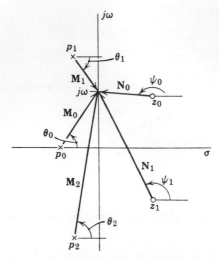

FIG. 7.17. Evaluation of amplitude and phase from pole-zero diagram.

In general, we can express the amplitude response $M(\omega)$ in terms of the following equation,

$$M(\omega) = \frac{\displaystyle\prod_{i=0}^{n} \text{ vector magnitudes from the zeros to the point on the } j\omega \text{ axis}}{\displaystyle\prod_{j=0}^{m} \text{ vector magnitudes from the poles to the point on the } j\omega \text{ axis}}$$

Similarly, the phase response is given as

$$\phi(\omega) = \sum_{i=0}^{n} \text{ angles of the vectors from the zeros to the } j\omega \text{ axis}$$

$$- \sum_{j=0}^{m} \text{ angles of the vectors from the poles to the } j\omega \text{ axis}$$

It is important to note that these relationships for amplitude and phase are point-by-point relationships only. In other words, we must draw vectors from the poles and zeros to every point on the $j\omega$ axis for which we wish to determine amplitude and phase. Consider the following example.

$$F(s) = \frac{4s}{s^2 + 2s + 2} = \frac{4s}{(s + 1 + j1)(s + 1 - j1)} \tag{7.36}$$

Let us find the amplitude and phase for $F(j2)$. From the poles and zeros of $F(s)$, we draw vectors to the point $\omega = 2$, as shown in Fig. 7.18. From the pole-zero diagram, it is clear that

$$M(j2) = 4\left(\frac{2}{\sqrt{2} \times \sqrt{10}}\right) = 1.78$$

and
$$\phi(j2) = 90° - 45° - 71.8° = -26.8°$$

With the values $M(j2)$ and $\phi(j2)$ and the amplitude and phase at three or four additional points, we have enough information for a rough estimate of the amplitude and phase response. First, at $\omega = 0$, we see that the vector magnitude from the zero at the origin to $\omega = 0$, is of course, zero. Consequently, $M(j0) = 0$. From Eq. 7.36 for $F(s)$, $F(j0)$ is

$$\lim_{\substack{\omega \to 0 \\ \omega > 0}} F(j\omega) = \frac{4(j0)}{(1 + j1)(1 - j1)} \tag{7.37}$$

From this equation, we see that the zero at the origin still contributes a 90° phase shift even though the vector magnitude is zero. From Fig. 7.19a we see that the net phase at $\omega = 0$ is

$$\phi(0) = 90° - 45° + 45° = 90°$$

Next, at a very high frequency ω_h, where $\omega_h \gg 1$, all the vectors are approximately equal to $\omega_h e^{j90°}$, as seen in Fig. 7.19b. Then,

$$M(\omega_h) \simeq \frac{4\omega_h}{\omega_h{}^2} = \frac{4}{\omega_h}$$

and
$$\phi(\omega_h) \simeq 90° - 90° - 90° = -90°$$

Extending this analysis for the frequencies listed in Table 7.1, we obtain

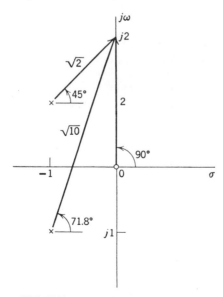

FIG. 7.18. Evaluation of amplitude and phase from pole-zero diagram.

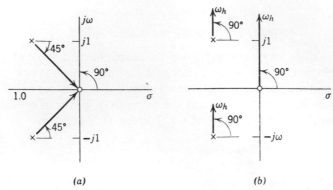

FIG. 7.19. Determining amplitude and phase at zero and very high frequencies.

values for amplitude and phase as given in the table. From this table, we can sketch the amplitude and phase curves shown in Fig. 7.20.

TABLE 7.1

Frequency, ω	Amplitude	Phase, degrees
1.0	1.8	25.8
1.5	2.0	−5.3
3.0	1.3	−50.0
5.0	0.8	−66.0
10.0	0.4	−78.5

Next, let us examine the effect of poles and zeros on the $j\omega$ axis upon frequency response. Consider the function,

$$F(s) = \frac{s^2 + 1.03}{s^2 + 1.23} = \frac{(s + j1.015)(s - j1.015)}{(s + j1.109)(s - j1.109)} \qquad (7.38)$$

whose pole-zero diagram is shown in Fig. 7.21. At $\omega = 1.015$, the vector from zero to that frequency is of zero magnitude. Therefore, at a zero on the $j\omega$ axis, the amplitude response is zero. At $\omega = 1.109$, the vector from the pole to that frequency is of zero magnitude. The amplitude response is therefore infinite at a pole as seen from Eq. 7.38. Next, consider the phase response. When $\omega < 1.015$, it is apparent from the pole-zero plot that the phase is zero. When $\omega > 1.015$, the vector from the zero at $\omega = 1.015$ is now pointing upwards, while the vectors from the other poles and zeros are oriented in the same direction as for $\omega < 1.015$. We see that, at a zero on the $j\omega$ axis, the phase response has a step discontinuity of $+180°$ for increasing frequency. Similarly, at a pole on the $j\omega$ axis, the phase response is discontinuous by $-180°$. These observations

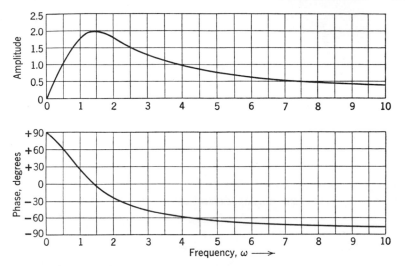

FIG. 7.20. Amplitude and phase response for $F(s)$ in Eq. 7.36.

are illustrated by the amplitude and phase plot for $F(s)$ in Eq. 7.38 for the frequency range, $0.9 \leq \omega \leq 1.3$, shown in Fig. 7.22.

With a simple extension of these ideas, we see that, if we have a zero at

$$z = -\sigma \pm j\omega_i$$

where σ is very small as compared to ω_i, then we will have a dip in the amplitude characteristic and a rapid change of phase near $\omega = \omega_i$, as seen in Fig. 7.23. Similarly, if there is a pole at

$$p = -\sigma \pm j\omega_j$$

with σ very small, then the amplitude will be peaked and the phase will decrease rapidly near $\omega = \omega_i$, as seen in Fig. 7.24. A contrasting situation occurs when we have poles and zeros far away from the $j\omega$ axis, i.e., σ is

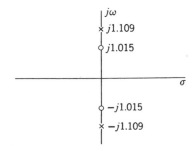

FIG. 7.21.

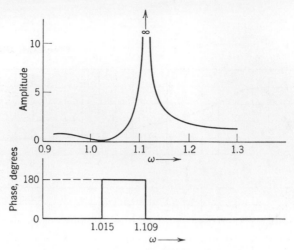

FIG. 7.22. Amplitude and phase for $F(s)$ in Fig. 7.21.

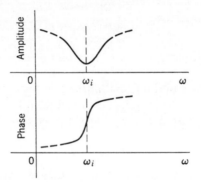

FIG. 7.23. Effect of zero very near the $j\omega$ axis.

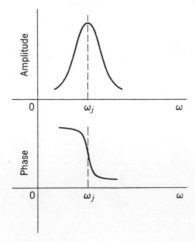

FIG. 7.24. Effect of pole very near the $j\omega$ axis.

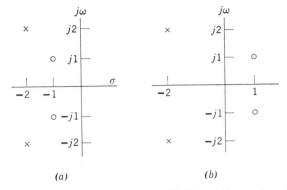

FIG. 7.25. (a) Minimum-phase function. (b) Nonminimum-phase function.

large when compared to the frequency range of interest. Then we see that these poles and zeros contribute little to the *shaping* of the amplitude and phase response curves. Their only effect is to scale up or down the over-all amplitude response.

From stability considerations, we know that there must be no poles in the right half of the s-plane. However, transfer functions may have zeros in the right-half plane. Consider the pole-zero diagrams in Figs. 7.25a and 7.25b. Both pole-zero configurations have the same poles; the only difference is that the zeros in (a) are in the left-half plane at $s = -1 \pm j1$ while the zeros in (b) are the mirror images of the zeros in (a) and are located at $s = +1 \pm j1$. Observe that the amplitude responses of the

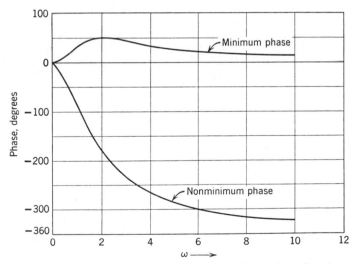

FIG. 7.26. Comparison of minimum and nonminimum phase functions.

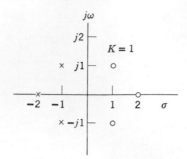

FIG. 7.27. All-pass function.

two configurations are the same because the lengths of the vectors correspond for both situations. We see that the absolute magnitude of the phase of (*b*) is greater than the phase of (*a*) for all frequencies. This is because the zeros in the right-half plane contribute more phase shift (on an absolute magnitude basis) than their counterparts in the left-half plane. From this reasoning, we have the following definitions. A system function with zeros in the left-half plane or on the *jω* axis only is called a *minimum phase* function. If the function has one or more zeros in the right-half plane, it is a *nonminimum phase* function. In Fig. 7.26, we see the phase responses of the minimum and nonminimum phase functions in Figs. 7.25*a* and 7.25*b*.

Let us next consider the pole-zero diagram in Fig. 7.27. Observe that

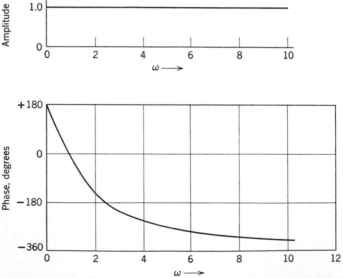

FIG. 7.28. Amplitude and phase of all-pass function in Fig. 7.27.

the zeros in the right-half plane are mirror images of the poles in the left-half plane. Consequently, the vector drawn from a pole to any point ω_1 on the $j\omega$ axis is identical in magnitude with the vector drawn from its mirror image to ω_1. It is apparent that the amplitude response must be constant for all frequencies. The phase response, however, is anything but constant, as seen from the amplitude and phase response curves given in Fig. 7.28 for the pole-zero configuration in Fig. 7.27.

A system function whose poles are only in the left-half plane and whose zeros are mirror images of the poles about the $j\omega$ axis is called an *all-pass* function. The networks which have all-pass response characteristics are often used to correct for phase distortion in a transmission system.

7.4 SINGLE-TUNED CIRCUITS

In this section, we will examine the amplitude response for a pair of conjugate poles. We will study a graphical method to obtain the maximum and half-power points for the amplitude response. For the purposes of our discussion here, we will describe the conjugate pole pair in terms of a magnitude ω_0 and an angle θ measured from the negative real axis, as shown in Fig. 7.29. Explicitly, the parameters which describe the pole positions are ω_0, which we call the *undamped frequency of oscillation*, and $\zeta = \cos \theta$ known as the *damping factor*. If the pole pair is given in terms of its real and imaginary parts,

$$p_{1,2} = -\alpha \pm j\beta \tag{7.39}$$

we can express α and β in terms of ω_0 and ζ by the following relations,

$$\alpha = \omega_0 \cos \theta = \omega_0 \zeta$$
$$\beta = \omega_0 \sin \theta = \omega_0 \sqrt{1 - \zeta^2} \tag{7.40}$$

Returning to the definition of the damping factor, $\zeta = \cos \theta$, we see

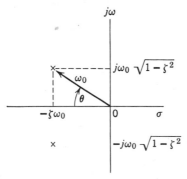

FIG. 7.29. Pole location in terms of ζ and ω_0.

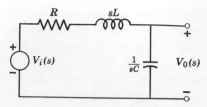

FIG. 7.30. Single-tuned circuit.

that for passive networks, $0 \leq \zeta \leq 1$, i.e., the poles must be restricted to the $j\omega$ axis or the left-half plane. Moreover, the closer the angle θ is to $\pi/2$, the smaller is the damping factor. When the angle θ is nearly zero degrees, the damping factor is nearly unity.

We will now apply these definitions to a study of a class of circuits whose system functions can be described by a pair of conjugate poles. These circuits are called *single-tuned* circuits because they only need two reactive elements—an inductor and a capacitor. The undamped frequency of oscillation of the circuit is then $\omega_0 = (LC)^{-\frac{1}{2}}$. An example of a single-tuned circuit is the *R-L-C* circuit in Fig. 7.30 whose voltage-ratio transfer function is

$$H(s) = \frac{V_0(s)}{V_i(s)} = \frac{1/sC}{R + sL + 1/sC} = \frac{1/LC}{s^2 + (R/L)s + 1/LC} \quad (7.41)$$

The poles of $H(s)$ are

$$p_{1,2} = -\frac{R}{2L} \pm \frac{j}{2}\left(\frac{4}{LC} - \frac{R^2}{L^2}\right)^{\frac{1}{2}} = -\alpha \pm j\beta \quad (7.42)$$

where we assume that

$$\frac{R^2}{L^2} < \frac{4}{LC}$$

In terms of α and β in Eq. 7.42, $H(s)$ is

$$H(s) = \frac{\alpha^2 + \beta^2}{(s + \alpha + j\beta)(s + \alpha - j\beta)} \quad (7.43)$$

From the pole-zero diagram of $H(s)$ shown in Fig. 7.31, we will determine the amplitude response, $|H(j\omega)|$. Let us denote the vectors from the poles to the $j\omega$ axis as $|\mathbf{M_1}|$ and $|\mathbf{M_2}|$ as seen in Fig. 7.31. We can then write

$$|H(j\omega)| = \frac{K}{|\mathbf{M_1}|\,|\mathbf{M_2}|} \quad (7.44)$$

where $K = \alpha^2 + \beta^2$ and

$$|\mathbf{M_1}| = [\alpha^2 + (\omega + \beta)^2]^{\frac{1}{2}}$$
$$|\mathbf{M_2}| = [\alpha^2 + (\omega - \beta)^2]^{\frac{1}{2}} \quad (7.45)$$

In characterizing the amplitude response, the point $\omega = \omega_{max}$ at which $|H(j\omega)|$ is maximum, is highly significant from both the analysis and design aspects. Since $|H(j\omega)|$ is always positive, the point at which $|H(j\omega)|^2$ is maximum corresponds exactly to the point at which $|H(j\omega)|$ is maximum. Since $|H(j\omega)|^2$ can be written as

$$|H(j\omega)|^2 = \frac{(\alpha^2 + \beta^2)^2}{[\alpha^2 + (\omega + \beta)^2][\alpha^2 + (\omega - \beta)^2]}$$

$$= \frac{(\alpha^2 + \beta^2)^2}{\omega^4 + 2\omega^2(\alpha^2 - \beta^2) + (\alpha^2 + \beta^2)^2} \tag{7.46}$$

we can find ω_{max} by taking the derivative of $|H(j\omega)|^2$ with respect to ω^2 and setting the result equal to zero. Thus we have

$$\frac{d\,|H(j\omega)|^2}{d\omega^2} = -\frac{(\alpha^2 + \beta^2)^2[2\omega^2 + 2(\alpha^2 - \beta^2)]}{[\omega^4 + 2\omega^2(\alpha^2 - \beta^2) + (\alpha^2 + \beta^2)^2]^2} \tag{7.47}$$

From the equation,

$$\frac{d\,|H(j\omega)|^2}{d\omega^2} = 0 \tag{7.48}$$

we determine

$$\omega_{max}^2 = \beta^2 - \alpha^2 \tag{7.49}$$

Expressed in terms of the natural frequency of oscillation ω_0 and the damping factor ζ, ω_{max}^2 is

$$\omega_{max}^2 = (\omega_0\sqrt{1 - \zeta^2})^2 - (\zeta\omega_0)^2 = \omega_0^2(1 - 2\zeta^2) \tag{7.50}$$

Since ω_{max} must always be real, the condition for ω_{max} to exist, i.e., the

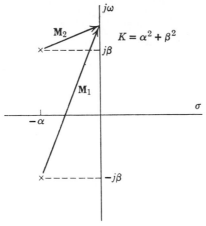

FIG. 7.31

condition for $|H(j\omega)|$ to possess a maximum, is given by the equation,

$$2\zeta^2 \leq 1 \tag{7.51}$$

so that

$$\zeta \leq 0.707$$

Since $\zeta = \cos\theta$, ω_{max} does not exist for $\theta < 45°$. When $\theta = 45°$, we have the limiting case for which ω_{max} exists. In this case, $\zeta = 0.707$ and the real and imaginary parts of the poles have the same magnitude, i.e., $\alpha = \beta$, or

$$\zeta\omega_0 = \omega_0\sqrt{1 - \zeta^2} \tag{7.52}$$

We see from Eq. 7.49 that, when $\alpha = \beta$, then $\omega_{max} = 0$. This is the lowest frequency at which ω_{max} may be located. For $\zeta > 0.707$, or

$$\zeta\omega_0 > \omega_0\sqrt{1 - \zeta^2} \tag{7.53}$$

ω_{max} is imaginary; it therefore does not exist. To summarize, the key point in this analysis is that the imaginary part of the pole must be greater or equal to the real part of the pole in order for ω_{max} to exist. Interpreted graphically, if we draw a circle in the s-plane with the center at $-\alpha$ and the radius equal to β, then the circle must intersect the $j\omega$ axis in order for ω_{max} to exist, as seen in Fig. 7.32. Moreover, the *point* at which the circle intersects the positive $j\omega$ axis is ω_{max}. This is readily seen from the triangle with sides α, β, ω_{max} in Fig. 7.32. By the Pythagorean theorem,

$$\omega_{max}^2 = \beta^2 - \alpha^2 \tag{7.54}$$

The circle described in Fig. 7.32 is called the *peaking circle*. When $\alpha = \beta$,

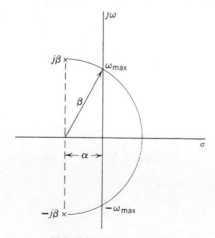

FIG. 7.32. Peaking circle.

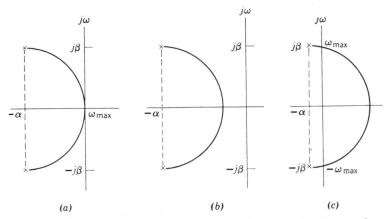

FIG. 7.33. Examples of peaking circles. (a) $\alpha = \beta$, $\omega_{max} = 0$. (b) $\alpha > \beta$, ω_{max} undetermined. (c) $\beta \gg \alpha$, $\omega_{max} \simeq \beta$.

the peaking circle intersects the $j\omega$ axis at $\omega = 0$, as seen in Fig. 7.33a. When $\alpha > \beta$, the circle does not intersect the $j\omega$ axis at all (Fig. 7.33b); therefore, ω_{max} cannot exist. When the imaginary part of the pole is much greater than the real part, i.e., when $\beta \gg \alpha$, then the circle intersects the $j\omega$ axis at approximately $\omega = \omega_0$, the natural frequency of oscillation of the circuit (Fig. 7.33c).

A figure of merit often used in describing the "peaking" of a tuned circuit is the circuit Q which is defined in pole-zero notation as

$$Q \triangleq \frac{1}{2\zeta} = \frac{1}{2\cos\theta} \tag{7.55}$$

From this definition, we see that poles near the $j\omega$ axis (ζ small) represent high-Q systems, as given in Fig. 7.33c, and poles far removed from the $j\omega$ axis represent *low-Q* circuits (Fig. 7.33a). Although the Q of the circuit given by the pole-zero plot of Fig. 7.33b is theoretically defined, it has no practical significance because the circuit does not possess a maximum point in its amplitude response.

By means of the peaking circle, we can also determine the half-power point, which is the frequency, ω_C, at which the amplitude response is

$$|H(j\omega_C)| = 0.707\,|H(j\omega_{max})|$$

We will now describe a method to obtain ω_C by geometrical construction. Consider the triangle in Fig. 7.34 whose vertices are the poles $\{p_1, p_1^*\}$ and a point ω_i on the $j\omega$ axis. The area of the triangle is

$$\text{Area}\,(\Delta p_1 p_1^* \omega_i) = \beta\alpha \tag{7.56}$$

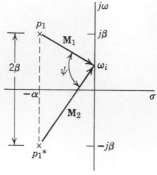

FIG. 7.34

In terms of the vectors $|M_1|$ and $|M_2|$ from the poles to ω_i, the area can also be expressed as

$$\text{Area } (\Delta p_1 p_1^* \omega_i) = \frac{|M_1||M_2| \sin \psi}{2} \qquad (7.57)$$

where ψ is the angle at ω_i as seen in the figure. From the last two equations, we see that the product $|M_1||M_2|$ is equal to

$$|M_1||M_2| = \frac{2\beta\alpha}{\sin \psi} \qquad (7.58)$$

Since the amplitude response is

$$|H(j\omega_i)| = \frac{K}{|M_1||M_2|} \qquad (7.59)$$

where K is a constant, then

$$|H(j\omega_i)| = \frac{K \sin \psi}{2\beta\alpha}. \qquad (7.60)$$

For a given pole-pair $\{p_1, p_1^*\}$ the parameters β, α, and K are prespecified. Therefore, we have derived $|H(j\omega)|$ in terms of a single variable parameter, the angle ψ. When the angle $\psi = \pi/2$ rad, then $\sin \psi = 1$, $\omega_i = \omega_{\max}$, and

$$|H(j\omega_{\max})| = \frac{K}{2\beta\alpha} \qquad (7.61)$$

When $\psi = \pi/4$ rad, then $\sin \psi = 0.707$ and

$$|H(j\omega_i)| = 0.707 \, |H(j\omega_{\max})|$$

so that $\omega_i = \omega_C$. Let us consider now a geometric construction to obtain ω_C. Let us first draw the peaking circle as shown in Fig. 7.35. We will denote by A the point at which the peaking circle intersects the positive real axis. Now we draw a second circle with its center at A, and its radius equal to AB, the distance from A to either one of the poles, as seen in

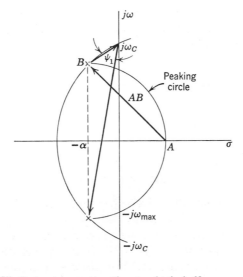

FIG. 7.35. Geometric construction to obtain half-power point.

Fig. 7.35. The point where this second circle intersects the $j\omega$ axis is ω_C. The reason is: at this point, the inscribed angle is $\psi_1 = \pi/4$ because it is equal to one-half the intercepted arc, which, by construction, is $\pi/2$.

When $\omega_{max} = 0$, the half-power point ω_C is also called the *half-power bandwidth* of the tuned circuit. In Fig. 7.36a the half-power point is given when $\omega_{max} = 0$. For a high-Q circuit, where $\omega_{max} \simeq \omega_0$, the amplitude is highly peaked at $\omega = \omega_{max}$, as shown in Fig. 7.36b. In this case, if

$$|H(j0)| < 0.707\,|H(j\omega_{max})|$$

there are two half-power points, ω_{C_1} and ω_{C_2} about the point ω_{max}, as

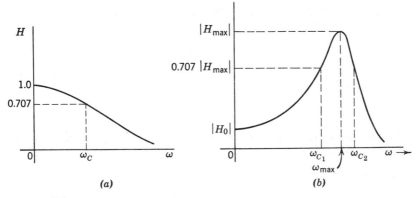

(a)   *(b)*

FIG. 7.36. (*a*) Low-Q circuit response. (*b*) High-Q circuit response.

seen in Fig. 7.36b. By the construction process just described, we obtain the upper half-power point ω_{C_2}. It can be shown* that the point $\omega_{\max}$ is the *geometric mean* of ω_{C_1} and ω_{C_2}, i.e.,

$$\omega_{C_1}\omega_{C_2} = \omega_{\max}^2 \tag{7.62}$$

As a result, the lower half-power point is

$$\omega_{C_1} = \frac{\omega_{\max}^2}{\omega_{C_2}} \tag{7.63}$$

The bandwidth of the system for a high-Q circuit of this type is described by

$$BW = \omega_{C_2} - \omega_{C_1} \tag{7.64}$$

In design applications, these high-Q circuits are used as narrow band-pass filters.

Finally, there are certain aspects of the phase response of high-Q circuits that are readily apparent. In Fig. 7.37, we see several steps in the process of obtaining the phase response. The phase shift at $\omega = 0$ is 0, as seen from Fig. 7.37a. At $\omega = \infty$, the phase shift is $-\pi$ rad, as shown in part (c) of the figure. Finally, in the neighborhood of $\omega = \omega_0 \simeq \omega_{\max}$, the phase shift resulting from the pole in the lower-half plane is approximately $-\theta_2 = -\pi/2$ (Fig. 7.37b). The change in phase in this region is controlled in large by the pole p_1. It is readily seen that the phase response in the

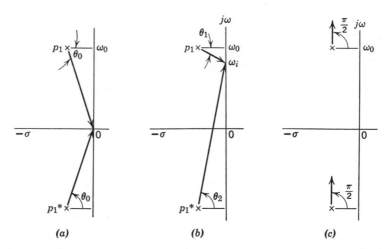

FIG. 7.37. Several steps in obtaining phase response for high-Q circuit. (a) $\omega_i = 0$. (b) $\omega_i \simeq \omega_0$. (c) $\omega_i = \alpha$.

---

* See for example, F. E. Terman, *Electronic and Radio Engineering*, McGraw-Hill Book Company, New York, 1953.

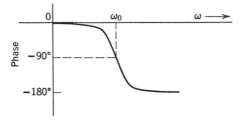

FIG. 7.38. Phase response of high-Q circuit.

region of ω_0 has the greatest negative slope, as seen from a typical phase response of a high-Q circuit shown in Fig. 7.38.

Finally, as an example to illustrate our discussion of single-tuned circuits, let us find the amplitude response for the system function,

$$H(s) = \frac{34}{s^2 + 6s + 34} \tag{7.65}$$

Now we determine the maximum and half-power points ω_{max} and ω_C, and also the amplitudes, $|H(j\omega_{max})|$ and $|H(j\omega_C)|$. In factored form, $H(s)$ is

$$H(s) = \frac{34}{(s + 3 + j5)(s + 3 - j5)} \tag{7.66}$$

and the poles of $H(s)$ are shown in Fig. 7.39. We next draw the peaking circle with the center at $s = -3$ and the radius equal to 5. At the point where the circle intersects the $j\omega$ axis, we see that $\omega_{max} = 4$. To check this result, the equation $\omega_{max}^2 = \beta^2 - \alpha^2$ gives

$$\omega_{max} = (5^2 - 3^2)^{1/2} = 4 \tag{7.67}$$

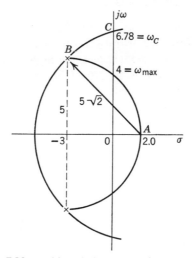

FIG. 7.39. Peaking circle construction example.

The amplitude $|H(j\omega_{max})|$ is then

$$|H(j4)| = \left| \frac{34}{(3+j9)(3-j1)} \right| = \frac{34}{30} = 1.133 \qquad (7.68)$$

The point A at which the peaking circle intersects the positive real axis is located at $s = 2.0$. With the center at A, we draw a circle of radius AB (equal to $5\sqrt{2}$ in this case). At the point C where this new circle intersects the $j\omega$ axis, we have ω_C. By measurement,

$$\omega_C \simeq 6.78 \qquad (7.69)$$

Let us check this result. Referring to Fig. 7.39, we know that the line segment AB is of length $5\sqrt{2}$; it follows that AC is also $5\sqrt{2}$ units long. The line segment AO is of length

$$AO = 5 - 3 = 2 \text{ units} \qquad (7.70)$$

Then ω_C is given as

$$\omega_C = \sqrt{(AC)^2 - (AO)^2} = \sqrt{46} = 6.782 \qquad (7.71)$$

Finally, we obtain $|H(j\omega_C)|$ as

$$|H(j6.782)| = \frac{34}{\sqrt{(34-46)^2 + (6\sqrt{46})^2}} = 0.802 \qquad (7.72)$$

which is precisely $0.707 \, |H(j\omega_{max})|$.

7.5 DOUBLE-TUNED CIRCUITS

In the previous section, we studied the frequency response for a pair of conjugate poles. Now, we will turn our attention to the amplitude response of two pairs of conjugate poles in a high-Q situation. The circuit which we will analyze here is the *double-tuned* or *stagger-tuned* circuit given in Fig. 7.40. We will consider the special case when the R, L, and C elements in the primary circuit are equal in value to their counterparts in the secondary. Since the primary and secondary inductances are equal, the mutual inductance is

$$M = KL \qquad (7.73)$$

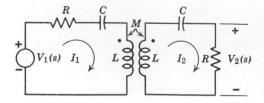

FIG. 7.40. Double-tuned circuit.

In this analysis we will assume the coefficient of coupling, K, to be a variable parameter. Let us determine the amplitude response for the voltage-ratio transfer function, $V_2(s)/V_1(s)$. From the mesh equations

$$V_1(s) = \left(R + sL + \frac{1}{sC}\right) I_1(s) - sM\, I_2(s)$$

$$0 = -sM\, I_1(s) + \left(R + sL + \frac{1}{sC}\right) I_2(s)$$

(7.74)

we readily determine

$$H(s) = \frac{V_2(s)}{V_1(s)} = \frac{s^3 RM/L^2}{[s^2 + (R/L)s + 1/LC]^2 - s^4 K^2}$$

(7.75)

Using tuned-circuit notation, we set

$$2\zeta\omega_0 = \frac{R}{L}$$

$$\omega_0^2 = \frac{1}{LC}$$

(7.76)

$H(s)$ can then be written as

$$H(s) = \frac{s^3 RM/L^2}{(1 - K^2)\left(s^2 + \frac{2\zeta\omega_0}{1 + K} s + \frac{\omega_0^2}{1 + K}\right)\left(s^2 + \frac{2\zeta\omega_0}{1 - K} s + \frac{\omega_0^2}{1 - K}\right)}$$

(7.77)

If we set

$$A = \frac{RM}{L^2(1 - K^2)} = \frac{2\zeta\omega_0 K}{1 - K^2}$$

(7.78)

then we can write

$$H(s) = \frac{As^3}{(s - s_1)(s - s_1{}^*)(s - s_2)(s - s_2{}^*)}$$

(7.79)

where

$$\{s_1, s_1{}^*\} = -\frac{\zeta\omega_0}{1 + K} \pm j\omega_0 \sqrt{\frac{1}{1 + K} - \frac{\zeta^2}{(1 + K)^2}}$$

$$\{s_2, s_2{}^*\} = -\frac{\zeta\omega_0}{1 - K} \pm j\omega_0 \sqrt{\frac{1}{1 - K} - \frac{\zeta^2}{(1 - K)^2}}$$

(7.80)

Let us restrict our analysis to a high-Q circuit so that $\zeta^2 \ll 1$. Furthermore, let us assume that the circuit is loosely coupled so that $K \ll 1$. Under these assumptions, we can approximate the pole locations by discarding the terms involving ζ^2 under the radicals in Eq. 7.80. Then the poles

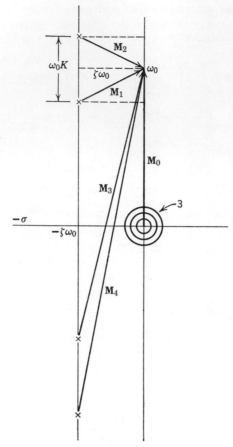

FIG. 7.41. Poles and zeros of a double-tuned circuit.

$\{s_1, s_1{}^*\}$ can be given approximately as

$$\{s_1, s_1{}^*\} \cong -\zeta\omega_0 \pm j\omega_0\left(1 - \frac{K}{2}\right) \tag{7.81}$$

Similarly, $\{s_2, s_2{}^*\}$ can be given as

$$\{s_2, s_2{}^*\} \cong -\zeta\omega_0 \pm j\omega_0\left(1 + \frac{K}{2}\right) \tag{7.82}$$

The pole-zero diagram of $H(s)$ is given in Fig. 7.41. The real part of the poles $-\zeta\omega_0$ is greatly enlarged in comparison to the imaginary parts for clarity purposes. Note that we have a triple zero at the origin. In terms of the vectors in Fig. 7.41, the amplitude response is

$$|H(j\omega)| = \frac{A\,|M_0|^3}{|M_1|\,|M_2|\,|M_3|\,|M_4|} \tag{7.83}$$

Since the circuit is high-Q, in the vicinity of $\omega = \omega_0$, we have

$$|\mathbf{M}_3| \simeq |\mathbf{M}_4| \simeq 2\,|\mathbf{M}_0| \simeq 2\omega_0 \qquad (7.84)$$

so that in the neighborhood of ω_0,

$$|H(j\omega)| \simeq \frac{A\omega_0}{4\,|\mathbf{M}_1|\,|\mathbf{M}_2|} \qquad (7.85)$$

It is evident that the amplitude response of $|H(j\omega)|$ in the neighborhood of ω_0 depends only upon the pair of vectors $|\mathbf{M}_1|$ and $|\mathbf{M}_2|$. The double-tuned problem has thus been reduced to a single-tuned problem in the neighborhood of ω_0. Consequently, we can use all of the results on the peaking circle derived in the previous section. Let us draw a peaking circle with the center at

$$s = -\zeta\omega_0 + j\omega_0 \qquad (7.86)$$

and with a radius equal to $\omega_0 K/2$, as shown in Fig. 7.42. The inscribed angle ψ then determines the location of the maxima and half-power points of the response. Without going into the derivation, the amplitude response can be expressed as a function of ψ according to the equation,

$$|H(j\omega)| = \frac{A\omega_0 \sin \psi}{4\omega_0\, K(\zeta\omega_0)} = \frac{\sin \psi}{2(1 - K^2)} \qquad (7.87)$$

Referring to the peaking circle in Fig. 7.42, let us consider the following situations:

1. $\omega_0\zeta > \omega_0 K/2$: In this case, the peaking circle never intersects the $j\omega$ axis; ψ is always less than $\pi/2$ (Fig. 7.43a), and the amplitude response

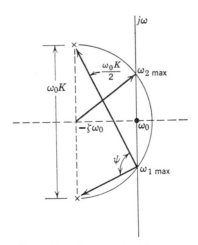

FIG. 7.42. Peaking circle for double-tuned circuit.

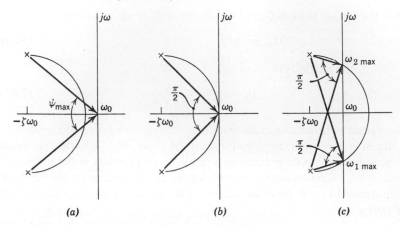

FIG. 7.43. (*a*) Undercoupling. (*b*) Critical coupling. (*c*) Overcoupling.

never attains the theoretical maximum,

$$H_{max} = \frac{1}{2(1 - K^2)} \tag{7.88}$$

as seen by the curve labeled (*a*) in Fig. 7.44. In this case, $K < 2\zeta$, and the circuit is said to be *undercoupled*.

2. $\omega_0\zeta = \omega_0 K/2$: Here the peaking circle intersects the $j\omega$ axis at a single point, $\omega = \omega_0$ (Fig. 7.43*b*). At ω_0, the amplitude is equal to H_{max} in Eq. 7.88. In this case, $\zeta = K/2$ and we have *critical coupling*.

3. $\omega_0\zeta < \omega_0 K/2$: The peaking circle intersects the $j\omega$ axis at two points, ω_1 and ω_2, as seen in Fig. 7.43*c*. The intersecting points are given by the equation,

$$\omega_{1,2} = \omega_0 \pm \omega_0\sqrt{\left(\frac{K}{2}\right)^2 - \zeta^2} \tag{7.89}$$

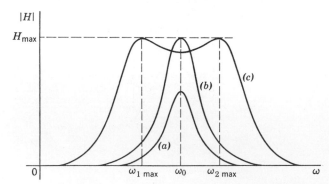

FIG. 7.44. (*a*) Undercoupled case. (*b*) Critically coupled case. (*c*) Overcoupled case.

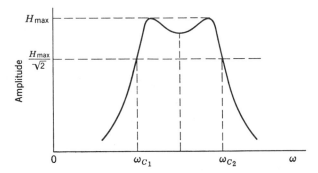

FIG. 7.45. Half-power points of overcoupled circuit.

Consequently, the amplitude response attains the theoretical maximum, H_{max}, at two points, as shown by curve (c) in Fig. 7.44. In this situation, the circuit is said to be *overcoupled*.

Note that in Fig. 7.44, the undercoupled and critically coupled curves have their maximum points at ω_0. The overcoupled curve, however, is maximum at ω_1 and ω_2. In the case of overcoupling and critical coupling, we can determine the half-power points by using the geometrical construction method given in the previous section. Observe there are two half-power points, ω_{C_2} and ω_{C_1}, as shown in the overcoupled curve in Fig. 7.45. The bandwidth of the circuit is then

$$BW = \omega_{C_2} - \omega_{C_1} \tag{7.90}$$

Example 7.1. The voltage-ratio transfer function of a double-tuned circuit is given as

$$H(s) = \frac{As^3}{(s + 2 + j100)(s + 2 - j100)(s + 2 + j106)(s + 2 - j106)} \tag{7.91}$$

From $H(s)$, let us determine the following: (a) the maximum points, ω_{1max} and ω_{2max}; (b) the 3-db bandwidth BW; (c) the damping factor ζ; (d) the coefficient of coupling K; (e) the gain constant A; and (f) the maximum of the amplitude response H_{max}.

Solution. (a) The natural frequency of oscillation ω_0 is taken to be approximately halfway between the two poles, i.e., $\omega_0 = 103$ rad. In the neighborhood of ω_0, we draw the poles $s = -2 + j100$ and $s = -2 + j106$, as shown in Fig. 7.46. From the peaking circle centered at the point $s = -2 + j\omega_0$, shown in Fig. 7.46, we obtain

$$\omega_{2max} - \omega_0 = \sqrt{3^2 - 2^2} = 2.236 \text{ rad} \tag{7.92}$$

so that

$$\omega_{2max} = \omega_0 + 2.236 = 105.236 \text{ rad}$$
$$\omega_{1max} = \omega_0 - 2.236 = 100.764 \text{ rad} \tag{7.93}$$

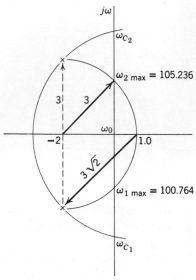

FIG. 7.46. Peaking circle for Example 7.1.

(b) Next we draw a circle centered at $s = 1 + j\omega_0$ with radius $3\sqrt{2}$. Where this circle intersects the $j\omega$ axis, we have ω_{C_2} so that

$$\omega_{C_2} - \omega_0 = \sqrt{(3\sqrt{2})^2 - 1} = 4.123 \text{ rad} \qquad (7.94)$$

The 3-db bandwidth is then

$$\text{BW} = 2(\omega_{C_2} - \omega_0) = 8.246 \text{ rad} \qquad (7.95)$$

(c) The damping factor ζ is obtained from the real part of the poles, $\zeta\omega_0 = 2$, from which we obtain

$$\zeta = \frac{2}{103} = 0.0194 \qquad (7.96)$$

(d) The coefficient of coupling K is obtained from the radius of the peaking circle which is

$$\frac{\omega_0 K}{2} = 3 \qquad (7.97)$$

We thus have

$$K = \frac{6}{\omega_0} = 0.0582 \qquad (7.98)$$

(e) The gain constant A is equal to

$$A = \frac{2\zeta\omega_0 K}{1 - K^2} = \frac{2(2)(0.0582)}{1 - (0.0582)^2} = 0.2328 \qquad (7.99)$$

(f) Finally, the maximum amplitude $H_{\max}$ is

$$H_{\max} = \frac{1}{2(1 - K^2)} = 0.5009 \qquad (7.100)$$

Problems

7.1   Given the pole-zero diagrams shown in (*a*) and (*b*) of the figure, write the rational functions $F_1(s)$ and $F_2(s)$ represented by the pole-zero plots as quotients of polynomials. What can you say about the relationship between the poles in the right-half plane and the signs of the coefficients of the denominator polynomial?

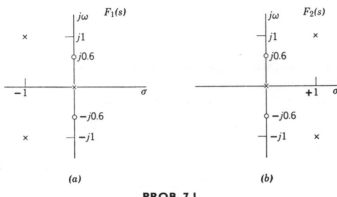

(*a*)   (*b*)

PROB. 7.1

7.2   Find the poles and zeros of the impedances of the following networks and plot on a scaled *s* plane.

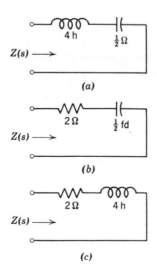

(*a*)

(*b*)

(*c*)

PROB. 7.2

7.3 Plot the poles and zeros for the following functions

(a)
$$F(s) = \frac{s^2 + 4s + 3}{s^2 + 2s}$$

(b)
$$F(s) = \frac{(s^2 + 4)(s - 2)}{(s^2 - 1)(s^2 + 2s + 2)}$$

(c)
$$F(s) = \frac{(s^2 + 3s)(s + 1)}{s(s^2 + 2s + 5)}$$

7.4 The circuit shown in the figure is a *shunt peaking* circuit often used in video amplifiers.

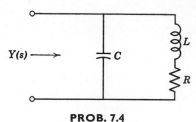

PROB. 7.4

(a) Show that the admittance $Y(s)$ is of the form

$$Y(s) = \frac{K(s - s_1)(s - s_2)}{(s - s_3)}$$

Express s_1, s_2, and s_3 in terms of R, L, and C.
(b) When $s_1 = -10 + j10^3$, $s_2 = -10 - j10^3$, and $Y(j0) = 10^{-2}$ mhos, find the values of R, L, and C and determine the numerical value of s_3.

7.5 Find the amplitude and phase response for the following functions and sketch.

(a) $F(s) = \dfrac{K}{s + K}$ (b) $F(s) = \dfrac{s}{s + K}$

(c) $F(s) = \dfrac{s}{s^2 + \omega_0^2}$ (d) $F(s) = \dfrac{\omega_0}{s^2 + \omega_0^2}$

Note that K and ω_0 are positive quantities.

7.6 For the pole-zero plots in Prob. 7.1, find the residues of the poles by the vector method.

7.7 For the pole-zero plots shown in the figure, find the residues of the poles.

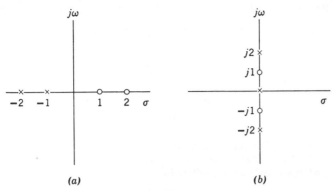

(a)   (b)

PROB. 7.7

7.8 Given the function

$$G(j\omega) = \frac{A(\omega) + jB(\omega)}{C(\omega) + jD(\omega)}$$

determine the amplitude and phase of $G(j\omega)$ in terms of A, B, C, D. Show that the amplitude function is even and the phase function is odd.

7.9 By means of the vector method, *sketch* the amplitude and phase response for

(a) $F(s) = \dfrac{s + 0.5}{s(s + 10)}$

(b) $F(s) = \dfrac{s}{s^2 + 2s + 2}$

(e) $F(s) = \dfrac{s + 1}{s - 1}$

(f) $F(s) = \dfrac{s^2 + 4}{(s + 2)(s^2 + 9)}$

(c) $F(s) = \dfrac{s - 1}{s + 1}$

(d) $F(s) = \dfrac{s}{s^2 - 2s + 2}$

(g) $F(s) = \dfrac{s^2 - 2s + 5}{(s + 2)(s + 1)}$

(h) $F(s) = \dfrac{s^2 + 2s + 5}{(s + 2)(s + 1)}$

7.10 For the function

$$F(s) = \frac{5}{s^2 + 2s + 5}$$

determine ω_{max}, $|F(j\omega_{max})|$, the half-power point ω_C and $|F(j\omega_C)|$. Sketch the amplitude and phase response.

7.11 For the circuit shown, determine the current ratio I_L/I_g and find: (a) the point ω_{max}, where its amplitude is maximum; (b) the half-power point ω_C; (c) the point ω_u where $|I_L(\omega_u)/I_g(\omega_u)| = 1$. Use geometric construction.

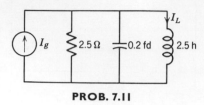

PROB. 7.11

7.12 A network function consists of two poles at $p_{1,2} = r_i e^{\pm j(\pi - \theta)} = -\sigma_i \pm j\omega_i$, as given in the figure. Show that the square of the amplitude response, $M^2(\omega)$ is maximum at $\omega_m{}^2 = r_i{}^2 |\cos 2\theta|$.

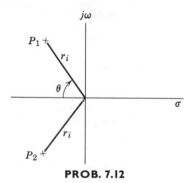

PROB. 7.12

7.13 In connection with Prob. 7.4, plot the poles and zeros of the impedance function $Z(s) = 1/Y(s)$. Find, approximately, the maximum point of the amplitude response. In addition, find the bandwidth at the half-power points and the circuit Q.

7.14 The pole configuration for a system function $H(s)$ is given in the figure. From the plot, calculate:

(a) The undamped frequency of oscillation ω_0
(b) the bandwidth and Q.

7.15 In connection with Prob. 7.12, determine the ratio $M^2(\omega_{max})/M^2(0)$.

7.16 Determine the amplitude and phase response for the admittance $Y(s)$ of the circuit shown. Is the peaking circle applicable here? What can you say about the shape of the amplitude response curve in a high-Q situation? Determine the bandwidth of the circuit and the circuit Q.

7.17 For the overcoupled case of a double-tuned circuit, derive an expression for the peak-to-valley ratio, i.e., $M(\omega_{max})/M(\omega_0)$, where $M(\cdot)$ denotes amplitude. Use the notation in Section 5 of this chapter. (*Hint:* see Prob. 7.15.)

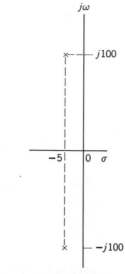

PROB. 7.14

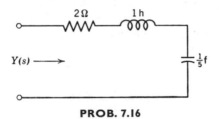

PROB. 7.16

7.18 For the voltage ratio of a double-tuned circuit,

$$H(s) = \frac{As^3}{(s + 4 + j50)(s + 4 - j50)(s + 4 + j60)(s + 4 - j60)}$$

Use the peaking circle to determine the maximum and half-power points and the circuit Q. Find the gain constant A and the coefficient of coupling K.

7.19 Derive Eq. 7.87.

chapter 8

Network analysis (II)

8.1 NETWORK FUNCTIONS

In electric network theory, the word *port* has a special meaning. A port may be regarded as a pair of terminals in which the current into one terminal equals the current out of the other. For the one-port network shown in Fig. 8.1, $I = I'$. A one-port network is completely specified when the voltage-current relationships at the terminals of the port are given. For example, if $V = 10v$ and $I = 2$ amp, then we know that the *input* or *driving-point* impedance of the one-port is

$$Z_{in} = \frac{V}{I} = 5\,\Omega \tag{8.1}$$

Whether the one-port is actually a single 5-Ω resistor, or two 2.5-Ω resistors in series, or two 10-Ω resistors in parallel is of little importance because the primary concern is the current-voltage relationship at the port. Consider the example when $I = 2s + 3$ and $V = 1$; then the input admittance of the one port is

$$Y_{in} = \frac{I}{V} = 2s + 3 \tag{8.2}$$

which corresponds to a 2-fd capacitor in parallel with a $\frac{1}{3}$-Ω resistor in its simplest case (Fig. 8.2).

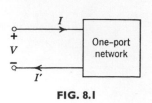

FIG. 8.1

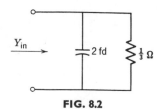

FIG. 8.2

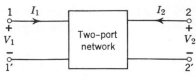

FIG. 8.3

A *two-port* network has two pairs of voltage-current relationships. The characterizing equations for the two-port network must indicate not only the voltage-current relationships for each port but also how the currents and voltages at the two ports are interrelated. Consider the general two-port network in Fig. 8.3. A particular set of equations that describe a two-port network are the z-parameter equations

$$V_1 = z_{11}I_1 + z_{12}I_2, \qquad V_2 = z_{21}I_1 + z_{22}I_2 \qquad (8.3)$$

where the individual z parameters are given by

$$z_{11} = \left.\frac{V_1}{I_1}\right|_{I_2=0} \qquad z_{12} = \left.\frac{V_1}{I_2}\right|_{I_1=0}$$

$$z_{21} = \left.\frac{V_2}{I_1}\right|_{I_2=0} \qquad z_{22} = \left.\frac{V_2}{I_2}\right|_{I_1=0} \qquad (8.4)$$

It is observed that all the z parameters have the dimensions of impedance. Moreover, the individual parameters are specified only when the current in one of the ports is zero. This corresponds to one of ports being *open-circuited* from which the z parameters also derive the name *open-circuit* parameters. Note that z_{11} relates the current and voltage in the 1–1′ port only whereas z_{22} gives the current voltage relationship for the 2–2′ port. Such parameters are called open-circuit driving-point impedances. On the other hand, the parameters z_{12} and z_{21} relate the voltage in one port to the current in the other. These are known as (open-circuit) transfer impedances.

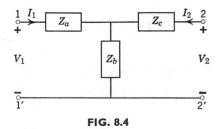

FIG. 8.4

As an example, let us find the open-circuit parameters for the T circuit in Fig. 8.4. We obtain the z parameters by inspection

$$z_{11} = \frac{V_1}{I_1}\bigg|_{I_2=0} = Z_a + Z_b$$

$$z_{22} = \frac{V_2}{I_2}\bigg|_{I_1=0} = Z_b + Z_c$$

$$z_{12} = \frac{V_1}{I_2}\bigg|_{I_1=0} = Z_b \tag{8.5}$$

$$z_{21} = \frac{V_2}{I_1}\bigg|_{I_2=0} = Z_b$$

Observe that $z_{12} = z_{21}$. When the open-circuit transfer impedances of a two-port network are equal, the network is said to be *reciprocal*. It will be shown later that most passive time-invariant networks are reciprocal.*

Most two-port networks, whether passive or active, can be characterized by a set of open-circuit parameters. Usually, the network is sufficiently complicated so that we cannot obtain the z parameters by inspection, as we did for the T circuit in Fig. 8.4. The question is now: how do we obtain the z parameters for *any* circuit in general? The procedure is as follows. We write a set of node equations with the voltages at the ports, V_1 and V_2, and other node voltages within the two port, V_3, V_4, $\cdots$, V_k as the dependent variables. The independent variables are the currents I_1 and I_2, which we will take to be current sources. We then proceed to write a set of node equations,

$$I_1 = n_{11}V_1 + n_{12}V_2 + n_{13}V_3 + \cdots + n_{1k}V_k$$
$$I_2 = n_{21}V_1 + n_{22}V_2 + \cdots \qquad \cdots + n_{2k}V_k$$
$$0 = n_{31}V_1 + \cdots \quad + \cdots \qquad \qquad + n_{3k}V_k$$
$$\cdots\cdots\cdots\cdots\cdots\cdots\cdots\cdots\cdots\cdots\cdots$$
$$0 = n_{k1}V_1 + \cdots \quad + \cdots \qquad \qquad + n_{kk}V_k \tag{8.6}$$

$\underline{I} = N\,V$

where n_{ij} represents the admittance between the ith and jth nodes, i.e.,

$$n_{ij} = G_{ij} + sC_{ij} + \frac{1}{sL_{ij}} \tag{8.7}$$

If the circuit is made up of R-L-C elements only, then it is clear that $n_{ij} = n_{ji}$. As a result, the ijth cofactor of the determinant of the node equations, Δ_{ij}, must be equal to the jith cofactor, Δ_{ji}, i.e.,

$$\Delta_{ij} = \Delta_{ji}$$

---

* One important exception is the *gyrator* discussed in Prob. 8.11.

This result leads directly to the reciprocity conditon $z_{21} = z_{12}$ as we shall see.

Returning to the set of node equations in Eq. 8.6, let us solve for V_1 and V_2. We obtain

$$V_1 = \frac{\Delta_{11}}{\Delta} I_1 + \frac{\Delta_{21}}{\Delta} I_2$$

$V = N^{-1} I$

(8.8)

$$V_2 = \frac{\Delta_{12}}{\Delta} I_1 + \frac{\Delta_{22}}{\Delta} I_2$$

Relating this last set of equations to the defining equations for the z parameters, it is clear that

$$z_{11} = \frac{\Delta_{11}}{\Delta} \qquad z_{12} = \frac{\Delta_{21}}{\Delta}$$

(8.9)

$$z_{21} = \frac{\Delta_{12}}{\Delta} \qquad z_{22} = \frac{\Delta_{22}}{\Delta}$$

Since for a passive network $\Delta_{21} = \Delta_{12}$, it follows that $z_{21} = z_{12}$; the network is then reciprocal.

As an example, let us find the z parameters of the Pi circuit in Fig. 8.5. First, the node equations are:

$$I_1 = (Y_A + Y_C)V_1 - Y_C V_2$$
$$I_2 = -Y_C V_1 + (Y_B + Y_C)V_2$$

(8.10)

The determinant for this set of equations is

$$\Delta Y = Y_A Y_B + Y_A Y_C + Y_B Y_C$$

(8.11)

In terms of ΔY, the open-circuit parameters for the Pi circuit are:

$$z_{11} = \frac{Y_B + Y_C}{\Delta Y} \qquad z_{21} = \frac{Y_C}{\Delta Y}$$

(8.12)

$$z_{12} = \frac{Y_C}{\Delta Y} \qquad z_{22} = \frac{Y_A + Y_C}{\Delta Y}$$

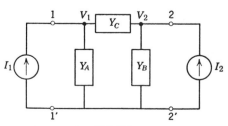

FIG. 8.5

Now, let us perform a *delta-wye* transformation for the circuits in Figs. 8.4 and 8.5. In other words, let us find relationships between the immittances of the two circuits so that they both have the same z parameters. We readily obtain

$$z_{12} = Z_b = \frac{Y_C}{\Delta Y}$$

$$z_{22} = Z_b + Z_c = \frac{Y_A + Y_C}{\Delta Y} \tag{8.13}$$

$$z_{11} = Z_a + Z_b = \frac{Y_B + Y_C}{\Delta Y}$$

We then find

$$Z_a = \frac{Y_B}{\Delta Y}$$

$$\tag{8.14}$$

$$Z_c = \frac{Y_A}{\Delta Y}$$

Suppose we were to write a set of mesh equations for the two port in Fig. 8.3. Then the voltages V_1 and V_2 would become independent sources and the currents I_1 and I_2 would be just two of the dependent mesh currents. Consider the general set of mesh equations,

$$V_1 = m_{11}I_1 + m_{12}I_2 + \cdots + m_{1k}I_k$$

$$V_2 = m_{21}I_1 + m_{22}I_2 + \cdots + m_{2k}I_k$$

$$0 = m_{31}I_1 + \quad \cdot \quad \cdots \quad + \cdot m_{3k}I_k$$

$$\cdots\cdots\cdots\cdots\cdots\cdots\cdots\cdots\cdots$$

$$0 = m_{k1}I_1 + \quad \cdot \quad \cdots \quad + m_{kk}I_k \tag{8.15}$$

where m_{ii} represents the sum of the impedances in the ith mesh and m_{ij} is the common impedance between mesh i and mesh j. We note here again that, for an *R-L-C* network, $m_{ij} = m_{ji}$ for all i and j. Thus reciprocity holds.

Solving the set of mesh equations for I_1 and I_2, we obtain the following equations:

$$I_1 = \frac{\Delta_{11}}{\Delta} V_1 + \frac{\Delta_{21}}{\Delta} V_2$$

$$\tag{8.16}$$

$$I_2 = \frac{\Delta_{12}}{\Delta} V_1 + \frac{\Delta_{22}}{\Delta} V_2$$

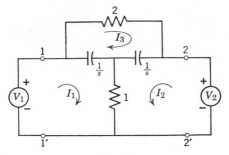

FIG. 8.6

The above equations define the *short-circuit admittance parameters* as

$$I_1 = y_{11}V_1 + y_{12}V_2$$
$$I_2 = y_{21}V_1 + y_{22}V_2 \tag{8.17}$$

where $y_{ij} = \Delta_{ji}/\Delta$ for all i and j.

Let us find the y parameters for the *bridged*-T circuit given in Fig. 8.6. The mesh equations for the circuit are

$$V_1 = \left(\frac{1}{s} + 1\right)I_1 + I_2 - \frac{1}{s}I_3$$

$$V_2 = I_1 + \left(\frac{1}{s} + 1\right)I_2 + \frac{1}{s}I_3 \tag{8.18}$$

$$0 = -\frac{1}{s}I_1 + \frac{1}{s}I_2 + 2\left(\frac{1}{s} + 1\right)I_3$$

In straightforward fashion we obtain

$$\Delta = \frac{2(2s + 1)}{s^2}$$

$$\Delta_{11} = \Delta_{22} = \frac{2s^2 + 4s + 1}{s^2} \tag{8.19}$$

$$\Delta_{12} = \Delta_{21} = -\frac{2s^2 + 2s + 1}{s^2}$$

The short-circuit parameters are then

$$y_{11} = y_{22} = \frac{2s^2 + 4s + 1}{2(2s + 1)}$$

$$y_{21} = y_{12} = -\frac{2s^2 + 2s + 1}{2(2s + 1)} \tag{8.20}$$

When $y_{11} = y_{22}$ or $z_{11} = z_{22}$, the network is *symmetrical*.*

---

* A symmetrical network is easily recognized because, by interchanging the (1–1') and (2–2') port designations, the network remains unchanged.

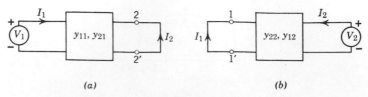

(a)   (b)

FIG. 8.7

Returning to Eq. 8.17 which defines the y parameters, we see that the y parameters are expressed explicitly as

$$y_{11} = \frac{I_1}{V_1}\bigg|_{V_2=0}$$

$$y_{12} = \frac{I_1}{V_2}\bigg|_{V_1=0}$$

$$y_{21} = \frac{I_2}{V_1}\bigg|_{V_2=0}$$

$$y_{22} = \frac{I_2}{V_2}\bigg|_{V_1=0}$$

(8.21)

The reason why the y parameters are also called *short-circuit admittance* parameters is now apparent. In obtaining y_{11} and y_{21}, the 2–2' port must be short-circuited, and when we find y_{22} and y_{12}, the 1–1' port must be short-circuited, as shown in Figs. 8.7a and 8.7b.

As a second example, let us obtain the y parameters of the *Pi* circuit in Fig. 8.5. To obtain y_{11} and y_{21}, we short-circuit terminals 2–2'. We then have

$$y_{11} = Y_A + Y_C$$

$$y_{21} = -Y_C$$

(8.22)

We next short-circuit terminals 1–1' to obtain

$$y_{22} = Y_B + Y_C$$

$$y_{12} = -Y_C$$

(8.23)

Given the z and y parameters of a two-port network, we may represent all other transfer functions involving V_1, I_1, V_2, and I_2. For example, the open-circuit transfer function V_2/V_1 can be represented in terms of z parameters in the following way. Now, let us consider the z parameter equations for the two-port network when the 2–2' port is assumed to be open-circuited:

$$V_2 = z_{21}I_1$$

$$V_1 = z_{11}I_1$$

(8.24)

If we take the ratio of V_2 to V_1, we obtain

$$\frac{V_2}{V_1} = \frac{z_{21}}{z_{11}} \tag{8.25}$$

By letting I_2 of the second y parameter equation go to zero, we derive

$$\frac{V_2}{V_1} = -\frac{y_{21}}{y_{22}} \tag{8.26}$$

As a third example, let us derive the transfer admittance I_2/V_1 of a two-port network which is terminated in a resistor of R ohms, as given in Fig. 8.8. For this two-port network, the following equations apply:

$$I_2 = y_{21}V_1 + y_{22}V_2$$
$$V_2 = -I_2R \tag{8.27}$$

By eliminating the variable V_2, we obtain

$$Y_{21} = \frac{I_2}{V_1} = \frac{y_{21}/R}{y_{22} + 1/R} \tag{8.28}$$

Note that Y_{21} and y_{21} are not the same. Y_{21} is the transfer admittance of the two-port network terminated in a resistor R, and y_{21} is the transfer admittance when the 2–2′ port is short-circuited. We must be careful to make this distinction in other cases of a similar nature.

In order to solve for transfer functions of two ports terminated at either port by an impedance Z_L, it is convenient to use the equivalent circuit of the two-port network given in terms of its z parameters (Fig. 8.9) or y parameters (Fig. 8.10). The equivalent voltage sources $z_{12}I_2$ and $z_{21}I_1$ in Fig. 8.9 are called *controlled sources* because they depend upon a current somewhere in the network.* Similarly, the current sources $y_{12}V_2$ and $y_{21}V_1$ are also controlled sources. For the circuit in Fig. 8.9, let us find the transfer impedance

$$Z_{21} = \frac{V_2}{I_1}$$

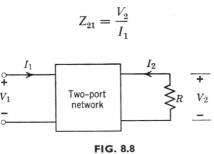

FIG. 8.8

* For a lucid treatment of controlled sources, see E. J. Angelo, *Electronic Circuits*, McGraw-Hill Book Co., New York, 1958.

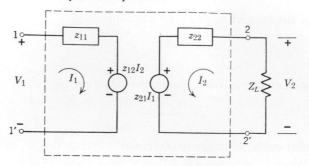

FIG. 8.9. Two-port equivalent.

with the 2–2' port terminated in a load impedance Z_L. If we write the mesh equation for the I_2 mesh, we have

$$-z_{21}I_1 = (z_{22} + Z_L)I_2 \qquad (8.29)$$

Since $V_2 = -I_2 Z_L$, we readily obtain

$$Z_{21} = \frac{V_2}{I_1} = \frac{z_{21}Z_L}{z_{22} + Z_L} \qquad (8.30)$$

Also, it is clear that the current-ratio transfer function for the terminated two-port network is

$$\frac{I_2}{I_1} = -\frac{z_{21}}{z_{22} + Z_L} \qquad (8.31)$$

In similar fashion, we obtain the voltage-ratio transfer function for the circuit represented in Fig. 8.10 as

$$\frac{V_2}{V_1} = -\frac{y_{21}}{Y_2 + y_{22}} \qquad (8.32)$$

As a final example, suppose we are required to find the transfer function V_2/V_g for the two-port network terminated at both ends, as shown in

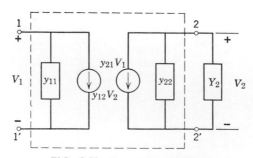

FIG. 8.10. Two-port equivalent.

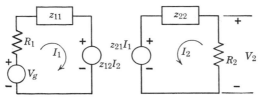

FIG. 8.11

Fig. 8.11. We first write the two mesh equations,

$$V_g = (R_1 + z_{11})I_1 + z_{12}I_2$$
$$0 = z_{21}I_1 + (z_{22} + R_2)I_2$$

(8.33)

Next, we solve for I_2 to give

$$I_2 = - \frac{V_g z_{21}}{(R_1 + z_{11})(R_2 + z_{22}) - z_{12}z_{21}}$$

(8.34)

From the equation $V_2 = -R_2 I_2$, we may now arrive at the following solution,

$$\frac{V_2}{V_g} = - \frac{R_2 I_2}{V_g} = \frac{z_{21}R_2}{(R_1 + z_{11})(R_2 + z_{22}) - z_{21}z_{12}}$$

(8.35)

8.2 MATRIX REPRESENTATION OF TWO PORTS

The use of matrix notation is extremely helpful in the analysis of two ports. Matrix representation not only clarifies the relationships between various two-port parameters but also serves to introduce other two-port representations. For example, the z-parameter equations

$$V_1 = z_{11}I_1 + z_{12}I_2$$
$$V_2 = z_{21}I_1 + z_{22}I_2$$

(8.36)

can be represented in matrix notation as

$$\begin{bmatrix} V_1 \\ V_2 \end{bmatrix} = \begin{bmatrix} z_{11} & z_{12} \\ z_{21} & z_{22} \end{bmatrix} \begin{bmatrix} I_1 \\ I_2 \end{bmatrix}$$

(8.37)

Similarly, the y-parameter equations can be written as shown in the following:

$$\begin{bmatrix} I_1 \\ I_2 \end{bmatrix} = \begin{bmatrix} y_{11} & y_{12} \\ y_{21} & y_{22} \end{bmatrix} \begin{bmatrix} V_1 \\ V_2 \end{bmatrix}$$

(8.38)

From these two sets of equations we can define the z matrix as

$$[Z] = \begin{bmatrix} z_{11} & z_{12} \\ z_{21} & z_{22} \end{bmatrix} \tag{8.39}$$

and the y matrix as

$$[Y] = \begin{bmatrix} y_{11} & y_{12} \\ y_{21} & y_{22} \end{bmatrix} \tag{8.40}$$

In simplified notation we can write the two sets of equations as

$$[V] = [Z][I] \tag{8.41}$$

and

$$[I] = [Y][V] \tag{8.42}$$

Replacing $[I]$ in Eq. 8.41 by $[Y][V]$, we obtain

$$[V] = [Z][Y][V] \tag{8.43}$$

so that the product $[Z][Y]$ must yield the unit matrix $[U]$. The matrices $[Z]$ and $[Y]$ must, therefore, be inverses of each other, i.e.,

$$[Z]^{-1} = [Y] \quad \text{and} \quad [Y]^{-1} = [Z] \tag{8.44}$$

From this relationship, we can find the relations between the open-circuit z parameters and the short-circuit y parameters:

$$y_{11} = \frac{z_{22}}{\Delta_z} \qquad y_{22} = \frac{z_{11}}{\Delta_z}$$

$$\tag{8.45}$$

$$y_{12} = -\frac{z_{12}}{\Delta_z} \qquad y_{21} = -\frac{z_{21}}{\Delta_z}$$

where $\Delta_z = z_{11}z_{22} - z_{12}z_{21}$; and

$$z_{11} = \frac{y_{22}}{\Delta_y} \qquad z_{22} = \frac{y_{11}}{\Delta_y}$$

$$\tag{8.46}$$

$$z_{12} = -\frac{y_{12}}{\Delta_y} \qquad z_{21} = -\frac{y_{21}}{\Delta_y}$$

where $\Delta_y = y_{11}y_{22} - y_{12}y_{21}$. Using these identities, we can derive the y parameters from the z parameters of a two-port network without having to refer back to the network itself.

A set of two-port parameters must relate the variables V_1, I_1, V_2, and I_2. Two of the four variables are chosen as the independent variables and two are chosen as the dependent ones. Since a combination of four quantities taken two at a time yields six possible combinations, there must be six sets of two-port parameters, of which the z and the y parameters are but two of the set. Let us take as the dependent variables, the voltage and current at the 1–1 port, and define the following matrix equations:

$$
\begin{bmatrix} V_1 \\ I_1 \end{bmatrix} = \begin{bmatrix} A & B \\ C & D \end{bmatrix} \begin{bmatrix} V_2 \\ -I_2 \end{bmatrix}
\tag{8.47}
$$

This matrix equation defines the A, B, C, D parameters, the matrix of which is known as the *transmission* matrix because it relates the voltage and current at the input port to their corresponding quantities at the output. The reason the current I_2 carries a negative sign is that most transmission engineers like to regard their output current as coming *out* of the output port instead of going into the port as per standard usage.

In explicit form the $ABCD$ parameters can be expressed as,

$$
A = \frac{V_1}{V_2}\bigg|_{I_2=0} \qquad B = -\frac{V_1}{I_2}\bigg|_{V_2=0}
$$
$$
C = \frac{I_1}{V_2}\bigg|_{I_2=0} \qquad D = -\frac{I_1}{I_2}\bigg|_{V_2=0}
\tag{8.48}
$$

From these relations, we see that A represents an open-circuit voltage transfer function; B is a short-circuit transfer impedance; C is an open-circuit transfer admittance; and D is a short-circuit current ratio. Note that all four parameters are transfer functions so that the term *transmission matrix* is a very appropriate one. Let us describe the short-circuit transfer functions B and D in terms of y parameters, and the open-circuit transfer functions A and C in terms of z parameters. Using straightforward algebraic operations, we obtain

$$
A = \frac{z_{11}}{z_{21}} \qquad B = -\frac{1}{y_{21}}
$$
$$
C = \frac{1}{z_{21}} \qquad D = -\frac{y_{11}}{y_{21}}
\tag{8.49}
$$

For the $ABCD$ parameters, the reciprocity condition is expressed by the equation,

$$
\det \begin{bmatrix} A & B \\ C & D \end{bmatrix} = AD - BC = 1
\tag{8.50}
$$

Let us find, as an example, the $ABCD$ parameter for the *ideal transformer* in Fig. 8.12, whose defining equations are:

$$
V_1 = nV_2
$$
$$
I_1 = \frac{1}{n}(-I_2)
\tag{8.51}
$$

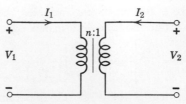

FIG. 8.12. Ideal transformer.

If we express Eq. 8.51 in matrix form, we have

$$\begin{bmatrix} V_1 \\ I_1 \end{bmatrix} = \begin{bmatrix} n & 0 \\ 0 & \dfrac{1}{n} \end{bmatrix} \begin{bmatrix} V_2 \\ -I_2 \end{bmatrix} \tag{8.52}$$

so that the transmission matrix of the ideal transformer is

$$\begin{bmatrix} A & B \\ C & D \end{bmatrix} = \begin{bmatrix} n & 0 \\ 0 & \dfrac{1}{n} \end{bmatrix} \tag{8.53}$$

Note, incidentally, that the ideal transformer does *not* possess an impedance or admittance matrix because the self- and mutual inductances are infinite.*

When we connect a pair of two ports, N_a and N_b, in tandem, as given in Fig. 8.13, we can find the transmission matrix of the over-all two-port network from the transmission matrices of the individual two ports in a very simple and straightforward manner. From Fig. 8.13, we see that,

$$\begin{bmatrix} V_{2a} \\ -I_{2a} \end{bmatrix} = \begin{bmatrix} V_{1b} \\ I_{1b} \end{bmatrix} \tag{8.54}$$

Writing the set of *ABCD* parameter equations for N_a, we obtain,

$$\begin{bmatrix} V_1 \\ I_1 \end{bmatrix} = \begin{bmatrix} A_a & B_a \\ C_a & D_a \end{bmatrix} \begin{bmatrix} V_{2a} \\ -I_{2a} \end{bmatrix} \tag{8.55}$$

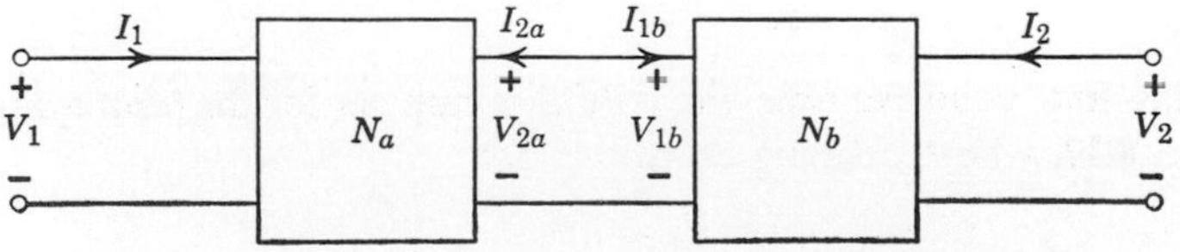

FIG. 8.13. Tandem connection of two ports.

---

* For a detailed discussion concerning ideal transformers, see M. E. Van Valkenburg, *Modern Network Synthesis*, John Wiley & Sons, New York, 1960.

We also know that

$$\begin{bmatrix} V_{2a} \\ -I_{2a} \end{bmatrix} = \begin{bmatrix} V_{1b} \\ I_{1b} \end{bmatrix} = \begin{bmatrix} A_b & B_b \\ C_b & D_b \end{bmatrix} \begin{bmatrix} V_2 \\ -I_2 \end{bmatrix} \tag{8.56}$$

Substituting the second matrix equation into the first, we obtain

$$\begin{bmatrix} V_1 \\ I_1 \end{bmatrix} = \begin{bmatrix} A_a & B_a \\ C_a & D_a \end{bmatrix} \begin{bmatrix} A_b & B_b \\ C_b & D_b \end{bmatrix} \begin{bmatrix} V_2 \\ -I_2 \end{bmatrix} \tag{8.57}$$

We see that the transmission matrix of the over-all two-port network is simply the product of the transmission matrices of the individual two ports.

As an example, consider the ideal transformer terminated by a resistor R, as shown in Fig. 8.14. If we consider the resistor as a separate two-port network, the $ABCD$ parameters for the resistor will be

$$\begin{bmatrix} 1 & 0 \\ \dfrac{1}{R} & 1 \end{bmatrix}$$

The $ABCD$ parameters for the circuit in Fig. 8.14 are obtained from the equation

$$\begin{bmatrix} A & B \\ C & D \end{bmatrix} = \begin{bmatrix} n & 0 \\ 0 & \dfrac{1}{n} \end{bmatrix} \begin{bmatrix} 1 & 0 \\ \dfrac{1}{R} & 1 \end{bmatrix} = \begin{bmatrix} n & 0 \\ \dfrac{1}{nR} & n \end{bmatrix} \tag{8.58}$$

Thus we obtain the following matrix equation for the two-port network,

$$\begin{bmatrix} V_1 \\ I_1 \end{bmatrix} = \begin{bmatrix} n & 0 \\ \dfrac{1}{nR} & n \end{bmatrix} \begin{bmatrix} V_2 \\ -I_2 \end{bmatrix} \tag{8.59}$$

For the circuit in Fig. 8.14, let us consider the case when V_1 is a voltage

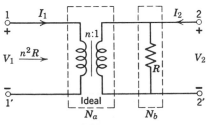

FIG. 8.14

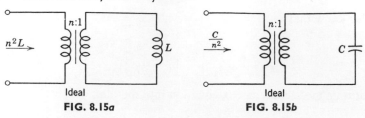

Ideal   Ideal
FIG. 8.15a   **FIG. 8.15b**

source and the 2–2′ port is open-circuited, i.e., $I_2 = 0$. Then the following set of equations apply.

$$V_1 = nV_2$$
$$I_1 = \frac{V_2}{nR}$$

(8.60)

Taking the ratio of V_1 to I_1, we find the input impedance at the 1–1′ port,

$$Z_1 = \frac{V_1}{I_1} = n^2R$$

(8.61)

We see that the equivalent circuit of Fig. 8.14 seen from the 1–1′ port is simply a resistor of n^2R ohms. From this example, we find that the ideal transformer acts as an *impedance transformer*. It can be similarly shown that, if we connect an inductor L in place of the resistor R in Fig. 8.14, the input impedance at the 1–1′ port would be

$$Z_1 = sn^2L$$

(8.62)

so that the inductor L appears as an equivalent inductor n^2L at the 1–1′ port (Fig. 8.15a). Also, if we connect a capacitor C in place of R, then the equivalent circuit as viewed from the 1–1′ port would consist of a capacitor of C/n^2 farads, as shown in Fig. 8.15b.

Next, consider the situation where a pair of two ports, N_a and N_b, are connected in parallel, as shown in Fig. 8.16. Let us find the y parameters

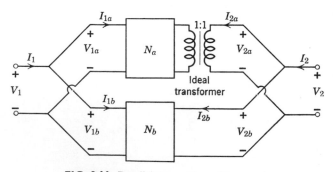

FIG. 8.16. Parallel connection of two ports.

for the over-all two-port network. The matrix equations for the individual two ports are:

$$\begin{bmatrix} I_{1a} \\ I_{2a} \end{bmatrix} = \begin{bmatrix} y_{11a} & y_{12a} \\ y_{21a} & y_{22a} \end{bmatrix} \begin{bmatrix} V_{1a} \\ V_{2a} \end{bmatrix} \tag{8.63}$$

and

$$\begin{bmatrix} I_{1b} \\ I_{2b} \end{bmatrix} = \begin{bmatrix} y_{11b} & y_{12b} \\ y_{21b} & y_{22b} \end{bmatrix} \begin{bmatrix} V_{1b} \\ V_{2b} \end{bmatrix} \tag{8.64}$$

From Fig. 8.13, we see that the following equations must hold:

$$V_1 = V_{1a} = V_{1b} \qquad V_2 = V_{2a} = V_{2b}$$
$$I_1 = I_{1a} + I_{1b} \qquad I_2 = I_{2a} + I_{2b}$$

In connecting two ports in series or in parallel, we must be careful lest the individual character of a two-port network is altered when connected in series or parallel with another two-port one. For example, when we connect the two ports in Fig. 8.17 in parallel, the impedances Z_7 and Z_8 will be short-circuited. Therefore, to ensure that a two-port network does not interfere with the internal affairs of the other, ideal transformers are used to provide the necessary isolation. In matrix notation, the sum of the individual $[I_i]$ matrices of the two ports in parallel must equal the $[I]$ matrix of the over-all two-port network. Thus,

$$\begin{bmatrix} I_1 \\ I_2 \end{bmatrix} = \begin{bmatrix} I_{1a} \\ I_{2a} \end{bmatrix} + \begin{bmatrix} I_{1b} \\ I_{2b} \end{bmatrix}$$
$$= \left[\begin{bmatrix} y_{11a} & y_{12a} \\ y_{21a} & y_{22a} \end{bmatrix} + \begin{bmatrix} y_{11b} & y_{12b} \\ y_{21b} & y_{22b} \end{bmatrix} \right] \begin{bmatrix} V_1 \\ V_2 \end{bmatrix} \tag{8.65}$$

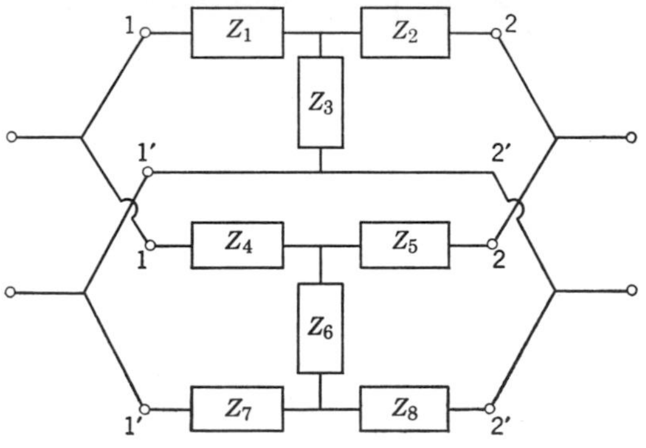

FIG. 8.17

so that the y parameters of the over-all two-port network can be expressed in terms of the y parameters of the individual two ports as

$$\begin{bmatrix} y_{11} & y_{12} \\ y_{21} & y_{22} \end{bmatrix} = \begin{bmatrix} y_{11a} + y_{11b} & y_{12a} + y_{12b} \\ y_{21a} + y_{21b} & y_{22a} + y_{22b} \end{bmatrix} \tag{8.66}$$

If we connect two ports in series, as shown in Fig. 8.18, we can express the z parameters of the over-all two-port network in terms of the z parameters of the individual two ports as

$$\begin{bmatrix} z_{11} & z_{12} \\ z_{21} & z_{22} \end{bmatrix} = \begin{bmatrix} z_{11a} + z_{11b} & z_{12a} + z_{12b} \\ z_{21a} + z_{21b} & z_{22a} + z_{22b} \end{bmatrix} \tag{8.67}$$

In summary, it can be said that

1. When two ports are connected in parallel, find the y parameters first and, from the y parameters, derive the other two-port parameters.

2. When two ports are connected in series, it is usually easiest to find the z parameters.

3. When two ports are connected in tandem, the transmission matrix is generally easier to obtain.

As a final example, let us find the y parameters of the bridged-T circuit in Fig. 8.6. We see that the bridged-T circuit could be decomposed into a parallel connection of two ports, as shown in Fig. 8.19. Our task is to first find the y parameters of the two ports N_a and N_b. The y parameters of N_b are obtained by inspection to be

$$y_{12b} = y_{21b} = -\tfrac{1}{2}, \qquad y_{11b} = y_{22b} = \tfrac{1}{2} \tag{8.68}$$

N_a is a T circuit so that the z parameters can be obtained by inspection.

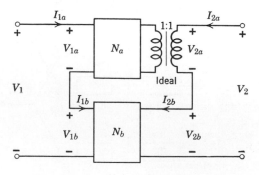

FIG. 8.18. Series connection of two ports.

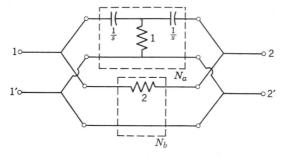

FIG. 8.19

These are:

$$z_{11a} = z_{22a} = \frac{s+1}{s}$$

$$z_{12a} = z_{21a} = 1 \tag{8.69}$$

We then find the y parameters from the equations,

$$y_{11a} = y_{22a} = \frac{z_{22a}}{\Delta z_a} = \frac{s(s+1)}{2s+1}$$

$$y_{12a} = y_{21a} = -\frac{z_{12a}}{\Delta z_a} = -\frac{s^2}{2s+1} \tag{8.70}$$

Since both N_a and N_b are symmetrical two ports, we know that $y_{11} = y_{22}$ for the over-all bridged-T circuit. The y parameters for the bridged-T circuit are now obtained as

$$y_{11} = y_{11a} + y_{11b}$$

$$= \frac{s(s+1)}{2s+1} + \frac{1}{2} = \frac{2s^2 + 4s + 1}{2(2s+1)}$$

$$y_{12} = y_{12a} + y_{12b} \tag{8.71}$$

$$= -\frac{s^2}{2s+1} - \frac{1}{2} = -\frac{2s^2 + 2s + 1}{2(2s+1)}$$

8.3 INCIDENTAL DISSIPATION

As we have seen, the system function $H(s)$ of an *R-L-C* network consists of a ratio of polynomials whose coefficients are functions of the resistances, inductances, and capacitances of the network. We have considered, up to this point, that the inductors and capacitors are *dissipationless*; i.e.,

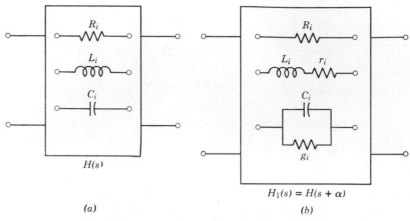

FIG. 8.20. (*a*) Original network. (*b*) Loaded network.

there are no *parasitic* resistances associated with the L and C. Since, at high frequencies, parasitic losses do play an important role in governing system performance, we must account for this incidental dissipation somehow. An effective way of accounting for parasitic resistances is to "load down" the pure inductances and capacitances with incidental dissipation by associating a resistance r_i in series with every inductor L_i, and, for every capacitor C_i, we associate a resistor whose admittance is g_i, as depicted in Fig. 8.20. Suppose we call the system function of the network without parasitic dissipation (Fig. 8.20a) $H(s)$, and the system function of the "loaded" network $H_1(s)$ (Fig. 8.20b). Let us consider the relationship between $H(s)$ and $H_1(s)$ when the dissipation is *uniform*, i.e., in a manner such that

$$\frac{r_i}{L_i} = \frac{g_i}{C} = \alpha \tag{8.72}$$

where the constant α is real and positive.

When a network has uniform dissipation or is *uniformly loaded*, then the sum of impedances in any mesh of the unloaded network,

$$m_{ij} = R_i + sL_i + \frac{1}{sC_i} \tag{8.73}$$

becomes, after loading,

$$m'_{ij} = R_i + sL_i + r_i + \frac{1}{sC_i + g_i}$$

$$= R_i + L_i(s + \alpha) + \frac{1}{C_i(s + \alpha)} \tag{8.74}$$

Similarly, on node basis, if the admittance between any two nodes of the original (unloaded) network is

$$n_{ij} = G_i + sC_i + \frac{1}{sL_i} \qquad (8.75)$$

then the same node admittance after loading is

$$n'_{ij} = G_i + sC_i + g_i + \frac{1}{sL_i + r_i}$$

$$= G_i + C_i(s + \alpha) + \frac{1}{L_i(s + \alpha)} \qquad (8.76)$$

Since any system function can be obtained through mesh or node equations, it is readily seen that the original system function $H(s)$ becomes $H(s + \alpha)$ after the network has been uniformly loaded, i.e., $H_1(s) = H(s + \alpha)$.

Consider the following example. Let us first find the y parameters for the unloaded network in Fig. 8.21. By inspection, we have

$$y_{11} = \frac{1}{2} + \frac{s}{3} + \frac{s}{4} = \frac{1}{2} + \frac{7s}{12}$$

$$y_{22} = 1 + \frac{1}{2s} + \frac{s}{4} = 1 + \frac{s^2 + 2}{4s} \qquad (8.77)$$

$$y_{12} = y_{21} = -\frac{s}{4}$$

Then, for a loading constant $\alpha = \frac{1}{2}$, the loaded network is shown in Fig. 8.22. In parallel with the capacitor $C_1 = \frac{1}{3}$ fd, we have an admittance

$$g_1 = \alpha C_1 = \frac{1}{6} \text{ mho} \qquad (8.78)$$

In parallel with the capacitor $C_2 = \frac{1}{4}$ fd, the associated admittance is

$$g_2 = \alpha C_2 = \frac{1}{8} \text{ mho} \qquad (8.79)$$

In series with the inductor $L = 2$ h, we have a resistor,

$$r_3 = \alpha L = 1 \ \Omega \qquad (8.80)$$

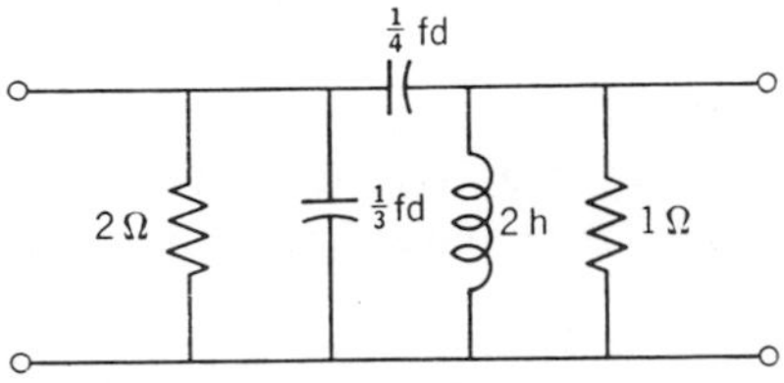

FIG. 8.21

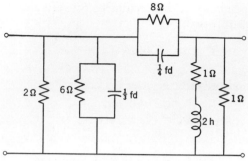

FIG. 8.22. Loaded network $\alpha = \frac{1}{2}$.

Now, we determine the y parameters for the loaded network to be

$$y'_{11} = \frac{1}{2} + \frac{s}{3} + \frac{1}{6} + \frac{s}{4} + \frac{1}{8}$$

$$= \tfrac{1}{2} + \tfrac{1}{3}(s + \tfrac{1}{2}) + \tfrac{1}{4}(s + \tfrac{1}{2})$$

$$= \tfrac{1}{2} + \tfrac{7}{12}(s + \tfrac{1}{2})$$

$$y'_{22} = 1 + \frac{1}{2s + 1} + \frac{s}{4} + \frac{1}{8}$$

$$= 1 + \frac{(s + \tfrac{1}{2})^2 + 2}{4(s + \tfrac{1}{2})}$$

$$y'_{12} = -\left(\frac{s}{4} + \frac{1}{8}\right) = -\frac{1}{4}\left(s + \frac{1}{2}\right) \tag{8.81}$$

We see that the y parameters of the loaded network could have been obtained from the y parameters of the unloaded network by the relationship $H_1(s) = H(s + \alpha)$.

We will make use of the uniform loading concept to prove an important theorem concerning network realizability in the next chapter.

8.4 ANALYSIS OF LADDER NETWORKS

In this section, we will consider a simple method to obtain the network functions of a ladder network in a single operation.* This method depends only upon relationships that exist between the branch currents and node voltages of the ladder. Consider the network shown in Fig. 8.23, where all the series branches are given as impedances and all the parallel branches

---

* F. F. Kuo and G. H. Leichner, "An Iterative Method for Determining Ladder Network Functions," *Proc. IRE*, **47**, No. 10 (Oct. 1959), 1782–1783.

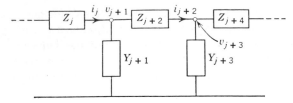

FIG. 8.23

are given as admittances. If the v denote node voltages and i denote branch currents, then the following relationships apply.

$$v_{j+1} = i_{j+2}Z_{j+2} + v_{j+3}$$
$$i_j = v_{j+1}Y_{j+1} + i_{j+2}$$

(8.82)

These equations form the basis of the method we will discuss here.

To illustrate this method, consider the network in Fig. 8.24, for which the following node voltage and branch current relationships apply.

$$V_2(s) = V_2(s)$$
$$I_2(s) = Y_4(s)\,V_2(s)$$
$$V_a(s) = I_2(s)\,Z_3(s) + V_2(s) = [1 + Z_3(s)\,Y_4(s)]\,V_2(s)$$
$$I_1(s) = Y_2(s)\,V_a(s) + I_2(s)$$
$$\qquad = \{Y_2(s)[1 + Z_3(s)\,Y_4(s)] + Y_4(s)\}\,V_2(s)$$
$$V_1(s) = I_1(s)\,Z_1(s) + V_a(s)$$
$$\qquad = \{Z_1[Y_2(1 + Z_3Y_4) + Y_4] + (1 + Z_3Y_4)\}\,V_2(s) \qquad (8.83)$$

We see upon examining the set of equations given above that each equation depends upon the two previous equations only. The first equation, $V_2 = V_2$ is, of course, unnecessary. But, as we shall see later, it is helpful as a starting point. In writing these equations, we begin at the 2–2′ port of the ladder and work towards the 1–1′ port. Each succeeding equation

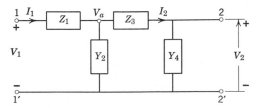

FIG. 8.24

takes into account one new immittance. We see, further, that, with the exception of the first two equations, each subsequent equation is obtained by multiplying the equation just preceding it by the immittance next down the line, and then adding to this product the equation twice preceding it. For example, we see that $I_2(s)$ is obtained by multiplying the preceding equation $V_2(s)$ by the admittance $Y_4(s)$. The next immittance is $Z_3(s)$. We obtain $V_a(s)$ by multiplying the previous equation $I_2(s)$ by $Z_3(s)$ to obtain I_2Z_3; then we add to this product the equation twice preceding it, $V_2(s)$, to obtain $V_a = I_2Z_3 + V_2$. The process is then easily *mechanized* according to the following rules: (1) alternate writing node voltage and branch current equations; (2) the next equation is obtained by multiplying the present equation by the next immittance (as we work from one port to the other), and adding to this product the results of the previous equation.

Using this set of equations, we obtain the input impedance $z_{11}(s)$ by dividing the equation for $V_1(s)$ by the equation for $I_1(s)$. We obtain the voltage-ratio transfer function $V_2(s)/V_1(s)$ by dividing the first equation $V_2(s)$ by the last equation $V_1(s)$. We obtain other network functions such as transfer immittances and current ratios in similar manner. Note that every equation contains $V_2(s)$ as a factor. In taking ratios of these equations, the $V_2(s)$ term is canceled. Therefore, our analysis can be simplified if we let $V_2(s) = 1$.

If the first equation of the set were a current variable $I_i(s)$ instead of the voltage $V_2(s)$, the subsequent equations would contain the current variable $I_i(s)$ as a factor which we could also normalize to $I_i(s) = 1$. An example where the first equation is a current rather than a voltage equation occurs in determining the y parameters of a two-port network.

Before we embark upon some numerical examples, it is important to note that we must represent the series branches as impedances and the shunt branches as admittances. Suppose the series branch consisted of a resistor $R = 1\ \Omega$ in parallel with a capacitor $C = \frac{1}{2}$ fd. Then the impedance of the branch is

$$Z(s) = \frac{R(1/sC)}{1/sC + R} = \frac{2}{s + 2} \tag{8.84}$$

and must be considered as a single entity in writing the equations for the ladder. Similarly, if a shunt branch consisted of a resistor $R_1 = 2\ \Omega$ and an inductor $L_1 = 1$ h, then the admittance of the branch is

$$Y(s) = \frac{1}{2 + s} \tag{8.85}$$

The key point in this discussion is that we must use the *total* impedance or admittance of a branch in writing the equations for the ladder.

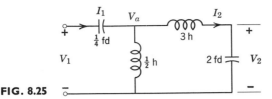

FIG. 8.25

Example 8.1. Let us find the voltage ratio V_2/V_1, the current ratio I_2/I_1, the input impedance $Z_1 = V_1/I_1$, and the transfer impedance $Z_{21} = V_2/I_1$ for the network in Fig. 8.25. First, we must represent the series branches as impedances and the shunt branches as admittances, as shown in Fig. 8.26. The branch current and node voltage equations for the network are:

$$V_2(s) = 1$$

$$I_2(s) = 2s$$

$$V_a(s) = 3s(2s) + 1 = 6s^2 + 1$$

$$I_1(s) = \frac{2}{s}(6s^2 + 1) + 2s = 14s + \frac{2}{s}$$

$$V_1(s) = \frac{4}{s}\left(14s + \frac{2}{s}\right) + 6s^2 + 1 = 6s^2 + 57 + \frac{8}{s^2} \qquad (8.86)$$

The various network functions are then obtained:

(a)
$$Z_{in} = \frac{V_1}{I_1} = \frac{6s^4 + 57s^2 + 8}{14s^3 + 2s}$$

(b)
$$\frac{V_2}{V_1} = \frac{s^2}{6s^4 + 57s^2 + 8}$$

(c)
$$\frac{I_2}{I_1} = \frac{2s^2}{14s^2 + 2}$$

(d)
$$Z_{21} = \frac{V_2}{I_1} = \frac{s}{14s^2 + 2} \qquad (8.87)$$

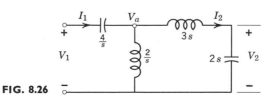

FIG. 8.26

8.5   For the circuit shown, find the voltage-ratio transfer function V_2/V_1 and the input impedance $Z_1 = V_1/I_1$ in terms of the z parameters of the two-port network N and the load resistor R_L.

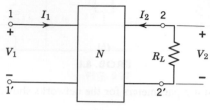

PROB. 8.5

8.6   For the bridged-T circuit given in the figure, show that when $Z_a Z_b = 1$, then the voltage-ratio transfer function is

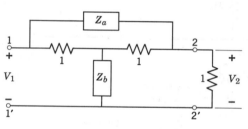

PROB. 8.6

8.7   For the cascade connection of two ports depicted in the figure, show that the transfer impedance z_{12} of the overall circuit is given in terms of the z parameters of the individual two ports by the equation,

$$z_{12} = \frac{z_{12a}z_{12b}}{z_{11b} + z_{22a}}$$

In addition, show that the short-circuit admittance y_{12} is given by

$$y_{12} = -\frac{y_{12a}y_{12b}}{y_{11b} + y_{22a}}$$

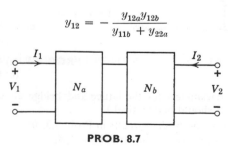

PROB. 8.7

8.8   Find the z and y parameters of the transformer (nonideal) shown below. Determine the T- and π-equivalent circuits for the transformer in terms of L_1, L_2, and M. (*Hint:* Use the z parameters for the T-equivalent circuit, and the y parameters for the π-equivalent circuit.)

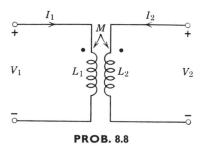

PROB. 8.8

8.9   The *hybrid* parameters of a two-port network are defined by the equations

$$\begin{bmatrix} V_1 \\ I_2 \end{bmatrix} = \begin{bmatrix} h_{11} & h_{12} \\ h_{21} & h_{22} \end{bmatrix}\begin{bmatrix} I_1 \\ V_2 \end{bmatrix}$$

and

$$\begin{bmatrix} I_1 \\ V_2 \end{bmatrix} = \begin{bmatrix} g_{11} & g_{12} \\ g_{21} & g_{22} \end{bmatrix}\begin{bmatrix} V_1 \\ I_2 \end{bmatrix}$$

Express the h and g parameters in terms of either the z or y parameters and give a physical interpretation of the meaning of these parameters; i.e., say whether a parameter is an open- or short-circuit parameter, and whether it is a driving point or transfer function. Finally, derive the conditions of reciprocity for the h and g parameters.

8.10   Prove that for a passive reciprocal network

$$AD - BC = 1$$

where A, B, C, D are the elements of the transmission matrix.

8.11   The *gyrator*, shown in part (*a*) of the figure is a nonreciprocal two-port network defined by the equation,

$$-\frac{V_1}{I_2} = \frac{V_2}{I_1} = K$$

where K is a constant. Find the $ABCD$ parameters of a gyrator and determine the $ABCD$ parameters of the configurations shown in parts (*b*) and (*c*) of the figure. Are these reciprocal?

8.12   Find the y parameters of the twin-T circuit in Prob. 8.2c by considering the circuit to be made up of two T circuits in parallel.

8.13   Find the z parameters of the circuits shown.

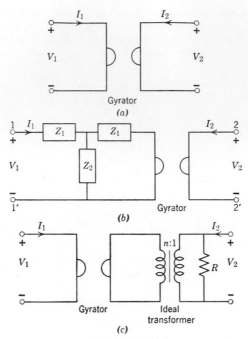

Gyrator
(a)

(b)

Gyrator

(c)

PROB. 8.11

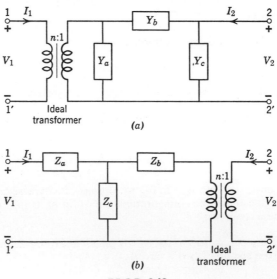

Ideal
transformer
(a)

(b)

Ideal
transformer

PROB. 8.13

8.14   Find the z parameters of the circuit shown.

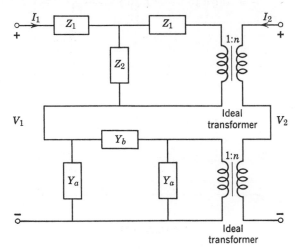

PROB. 8.14

8.15   Find the z parameters of the circuit shown.

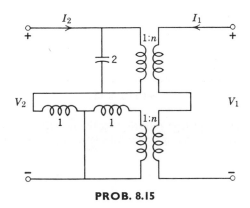

PROB. 8.15

8.16   For the circuit in Prob. 8.2b, determine the y parameters of the uniformly loaded circuit derived from the original circuit with the dissipation $\alpha = 0.1$. Plot the poles and zeros of both cases.

8.17   Find the transfer impedance V_2/I_1 for the circuit in part (a) and the voltage ratio V_2/V_1 for the circuit in part (b). Plot the poles and zeros for the transfer functions obtained.

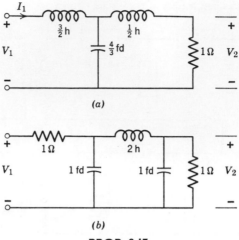

(a)

(b)

PROB. 8.17

8.18 Find the short-circuit parameters for the ladder network utilizing the method in Section 8.4.

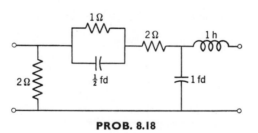

PROB. 8.18

8.19 Determine the voltage ratio V_2/V_1, the current ratio I_2/I_1, the transfer impedance V_2/I_1, and the driving point impedance V_1/I_1 for the network shown.

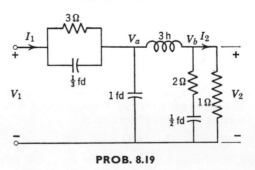

PROB. 8.19

chapter 9

Elements of realizability
theory

9.1 CAUSALITY AND STABILITY

In previous chapters, we have been primarily concerned with the problem of determining the response given the excitation and the network; this problem lies in the domain of network analysis. In the next five chapters we will be dealing with the problem of synthesizing a network, given the excitation $E(s)$ and the response $R(s)$. The starting point for any synthesis problem is the system function,

$$H(s) = \frac{R(s)}{E(s)} \tag{9.1}$$

Our task is to synthesize a network from a given system function.

The first step in a synthesis procedure is to determine whether $H(s)$ could be realized as a physical passive network. There are two important considerations—*causality* and *stability*. By causality we mean that a voltage cannot appear between any pair of terminals in the network before a current is impressed, or vice versa. In other words, the impulse response of the network must be zero for $t < 0$, i.e.,

$$h(t) = 0 \qquad t < 0 \tag{9.2}$$

As an example, the impulse response

$$h(t) = e^{-at}\, u(t) \tag{9.3}$$

is causal, whereas,

$$h(t) = e^{-a|t|} \tag{9.3a}$$

is not causal. In certain cases, the impulse response could be made

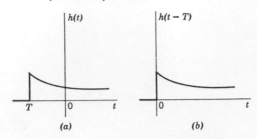

FIG. 9.1. (*a*) Nonrealizable impulse response.
(*b*) Realizable impulse response.

realizable (causal) by delaying it appropriately. For example, the impulse response in Fig. 9.1*a* is not realizable. If we delay the response by T sec, we find that the delayed response $h(t - T)$ is realizable (Fig. 9.1*b*).

In the frequency domain, causality is implied when the Paley-Wiener Criterion* is satisfied for the amplitude function $|H(j\omega)|$. The Paley-Wiener criterion states that a necessary and sufficient condition for an amplitude function $|H(j\omega)|$ to be realizable (causal) is that

$$\int_{-\infty}^{\infty} \frac{\left|\log |H(j\omega)|\,\right|}{1 + \omega^2}\, d\omega < \infty \tag{9.4}$$

The following conditions must be satisfied before the Paley-Wiener criterion is valid: (*a*) $h(t)$ must possess a Fourier transform $H(j\omega)$; (*b*) the square magnitude function $|H(j\omega)|^2$ must be integrable, i.e.,

$$\int_{-\infty}^{\infty} |H(j\omega)|^2\, d\omega < \infty \tag{9.5}$$

The physical implication of the Paley-Wiener criterion is that the amplitude $|H(j\omega)|$ of a realizable network must not be zero over a finite band of frequencies. Another way of looking at the Paley-Wiener criterion is that the amplitude function cannot fall off to zero faster than exponential

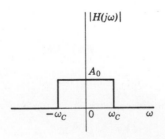

FIG. 9.2. Ideal filter characteristic.

---

* R. E. A. C. Paley and N. Wiener, "Fourier Transforms in the Complex Domain," *Am. Math. Soc. Colloq. Pub.*, **19** (1934), 16–17.

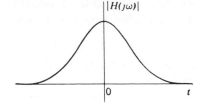

FIG. 9.3. Gaussian filter characteristic.

order. For example, the ideal low-pass filter in Fig. 9.2 is not realizable because beyond ω_C the amplitude is zero. The *Gaussian* shaped curve,

$$|H(j\omega)| = e^{-\omega^2} \tag{9.6}$$

shown in Fig. 9.3 is not realizable because

$$|\log |H(j\omega)|| = \omega^2 \tag{9.7}$$

so that the integral

$$\int_{-\infty}^{\infty} \frac{\omega^2}{1 + \omega^2} \, d\omega \tag{9.8}$$

is not finite. On the other hand, the amplitude function

$$|H(j\omega)| = \frac{1}{\sqrt{1 + \omega^2}} \tag{9.9}$$

does represent a realizable network. In fact, the voltage-ratio transfer function of the *R-C* network in Fig. 9.4 has an amplitude characteristic given by $|H(j\omega)|$ in Eq. 9.9.

For the ideal filter in Fig. 9.2, the inverse transform $h(t)$ has the form

$$h(t) = \frac{A_0 \sin \omega_C t}{t} \tag{9.10}$$

where A_0 is a constant. From the $\sin t/t$ curve in Fig. 2.47, we see that $h(t)$ is nonzero for t less than zero. In fact, in order to make $h(t)$ causal, it must be delayed by an infinite amount. In practice, however, if we delay

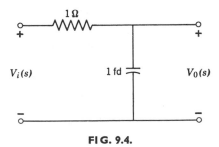

FIG. 9.4.

$h(t)$ by a large but finite amount t_d such that for $t < 0$ the magnitude of $h(t - t_d)$ is less than a very small quantity ϵ, i.e.,

$$|h(t - t_d)| < \epsilon \qquad t < 0$$

we then can approximate $h(t - t_d)$ by a causal response $h_1(t)$ which is zero for $t < 0$.

For a more detailed discussion of the Paley-Wiener criterion, the reader is referred to an excellent treatment by Wallman.*

If a network is stable, then for a bounded excitation $e(t)$ the response $r(t)$ is also bounded. In other words, if

$$|e(t)| < C_1 \qquad 0 \le t < \infty$$

then

$$|r(t)| < C_2 \qquad 0 \le t < \infty$$

where C_1 and C_2 are real, positive, finite quantities. If a linear system is stable, then from the convolution integral we obtain,

$$|r(t)| < C_1 \int_{-\infty}^{\infty} |h(\tau)|\, d\tau < C_2 \tag{9.11}$$

Equation 9.11 requires that the impulse response be absolutely integrable, or

$$\int_{-\infty}^{\infty} |h(\tau)|\, d\tau < \infty \tag{9.12}$$

One important requirement for $h(t)$ to be absolutely integrable is that the impulse response approach zero as t approaches infinity, i.e.,

$$\lim_{t \to \infty} h(t) \to 0$$

Generally, it can be said that, with the exception of isolated impulses, the impulse response must be bound for all t, i.e.,

$$|h(t)| < C \qquad \text{all } t \tag{9.13}$$

where C is a real, positive, finite number.

Observe that our definition of stability precludes such terms as $\sin \omega_0 t$ from the impulse response because $\sin \omega_0 t$ is not absolutely integrable. These undamped sinusoidal terms are associated with simple poles on the $j\omega$ axis. Since pure L-C networks have system functions with simple poles on the $j\omega$ axis and since we do not wish to call these networks unstable, we say that a system is *marginally* stable if its impulse response is bounded according to Eq. 9.13 but does not approach zero as t approaches infinity.

---

* G. E. Valley Jr., and H. Wallman, *Vacuum Tube Amplifiers*, McGraw-Hill Book Co., New York, 1948, Appendix A, pp. 721–727.

In the frequency domain, the stability criterion requires that the system function possess poles in the left-half plane or on the $j\omega$ axis only. Moreover, the poles on the $j\omega$ axis must be simple.* As a result of the requirement of simple poles on the $j\omega$ axis, if $H(s)$ were given as

$$H(s) = \frac{a_n s^n + a_{n-1} s^{n-1} + \cdots + a_1 s + a_0}{b_m s^m + b_{m-1} s^{m-1} + \cdots + b_1 s + b_0} \qquad (9.14)$$

then the order of the numerator n cannot exceed the order of the denominator m by more than unity, i.e.,

$$n - m \leq 1$$

If n exceeded m by more than unity, this would imply that at $s = j\omega = \infty$, and there would be a multiple pole. To summarize, in order for a network to be stable, the following three conditions on its system function $H(s)$ must be satisfied:

1. $H(s)$ cannot have poles in the right-half plane.
2. $H(s)$ cannot have multiple poles in the $j\omega$ axis.
3. The degree of the numerator of $H(s)$ cannot exceed the degree of the denominator by more than unity.

Finally, it should be pointed out that a rational function $H(s)$ with poles in the left-half plane only has an inverse transform $h(t)$ which is zero for $t < 0$.† In this respect, stability implies causality. Since system functions of passive linear networks with lumped elements are rational functions with poles in the left-half plane or $j\omega$ axis only, causality ceases to be a problem when we deal with system functions of this type. We are only concerned with the problem of causality when we have to design a filter for a given amplitude characteristic such as the ideal filter in Fig. 9.2. We know we could never hope to realize exactly a filter of this type because the impulse response would not be causal. To this extent the Paley-Wiener criterion is helpful in defining the limits of our capability.

9.2 HURWITZ POLYNOMIALS

In the previous section we have seen that, in order for a system function to be stable, its poles must be restricted to the left-half plane or the $j\omega$ axis.

---

* In Chapter 7 it was shown that multiple poles on the $j\omega$ axis gave rise to terms as $A_0 t \sin \omega_0 t$.

† G. Raisbeck, "A Definition of Passive Linear Networks in Terms of Time and Energy," *J. Appl. Phys.*, (Dec. 25, 1954) 1510–1514. The proof follows straightforwardly from the properties of the Laplace transform.

Moreover, the poles on the $j\omega$ axis must be simple. The denominator polynomial of the system function belongs to a class of polynomials known as *Hurwitz* polynomials. A polynomial $P(s)$ is said to be Hurwitz if the following conditions are satisfied:

1. $P(s)$ is real when s is real.
2. The roots of $P(s)$ have real parts which are zero or negative.

As a result of these conditons, if $P(s)$ is a Hurwitz polynomial given by

$$P(s) = a_n s^n + a_{n-1} s^{n-1} + \cdots + a_1 s + a_0 \qquad (9.15)$$

then all the coefficients a_i must be real; if $s_i = \alpha_i + j\beta$ is a root of $P(s)$, then α_i must be negative. The polynomial

$$P(s) = (s + 1)(s + 1 + j\sqrt{2})(s + 1 - j\sqrt{2}) \qquad (9.16)$$

is Hurwitz because all of its roots have negative real parts. On the other hand,

$$G(s) = (s - 1)(s + 2)(s + 3) \qquad (9.17)$$

is not Hurwitz because of the root $s = 1$ which has a positive real part. Hurwitz polynomials have the following properties:

1. All the coefficients a_i are nonnegative. This is readily seen by examining the three types of roots that a Hurwitz polynomial might have. These are:

$$s = -\gamma_i \qquad \gamma_i \text{ real and positive}$$
$$s = \pm j\omega_i \qquad \omega_i \text{ real}$$
$$s = -\alpha_i \pm j\beta_i \qquad \alpha_i \text{ real and positive}$$

The polynomial $P(s)$ which contains these roots can be written as

$$P(s) = (s + \gamma_i)(s^2 + \omega_i^2)[(s + \alpha_i)^2 + \beta_i^2] \cdots \qquad (9.18)$$

Since $P(s)$ is the product of terms with only positive coefficients, it follows that the coefficients of $P(s)$ must be positive. A corollary is that, between the highest order term in s and the lowest order term, none of the coefficients may be zero unless the polynomial is even or odd. In other words, $a_{n-1}, a_{n-2}, \cdots, a_2, a_1$ must not be zero if the polynomial is neither even nor odd. This is readily seen because the absence of a term a_i implies cancellation brought about by a root $(s - \gamma_i)$ with a positive real part.

2. Both the odd and even parts of a Hurwitz polynomial $P(s)$ have roots on the $j\omega$ axis only. If we denote the odd part of $P(s)$ as $n(s)$ and the even part as $m(s)$, so that

$$P(s) = n(s) + m(s) \qquad (9.19)$$

then $m(s)$ and $n(s)$ both have roots on the $j\omega$ axis only. The reader is referred to a proof of this property by Guillemin.*

3. As a result of property 2, if $P(s)$ is either even or odd, all its roots are on the $j\omega$ axis.

4. The continued fraction expansion of the ratio of the odd to even parts or the even to odd parts of a Hurwitz polynomial yields all positive quotient terms. Suppose we denote the ratios as $\psi(s) = n(s)/m(s)$ or $\psi(s) = m(s)/n(s)$, then the continued fraction expansion of $\psi(s)$ can be written as:

$$\psi(s) = q_1 s + \cfrac{1}{q_2 s + \cfrac{1}{q_3 s + \cfrac{1}{\ddots \; + \cfrac{1}{q_n s}}}} \qquad (9.20)$$

where the quotients $q_1, q_2, \cdots, q_n$ must be positive if the polynomial $P(s) = n(s) + m(s)$ is Hurwitz.† To obtain the continued fraction expansion, we must perform a series of long divisions. Suppose $\psi(s)$ is

$$\psi(s) = \frac{m(s)}{n(s)} \qquad (9.21)$$

where $m(s)$ is of one higher degree than $n(s)$. Then, if we divide $n(s)$ into $m(s)$, we obtain a single quotient and a remainder,

$$\psi(s) = q_1 s + \frac{R_1(s)}{n(s)} \qquad (9.22)$$

The degree of the term $R_1(s)$ is one lower than the degree of $n(s)$. Therefore, if we invert the remainder term and divide, we have

$$\frac{n(s)}{R_1(s)} = q_2 s + \frac{R_2(s)}{R_1(s)} \qquad (9.23)$$

---

* E. Guillemin, *The Mathematics of Circuit Analysis*, John Wiley & Sons, New York, 1949. An excellent treatment of Hurwitz polynomials is given here.

† A proof can be undertaken in connection with *L-C* driving-point functions; see M. E. Van Valkenburg, *Modern Network Synthesis*, John Wiley & Sons, New York, 1960.

Inverting and dividing again, we obtain

$$\frac{R_1(s)}{R_2(s)} = q_3 s + \frac{R_3(s)}{R_2(s)} \tag{9.24}$$

We see that the process of obtaining the continued fraction expansion of $\psi(s)$ simply involves division and inversion. At each step we obtain a quotient term $q_i s$ and a remainder term, $R_{i+1}(s)/R_i(s)$. We then invert the remainder term and divide $R_{i+1}(s)$ into $R_i(s)$ to obtain a new quotient. There is a theorem in the theory of continued fractions which states that the continued fraction expansion of the even to odd or odd to even parts of a polynomial must be finite in length.* Another theorem states that, if the continued fraction expansion of the odd to even or even to odd parts of a polynomial yields positive quotient terms, then the polynomial must be Hurwitz to within an even multiplicative factor $W(s)$.* That is, if we write

$$F_1(s) = W(s) F(s) \tag{9.25}$$

then $F(s)$ is Hurwitz. If $W(s)$ is also Hurwitz, $F_1(s)$ must be Hurwitz. For example, let us test whether the polynomial,

$$F(s) = s^4 + s^3 + 5s^2 + 3s + 4 \tag{9.26}$$

is Hurwitz. The even and odd parts of $F(s)$ are

$$m(s) = s^4 + 5s^2 + 4$$
$$n(s) = s^3 + 3s \tag{9.27}$$

We will now perform a continued fraction expansion of $\psi(s) = m(s)/n(s)$ by dividing $n(s)$ by $m(s)$, and then inverting and dividing again, as given by the operation,

$$
\begin{array}{r}
s^3 + 3s \overline{)\, s^4 + 5s^2 + 4 \,}\,(s \\
s^4 + 3s^2 \\
\hline
2s^2 + 4 \,)\, s^3 + 3s \,(s/2 \\
s^3 + 2s \\
\hline
s \,)\, 2s^2 + 4 \,(2s \\
2s^2 \\
\hline
4 \,)\, s \,(s/4 \\
s \\
\hline
\end{array}
$$

---

* See Van Valkenburg, *loc. cit.*

so that the continued fraction expansion of $F(s)$ is

$$F(s) = \frac{m(s)}{n(s)} = s + \cfrac{1}{\frac{s}{2} + \cfrac{1}{2s + \cfrac{1}{s/4}}} \tag{9.28}$$

Since all of the quotient terms of the continued fraction expansion are positive, $F(s)$ is Hurwitz.

Example 9.1. Let us test whether the polynomial

$$G(s) = s^3 + 2s^2 + 3s + 6 \tag{9.29}$$

is Hurwitz. The continued fraction expansion of $n(s)/m(s)$ is obtained from the division,

$$2s^2 + 6\overline{)s^3 + 3s}\ (s/2$$
$$\underline{s^3 + 3s}$$
$$\underset{=}{0}$$

We see that the division has been terminated abruptly by a common factor, $s^3 + 3s$. The polynomial can then be written as

$$G(s) = (s^3 + 3s)\left(1 + \frac{2}{s}\right) \tag{9.30}$$

We know that the term $1 + \dfrac{2}{s}$ is Hurwitz. Since the multiplicative factor $s^3 + 3s$ is also Hurwitz, then $G(s)$ is Hurwitz. The term $s^3 + 3s$ is the multiplicative factor $s\,W(s)$ which we referred to earlier.

Example 9.2. Next, consider a case where $W(s)$ is non-Hurwitz.

$$F(s) = s^7 + 2s^6 + 2s^5 + s^4 + 4s^3 + 8s^2 + 8s + 4 \tag{9.31}$$

The continued fraction expansion of $F(s)$ is now obtained.

$$\frac{n(s)}{m(s)} = \frac{s}{2} + \cfrac{1}{\frac{4}{3}s + \cfrac{1}{\frac{3}{2}s(s^4+4)}} \tag{9.32}$$

We thus see that $W(s) = s^4 + 4$ which can be factored into

$$W(s) = (s^2 + 2s + 2)(s^2 - 2s + 2) \tag{9.33}$$

It is clear that $F(s)$ is not Hurwitz.

Example 9.3. Let us consider a more obvious non-Hurwitz polynomial

$$F(s) = s^4 + s^3 + 2s^2 + 3s + 2 \tag{9.34}$$

The continued fraction expansion is

$$s^3 + 3s)\overline{s^4 + 2s^2 + 2}\,(s$$
$$\underline{s^4 + 3s^2}$$
$$-s^2 + 2)\ s^3 + 3s\ (-s$$
$$\underline{s^3 - 2s}$$
$$5s)\ -s^2 + 2\ (-s/5$$
$$\underline{-s^2}$$
$$2)5s(\tfrac{5}{2}s$$
$$\underline{5s}$$

We see that $F(s)$ is not Hurwitz because of the negative quotients.

Example 9.4. Consider the case where $F(s)$ is an odd or even function. It is impossible to perform a continued fraction expansion on the function as it stands. However, we can test the ratio of $F(s)$ to its derivative, $F'(s)$.* If the ratio $F(s)/F'(s)$ gives a continued fraction expansion with all positive coefficients, then $F(s)$ is Hurwitz. For example, if $F(s)$ is given as

$$F(s) = s^7 + 3s^5 + 2s^3 + s \qquad (9.35)$$

then $F'(s)$ is

$$F'(s) = 7s^6 + 15s^4 + 6s^2 + 1 \qquad (9.36)$$

Without going into the details, it can be shown that the continued fraction expansion of $F(s)/F'(s)$ does not yield all positive quotients. Therefore, $F(s)$ is not Hurwitz.

9.3 POSITIVE REAL FUNCTIONS

In this section, we will study the properties of a class of functions known as *positive real functions*. These functions are important because they represent physically realizable passive driving-point immittances. A function $F(s)$ is positive real (p.r.) if the following conditions are satisfied:

1. $F(s)$ is real for real s; i.e., $F(\sigma)$ is real.
2. The real part of $F(s)$ is greater than or equal to zero when the real part of s is greater than or equal to zero, i.e.,

$$\text{Re}\,[F(s)] \geq 0 \qquad \text{for} \qquad \text{Re}\,s \geq 0$$

Let us consider a complex plane interpretation of a p.r. function. Consider the s-plane and the $F(s)$-plane in Fig. 9.5. If $F(s)$ is p.r., then a point σ_0 on the positive real axis of the s-plane would correspond to, or *map onto*, a point $F(\sigma_0)$ which must be on the positive real axis of the $F(s)$-plane. In addition, a point s_i in the right half of the s-plane would

---

* See Guillemin, *loc. cit.*

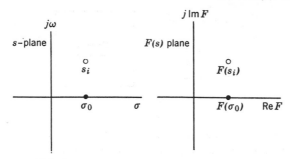

FIG. 9.5. Mapping of s-plane onto $F(s)$-plane.

map onto a point $F(s_i)$ in the right half of the $F(s)$-plane. In other words, for a positive real function, the right half of the s-plane maps onto the right half of the $F(s)$-plane. The real axis of the s-plane maps onto the real axis of the $F(s)$-plane.

A further restriction we will impose is that $F(s)$ be rational. Consider the following examples of p.r. functions,

1. $F(s) = Ls$, where L is a real, positive number, is p.r. by definition. If $F(s)$ is an impedance function, then L is an inductance.

2. $F(s) = R$, where R is real and positive, is p.r. by definition. If $F(s)$ is an impedance function, R is a resistance.

3. $F(s) = K/s$ (K real and positive) is p.r. because, when s is real, $F(s)$ is real. In addition, when the real part of s is greater than zero,

$$\text{Re}\,(s) = \sigma > 0$$

then

$$\text{Re}\left(\frac{K}{s}\right) = \frac{K\sigma}{\sigma^2 + \omega^2} > 0 \tag{9.37}$$

therefore, $F(s)$ is p.r. If $F(s)$ is an impedance function, then the corresponding element is a capacitor of $1/K$ farads.

We thus see that the basic passive impedances are p.r. functions, Similarly, it is clear that the admittances,

$$Y(s) = K$$
$$Y(s) = Ks \tag{9.38}$$
$$Y(s) = \frac{K}{s}$$

are positive real if K is real and positive. We will now show that all driving-point immittances of passive networks must be p.r. The proof depends upon the following assertion: for a sinusoidal input, the average

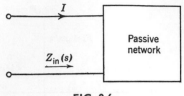

FIG. 9.6

power dissipated by a passive network is nonnegative. For the passive network in Fig. 9.6, the average power dissipated by the network is

$$\text{Average power} = \tfrac{1}{2} \, \text{Re} \, [Z_{\text{in}}(j\omega)] \, |I|^2 \geq 0 \qquad (9.39)$$

We then conclude that, for any passive network,

$$\text{Re} \, [Z_{\text{in}}(j\omega)] \geq 0 \qquad (9.40)$$

We can now prove that, for Re $s = \sigma \geq 0$, Re $Z_{\text{in}}(\sigma + j\omega) \geq 0$. Consider the network in Fig. 9.6 whose driving-point impedance is $Z_{\text{in}}(s)$. Let us load the network with incidental dissipation such that, if the driving-point impedance of the uniformly loaded network is $Z_1(s)$, then

$$Z_1(s) = Z_{\text{in}}(s + \alpha) \qquad (9.41)$$

where α, the dissipation constant, is real and positive. Since $Z_1(s)$ is the impedance of a passive network,

$$\text{Re} \, Z_1(j\omega) \geq 0 \qquad (9.42)$$

so that

$$\text{Re} \, Z_{\text{in}}(\alpha + j\omega) \geq 0 \qquad (9.43)$$

Since α is an arbitrary real positive quantity, it can be taken to be σ. Thus the theorem is proved.

Next let us consider some useful properties of p.r. functions. The proofs of these properties are given in Appendix C.

1. If $F(s)$ is p.r. then $1/F(s)$ is also p.r. This property implies that, if a driving-point impedance is p.r., then its reciprocal, the driving-point admittance, is also p.r.

2. The sum of p.r. functions is p.r. From an impedance standpoint, we see that, if two impedances are connected in series, the sum of the impedances is p.r. An analogous situation holds for two admittances in parallel. Note that the difference of two p.r. functions is not necessarily p.r.; e.g.,

$$F(s) = s - \frac{1}{s}$$

is not p.r.

3. The poles and zeros of a p.r. function cannot have positive real parts, i.e., they cannot be in the right half of the s-plane.

4. Only simple poles with real positive residues can exist on the $j\omega$ axis.

5. The poles and zeros of a p.r. function are real or occur in conjugate pairs. We know that the poles and zeros of a network function are functions of the elements in the network. Since the elements themselves are real, there cannot be complex poles or zeros without conjugates because this would imply imaginary elements.

6. The highest powers of the numerator and denominator polynomials may differ at most by unity. This condition prohibits multiple poles and zeros at $s = \infty$.

7. The lowest powers of the denominator and numerator polynomials may differ by at most unity. This condition prevents the possibility of multiple poles or zeros at $s = 0$.

8. The necessary and sufficient conditions for a rational function with real coefficients $F(s)$ to be p.r. are:

   a. $F(s)$ must have no poles in the right-half plane.
   b. $F(s)$ may have only simple poles on the $j\omega$ axis with real and positive residues.
   c. Re $F(j\omega) \geq 0$ for all ω.

Let us compare this new definition with the original one which requires the two conditions.

1. $F(s)$ is real when s is real.
2. Re $F(s) \geq 0$, when Re $s \geq 0$.

In order to test condition 2 of the original definition, we must test every single point in the right-half plane. In the alternate definition, condition (c) merely requires that we test the behavior of $F(s)$ along the $j\omega$ axis. It is apparent that testing a function for the three conditions given by the alternate definition represents a considerable saving of effort, except in simple cases, as $F(s) = 1/s$.

Let us examine the implications of each criterion of the second definition. Condition (a) requires that we test the denominator of $F(s)$ for roots in the right-half plane, i.e., we must determine whether the denominator of $F(s)$ is Hurwitz. This is readily accomplished through a continued fraction expansion of the odd to even or even to odd parts of the denominator. The second requirement [condition (b)] is tested by making a partial fraction expansion of $F(s)$, and checking whether the residues of the poles on the $j\omega$ axis are positive and real. Thus, if $F(s)$ has a pair of poles at $s = \pm j\omega_1$, a partial fraction expansion will give terms of the form shown below

$$\frac{K_1}{s - j\omega_1} + \frac{K_1{}^*}{s + j\omega_1}$$

which simplifies to

$$A(\omega) = (b - a)\omega^2 + c \geq 0 \qquad (9.58a)$$

It is evident that, in order to prevent $A(\omega)$ from having positive real roots of ω, b must be greater than or equal to a, i.e,

$$b \geq a$$

As a result, when $b = 0$, then $a = 0$. To summarize, the conditions that must be fulfilled in order for $F(s)$ to be positive real are:

1. $a, b, c \geq 0$.
2. $b \geq a$.

We see that

$$F_1(s) = \frac{s + 2}{s^2 + 3s + 2} \qquad (9.59)$$

is p.r., while the functions,

$$F_2(s) = \frac{s + 1}{s^2 + 2} \qquad (9.60)$$

$$F_3(s) = \frac{s + 4}{s^2 + 2s + 1} \qquad (9.61)$$

are not p.r. As a second example, let us determine the conditions for the *biquadratic* function

$$F(s) = \frac{s^2 + a_1 s + a_0}{s^2 + b_1 s + b_0} \qquad (9.62)$$

to be p.r. We will assume that the coefficients a_1, a_0, b_1, b_0 are all real, positive constants. Let us test whether $F(s)$ is p.r. by testing each requirement of the second definition.

First, if the coefficients of the denominator b_1 and b_0 are positive, the denominator must be Hurwitz. Secondly, if b_1 is positive, we have no poles on the $j\omega$ axis. Therefore, we can ignore the second condition.

The third condition can be checked by first finding the even part of $F(s)$, which is

$$\text{Ev}\,[F(s)] = \frac{(s^2 + a_0)(s^2 + b_0) - a_1 b_1 s^2}{(s^2 + b_0)^2 - b_1^2 s^2}$$

$$= \frac{s^4 + [(a_0 + b_0) - a_1 b_1]s^2 + a_0 b_0}{(s^2 + b_0)^2 - b_1^2 s^2} \qquad (9.63)$$

The real part of $F(j\omega)$ is then

$$\text{Re}\,[F(j\omega)] = \frac{\omega^4 - [(a_0 + b_0) - a_1 b_1]\omega^2 + a_0 b_0}{(-\omega^2 + b_0)^2 + b_1^2 \omega^2} \qquad (9.64)$$

We see that the denominator of Re $[F(j\omega)]$ is truly always positive, so it remains for us to determine whether the numerator of Re $[F(j\omega)]$ ever goes negative. Factoring the numerator, we obtain,

$$\omega_{1,2}^2 = \frac{(a_0 + b_0) - a_1b_1}{2} \pm \frac{1}{2}\sqrt{[(a_0 + b_0) - a_1b_1]^2 - 4a_0b_0} \quad (9.65)$$

In order for Re $[F(j\omega)]$ to possess no simple real zero, the quantity under the radical sign must be either zero or negative, i.e.,

$$[(a_0 + b_0) - a_1b_1]^2 - 4a_0b_0 \leq 0 \quad (9.66)$$

so that

$$-a_1b_1 \leq -a_0 + 2\sqrt{a_0b_0} - b_0 \quad (9.67)$$

or, in a simplified form,

$$a_1b_1 \geq (\sqrt{a_0} - \sqrt{b_0})^2 \quad (9.68)$$

The equation just derived can be used to test a function which is the ratio of one second-degree polynomial to another. If

$$a_1b_1 = (\sqrt{a_0} - \sqrt{b_0})^2 \quad (9.69)$$

then we will have double zeros for Re $[F(j\omega)]$.

Consider the following example:

$$F(s) = \frac{s^2 + 2s + 25}{s^2 + 5s + 16} \quad (9.70)$$

We see that

$$a_1b_1 = 2 \times 5 \geq (\sqrt{a_0} - \sqrt{b_0})^2 = (\sqrt{25} - \sqrt{16})^2 \quad (9.71)$$

so that $F(s)$ is p.r.

The examples just given are, of course, special cases. But they do illustrate the procedure by which functions are tested for the p.r. property. Let us consider a number of other helpful points by which a function might be tested quickly. First, if $F(s)$ has poles on the $j\omega$ axis, a partial fraction expansion will show if the residues of these poles are positive and real. For example,

$$F(s) = \frac{3s^2 + 5}{s(s^2 + 1)} \quad (9.72)$$

has a pair of poles at $s = \pm j1$. The partial fraction expansion of $F(s)$,

$$F(s) = \frac{-2s}{s^2 + 1} + \frac{5}{s} \quad (9.73)$$

shows that the residue of the poles at $s = \pm j$ is negative. Therefore $F(s)$ is not p.r.

Since impedances and admittances of passive time-invariant networks are p.r. functions, we can make use of our knowledge of impedances connected in series or parallel in our testing for the p.r. property. For example, if $Z_1(s)$ and $Z_2(s)$ are passive impedances, then Z_1 connected in parallel with Z_2 gives an over-all impedance

$$Z(s) = \frac{Z_1(s)\, Z_2(s)}{Z_1(s) + Z_2(s)} \tag{9.74}$$

Since the connecting of the two impedances in parallel has not affected the passivity of the network, we know that $Z(s)$ must also be p.r. We see that, if $F_1(s)$ and $F_2(s)$ are p.r. functions, then

$$F(s) = \frac{F_1(s)\, F_2(s)}{F_1(s) + F_2(s)} \tag{9.75}$$

must also be p.r. Consequently, the functions

$$F(s) = \frac{Ks}{s + \alpha} \tag{9.76}$$

and

$$F(s) = \frac{K}{s + \alpha} \tag{9.77}$$

where α and K are real and positive quantities, must be p.r. We then observe that functions of the type

$$F(s) = \frac{s + \beta}{s + \alpha} \qquad \alpha, \beta \geq 0$$

$$= \frac{s}{s + \alpha} + \frac{\beta}{s + \alpha} \tag{9.78}$$

must be p.r. also.

Finally, let us determine whether

$$F(s) = \frac{Ks}{s^2 + \alpha} \qquad \alpha, K \geq 0 \tag{9.79}$$

is p.r. If we write $F(s)$ as

$$F(s) = \frac{1}{s/K + \alpha/Ks} \tag{9.80}$$

we see that the terms s/K and α/Ks are p.r. Therefore, the sum of the two terms must be p.r. Since the reciprocal of a p.r. function is also p.r., we conclude that $F(s)$ is p.r.

9.4 ELEMENTARY SYNTHESIS PROCEDURES

The basic philosophy behind the synthesis of driving point functions is to break up a p.r. function $Z(s)$ into a sum of simpler p.r. functions, $Z_1(s), Z_2(s), \cdots, Z_n(s)$, and then to synthesize these individual $Z_i(s)$ as elements of the overall network whose driving-point impedance is $Z(s)$.

$$Z(s) = Z_1(s) + Z_2(s) + \cdots + Z_n(s) \qquad (9.81)$$

First, consider the "breaking-up" process of the function $Z(s)$ into the sum of functions $Z_i(s)$. One important restriction is that all $Z_i(s)$ must be p.r. Certainly, if all $Z_i(s)$ were given to us, we could synthesize a network whose driving-point impedance is $Z(s)$ by simply connecting all the $Z_i(s)$ in series. However, if we were to start with $Z(s)$ alone, how would we decompose $Z(s)$ to give us the individual $Z_i(s)$? Suppose $Z(s)$ is given in general as

$$Z(s) = \frac{a_n s^n + a_{n-1}s^{n-1} + \cdots + a_1 s + a_0}{b_m s^m + b_{m-1}s^{m-1} + \cdots + b_1 s + b_0} = \frac{P(s)}{Q(s)} \qquad (9.82)$$

Consider the case where $Z(s)$ has a pole at $s = 0$, (i.e., $b_0 = 0$). Let us divide $P(s)$ by $Q(s)$ to give a quotient D/s and a remainder $R(s)$, which we can denote as $Z_1(s)$ and $Z_2(s)$.

$$Z(s) = \frac{D}{s} + R(s) \qquad D \geq 0$$

$$= Z_1(s) + Z_2(s) \qquad (9.83)$$

Are Z_1 and Z_2 p.r.? From previous discussions, we know that $Z_1 = D/s$ is p.r. Is $Z_2(s)$ p.r.? Consider the p.r. criteria given previously,

1. $Z_2(s)$ must have no poles in the right-half plane.
2. Poles of $Z_2(s)$ on the imaginary axis must be simple, and their residues must be real and positive.
3. Re $[Z_2(j\omega)] \geq 0$ for all ω.

Let us examine these cases one by one. Criterion 1 is satisfied because the poles of $Z_2(s)$ are also poles of $Z(s)$. Criterion 2 is satisfied by this same argument. A simple partial fraction expansion does not affect the residues of the other poles. When $s = j\omega$, Re $[Z(j\omega) = D/j\omega] = 0$. Therefore,

$$\text{Re } Z_2(j\omega) = \text{Re } Z(j\omega) \geq 0 \qquad (9.84)$$

From the above discussion, it is seen that, if $Z(s)$ has a pole at $s = 0$, a partial fraction expansion can be made such that one of the terms is of the form K/s and the other terms combined still remain p.r.

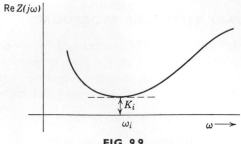

FIG. 9.9

A similar argument shows that, if $Z(s)$ has a pole at $s = \infty$ (i.e., $n - m = 1$), we can divide the numerator by the denominator to give a quotient Ls and a remainder term $R(s)$, again denoted as $Z_1(s)$ and $Z_2(s)$.

$$Z(s) = Ls + R(s) = Z_1(s) + Z_2(s). \tag{9.85}$$

Here $Z_2(s)$ is also p.r. If $Z(s)$ has a pair of conjugate imaginary poles on the imaginary axis, say poles at $s = \pm j\omega_1$, then $Z(s)$ can be expanded into partial fractions, so that

$$Z(s) = \frac{2Ks}{s^2 + \omega_1^2} + Z_2(s) \tag{9.86}$$

Here

$$\operatorname{Re}\left(\frac{2Ks}{s^2 + \omega_1^2}\right)_{s=j\omega} = \operatorname{Re}\left(\frac{j2\omega K}{-\omega^2 + \omega_1^2}\right) = 0 \tag{9.87}$$

so that $Z_2(s)$ is p.r.

Finally, if Re $[Z(j\omega)]$ is minimum at some point ω_i and if the value of Re $Z(j\omega_i) = K_i$ as shown in Fig. 9.9, we can remove a constant $K \le K_i$ from Re $[Z(j\omega)]$ so that the remainder is still p.r. This is because Re $[Z(j\omega)]$ will still be greater than or equal to zero for all values of ω.

Suppose, now, we have a p.r. function $Z(s)$, which is a driving-point impedance function. Let $Z(s)$ be decomposed as above, so that

$$Z(s) = Z_1(s) + Z_2(s) \tag{9.88}$$

where both Z_1 and Z_2 are p.r. Now let us "remove" $Z_1(s)$ from $Z(s)$ to give us a remainder $Z_2(s)$. This removal process is illustrated in Fig. 9.10 and shows that removal corresponds to synthesis of $Z_1(s)$.

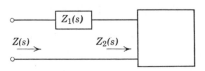

FIG. 9.10

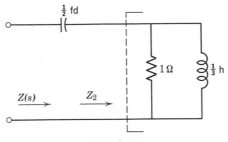

FIG. 9.11

Example 9.5. Consider the following p.r. function

$$Z(s) = \frac{s^2 + 2s + 6}{s(s + 3)} \tag{9.89}$$

We see that $Z(s)$ has a pole at $s = 0$. A partial fraction expansion of $Z(s)$ yields

$$Z(s) = \frac{2}{s} + \frac{s}{s + 3} \tag{9.90}$$

$$= Z_1(s) + Z_2(s)$$

If we remove $Z_1(s)$ from $Z(s)$, we obtain $Z_2(s)$, which can be shown by a resistor in parallel with an inductor, as illustrated in Fig. 9.11.

Example 9.6.

$$Y(s) = \frac{7s + 2}{2s + 4} \tag{9.91}$$

where $Y(s)$ is also a p.r. function.

Let us synthesize the network by first removing min [Re $Y(j\omega)$]. The real part of $Y(j\omega)$ can be easily obtained as

$$\text{Re}\,[Y(j\omega)] = \frac{8 + 14\omega^2}{16 + 4\omega^2} \tag{9.92}$$

We see that the minimum of Re $[Y(j\omega)]$ occurs at $\omega = 0$, and is equal to min $[\text{Re } Y(j\omega)] = \frac{1}{2}$. Let us then remove $Y_1 = \frac{1}{2}$ mho from $Y(s)$ and denote the remainder as $Y_2(s)$, as shown in Fig. 9.12. The remainder function $Y_2(s)$ is

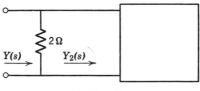

FIG. 9.12

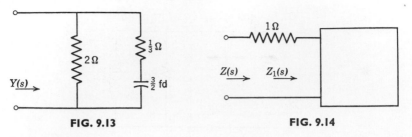

FIG. 9.13   **FIG. 9.14**

p.r. because we have removed only the minimum real part of $Y_2(j\omega)$. $Y_2(s)$ is obtained as

$$Y_2(s) = Y(s) - \frac{1}{2} = \frac{3s}{s+2} \qquad (9.93)$$

It is readily seen that $Y_2(s)$ is made up of a ⅓-Ω resistor in series with a ¾-fd capacitor. Thus the final network is that shown in Fig. 9.13.

Example 9.7. Consider the p.r. impedance,

$$Z(s) = \frac{6s^3 + 3s^2 + 3s + 1}{6s^3 + 3s} \qquad (9.94)$$

The real part of the function is a constant, equal to unity. Removing a constant of 1 Ω, we obtain (Fig. 9.14),

$$Z_1 = Z(s) - 1 = \frac{3s^2 + 1}{6s^3 + 3s} \qquad (9.95)$$

The reciprocal of $Z_1(s)$ is an admittance

$$Y_1(s) = \frac{6s^3 + 3s}{3s^2 + 1} \qquad (9.96)$$

which has a pole at $s = \infty$. This pole is removed by finding the partial fraction expansion of $Y_1(s)$,

$$Y_1(s) = 2s + \frac{s}{3s^2 + 1} \qquad (9.97)$$

and then removing the term with the pole at $s = \infty$ to give a capacitor of 2 fd in parallel with $Y_2(s)$ below (Fig. 9.15). $Y_2(s)$ is now obtained as

$$Y_2(s) = Y_1(s) - 2s = \frac{s}{3s^2 + 1} \qquad (9.98)$$

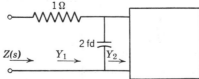

FIG. 9·15

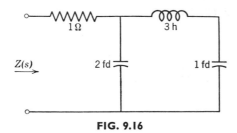

FIG. 9.16

The reciprocal of $Y_2(s)$ is

$$Z_2(s) = 3s + \frac{1}{s} \tag{9.99}$$

which is, clearly, an inductor of 3 h in series with a capacitor of 1 fd. The final network is shown in Fig. 9.16.

These examples are, of course, special cases of the driving-point synthesis problem. However, they do illustrate the basic techniques involved. In the next chapter, we will discuss the problem of synthesizing a network with two kinds of elements, either L-C, R-C, or R-L networks. The synthesis techniques involved, however, will be the same.

Problems

9.1   Test the following polynomials for the Hurwitz property.

(a) $s^3 + s^2 + 2s + 2$

(b) $s^4 + s^2 + s + 1$

(c) $s^7 + s^5 + s^3 + s$

(d) $s^3 + 4s^2 + 5s + 2$

(e) $s^5 + 2s^3 + s$

(f) $s^7 + 2s^6 + 2s^5 + s^4 + 4s^3 + 8s^2 + 8s + 4$

9.2   Determine whether the following functions are p.r. For the functions with the denominator already factored, perform a partial fraction expansion first.

(a) $$F(s) = \frac{s^2 + 1}{s^3 + 4s}$$

(b) $$F(s) = \frac{2s^2 + 2s + 4}{(s + 1)(s^2 + 2)}$$

(c) $$F(s) = \frac{(s + 2)(s + 4)}{(s + 1)(s + 3)}$$

(d) $$F(s) = \frac{s^2 + 4}{s^3 + 3s^2 + 3s + 1}$$

(e) $$F(s) = \frac{5s^2 + s}{s^2 + 1}$$

9.3 Suppose $F_1(s)$ and $F_2(s)$ are both p.r. Discuss the conditions such that

$$F(s) = F_1(s) - F_2(s)$$

is also p.r.

9.4 Show that the product of two p.r. functions need not be p.r. Also show that the ratio of one p.r. function to another may not be p.r. (Give one example of each.)

9.5 Given $Z(s) = \dfrac{s^2 + Xs}{s^2 + 5s + 4}$:

(a) What are the restrictions on X for $Z(s)$ to be a p.r. function?
(b) Find X for Re $[Z(j\omega)]$ to have a second-order zero at $\omega = 0$.
(c) Choose a numerical value for X and synthesize $Z(s)$.

9.6 Prove that, if $Z_1(s)$ and $Z_2(s)$ are both p.r.,

$$Z(s) = \frac{Z_1(s) Z_2(s)}{Z_1(s) + Z_2(s)}$$

must also be positive real.

9.7 $Z(s) = \dfrac{2s^2 + s + 2}{s^2 + s + 1}$ is p.r. Determine Min [Re $Z(j\omega)$] and synthesize $Z(s)$ by first removing Min [Re $Z(j\omega)$].

9.8 Perform a continued fraction expansion on the ratio,

$$Y(s) = \frac{s^3 + 2s^2 + 3s + 1}{s^3 + s^2 + 2s + 1}$$

What does the continued fraction expansion imply if $Y(s)$ is the driving-point admittance of a passive network? Draw the network from the continued fraction.

9.9 The following functions are impedance functions. Synthesize the impedances by successive removals of $j\omega$ axis poles or by removing min [Re $Z(j\omega)$].

(a) $\dfrac{s^3 + 4s}{s^2 + 2}$

(b) $\dfrac{s + 1}{s(s + 2)}$

(c) $\dfrac{2s + 4}{2s + 3}$

(d) $\dfrac{s^2 + 3s + 1}{s^2 + 1}$

chapter 10

Synthesis of one-port networks
with two kinds of elements

In this chapter, we will study methods for synthesizing one-port networks with two kinds of elements. Since we have three elements to choose from, the networks to be synthesized are either R-C, R-L, or L-C networks. We will proceed according to the following plan. First we will discuss the properties of a particular type of one-port network, and then we will synthesize it. Let us first examine some properties of L-C driving-point functions.

10.1 PROPERTIES OF L-C IMMITTANCE FUNCTIONS

Consider the impedance $Z(s)$ of a passive one-port network. Let us represent $Z(s)$ as

$$Z(s) = \frac{M_1(s) + N_1(s)}{M_2(s) + N_2(s)} \tag{10.1}$$

where M_1, M_2 are even parts of the numerator and denominator, and N_1, N_2 are odd parts. The average power dissipated by the one port is

$$\text{Average power} = \tfrac{1}{2} \operatorname{Re} [Z(j\omega)] |I|^2 \tag{10.2}$$

where I is the input current. For a pure reactive network, it is known that the power dissipated is zero. We therefore conclude that the real part of $Z(j\omega)$ is zero; i.e.,

$$\operatorname{Re} Z(j\omega) = \operatorname{Ev} Z(j\omega) = 0 \tag{10.3}$$

where

$$\operatorname{Ev} Z(s) = \frac{M_1(s) M_2(s) - N_1(s) N_2(s)}{M_2{}^2(s) - N_2{}^2(s)} \tag{10.4}$$

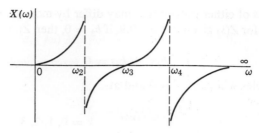

FIG. 10.1

Consider the following example. $Z(s)$ is given as

$$Z(s) = \frac{Ks(s^2 + \omega_3^2)}{(s^2 + \omega_2^2)(s^2 + \omega_4^2)}$$

(10.18)

Letting $s = j\omega$, we obtain $X(\omega)$ as

$$Z(j\omega) = jX(\omega) = +j\left[\frac{K\omega(-\omega^2 + \omega_3^2)}{(-\omega^2 + \omega_2^2)(-\omega^2 + \omega_4^2)}\right]$$

(10.19)

Let us draw a curve of $X(\omega)$ versus ω. Beginning with the zero at $\omega = 0$, let us examine the sequence of critical frequencies encountered as ω increases. Since the slope of the $X(\omega)$ curve is always positive, the next critical frequency we encounter is when $X(\omega)$ becomes infinitely large or the pole is at ω_2. As we pass ω_2, $X(\omega)$ changes sign, from $+$ to $-$. In general, whenever we pass through any critical frequency, there will always be a change of sign as seen from the way $jX(\omega)$ is written in the last equation. After we pass through ω_2, with the slope of $X(\omega)$ always positive, it is easy to see that the next critical frequency is the zero at ω_3. Thus, if an impedance function is an L-C immittance, the poles and zeros of the function must alternate. The particular $X(\omega)$ under discussion takes the form shown in Fig. 10.1. Since the highest powers of the numerator and the denominator always differ by unity and the lowest powers also differ by one, we observe that, at $s = 0$ and at $s = \infty$, there is always a critical frequency, whether a zero or a pole.

For the example just discussed, there is a zero at $s = 0$ and a zero at $s = \infty$. The critical frequencies at $s = 0$ and $s = \infty$ are called "external" critical frequencies, whereas the remaining finite critical frequencies are referred to as "internal." Thus, in the previous example, ω_2, ω_3, and ω_4 are internal critical frequencies.

Finally, let us summarize the properties of L-C impedance or admittance functions.

1. $Z_{LC}(s)$ or $Y_{LC}(s)$ is the ratio of odd to even or even to odd polynomials.

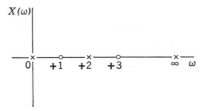

FIG. 10.2

2. The poles and zeros are simple and lie on the $j\omega$ axis.

3. The poles and zeros interlace on the $j\omega$ axis.

4. The highest powers of numerator and denominator must differ by unity; the lowest powers also differ by unity.

5. There must be either a zero or a pole at the origin and infinity.

The following functions are not L-C for the reasons listed at the left.

3.
$$Z(s) = \frac{Ks(s^2 + 4)}{(s^2 + 1)(s^2 + 3)}$$

2.
$$Z(s) = \frac{s^5 + 4s^3 + 2s}{3s^4 + 6s^2} \tag{10.20}$$

1.
$$Z(s) = \frac{K(s^2 + 1)(s^2 + 9)}{(s^2 + 2)(s^2 + 10)}$$

On the other hand, the function $Z(s)$ below, whose pole-zero diagram is shown in Fig. 10.2, is an L-C immittance.

$$Z(s) = \frac{2(s^2 + 1)(s^2 + 9)}{s(s^2 + 4)} \tag{10.21}$$

10.2 SYNTHESIS OF L-C DRIVING-POINT IMMITTANCES

We saw in the preceding section that an L-C immittance is a positive real function with poles and zeros on the $j\omega$ axis only. The partial fraction expansion of an L-C function is expressed in general terms as

$$F(s) = \frac{K_0}{s} + \frac{2K_2 s}{s^2 + \omega_2{}^2} + \cdots + K_\infty s \tag{10.22}$$

The synthesis is accomplished directly from the partial fraction expansion by associating the individual terms in the expansion with network elements.

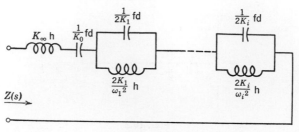

FIG. 10.3

If $F(s)$ is an impedance $Z(s)$ then the term K_0/s represents a capacitor of $1/K_0$ farads; the term $K_\infty s$ is an inductance of K_∞ henrys, and the term

$$\frac{2K_i s}{s^2 + \omega_i^2}$$

is a parallel tank circuit which consists of a capacitor of $1/2K_i$ farads in parallel with an inductance of $2K_i/\omega_i^2$. Thus a partial fraction expansion of a general L-C impedance would yield the network shown in Fig. 10.3. For example, consider the following L-C function,

$$Z(s) = \frac{2(s^2 + 1)(s^2 + 9)}{s(s^2 + 4)} \tag{10.23}$$

A partial fraction expansion of $Z(s)$ gives

$$Z(s) = 2s + \frac{\frac{9}{2}}{s} + \frac{\frac{15}{2}s}{s^2 + 4} \tag{10.24}$$

We then obtain the synthesized network in Fig. 10.4.

The partial fraction expansion method is based upon the elementary synthesis procedure of removing poles on the $j\omega$ axis. The advantage with L-C functions is that *all* the poles of the function lie on the $j\omega$ axis so that we can remove all the poles simultaneously. Suppose $F(s)$ in Eq. 10.22 is an admittance $Y(s)$. Then the partial fraction expansion of $Y(s)$ gives us a

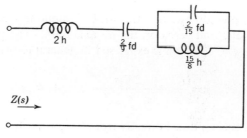

FIG. 10.4

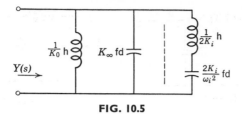

FIG. 10.5

circuit consisting of parallel branches shown in Fig. 10.5. For example,

$$Y(s) = \frac{s(s^2 + 2)(s^2 + 4)}{(s^2 + 1)(s^2 + 3)} \tag{10.25}$$

The partial fraction expansion of $Y(s)$ is

$$Y(s) = s + \frac{\frac{1}{2}s}{s^2 + 3} + \frac{\frac{3}{2}s}{s^2 + 1} \tag{10.26}$$

from which we synthesize the network shown in Fig. 10.6. The *L-C* networks synthesized by partial fraction expansions are sometimes called *Foster* type networks.[*] The impedance form is sometimes called a Foster series network and the admittance form is a Foster parallel network.

A useful property of *L-C* immittances is that the numerator and the denominator always differ in degree by unity. Therefore, there is always a zero or a pole at $s = \infty$. Suppose we consider the case of an *L-C* impedance $Z(s)$ whose numerator is of degree $2n$ and denominator is of degree $2n - 1$, giving $Z(s)$ a pole at $s = \infty$. We can remove this pole by removing an impedance $L_1 s$ so that the remainder function $Z_2(s)$ is still *L-C*:

$$Z_2(s) = Z(s) - L_1 s. \tag{10.27}$$

The degree of the denominator of $Z_2(s)$ is $2n - 1$, but the numerator is of degree $2n - 2$, because the numerator and denominator must differ in degree by 1. Therefore, we see that $Z_2(s)$ has a zero at $s = \infty$. If we invert

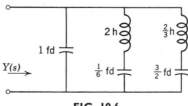

FIG. 10.6

* R. M. Foster, "A Reactance Theorem," *Bell System Tech. J.*, No. 3 (1924) 259–267.

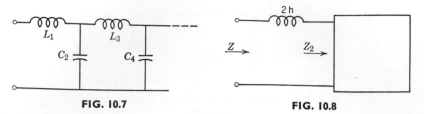

FIG. 10.7   FIG. 10.8

$Z_2(s)$ to give $Y_2(s) = 1/Z_2(s)$, $Y_2(s)$ would have a pole at $s = \infty$, which we can again remove to give a capacitor $C_2 s$ and a remainder $Y_3(s)$, which is

$$Y_3(s) = Y_2(s) - C_2 s. \tag{10.28}$$

We readily see that $Y_3(s)$ has a zero at $s = \infty$ which we can invert and remove. This process continues until the remainder is zero. Every time we remove a pole, we remove an inductor or a capacitor depending upon whether the function is an impedance or an admittance. Note that the final structure of the network synthesized is a ladder whose series arms are inductors and whose shunt arms are capacitors, as shown in Fig. 10.7. Consider the following example,

$$Z(s) = \frac{2s^5 + 12s^3 + 16s}{s^4 + 4s^2 + 3} \tag{10.29}$$

We see that $Z(s)$ has a pole at $s = \infty$, which we can remove by first dividing the denominator into the numerator to give a quotient $2s$ and a remainder $Z_2(s)$, as shown in Fig. 10.8. Then

$$Z_2(s) = Z(s) - 2s = \frac{4s^3 + 10s}{s^4 + 4s^2 + 3} \tag{10.30}$$

Observe that $Z_2(s)$ has a zero at $s = \infty$. Inverting $Z_2(s)$, we again remove the pole at infinity. Then we realize a capacitor of $\frac{1}{4}$ fd and a remainder $Y_3(s)$ (Fig. 10.9).

$$Y_3(s) = Y_2(s) - \frac{1}{4} s = \frac{\frac{3}{2}s^2 + 3}{4s^3 + 10s} \tag{10.31}$$

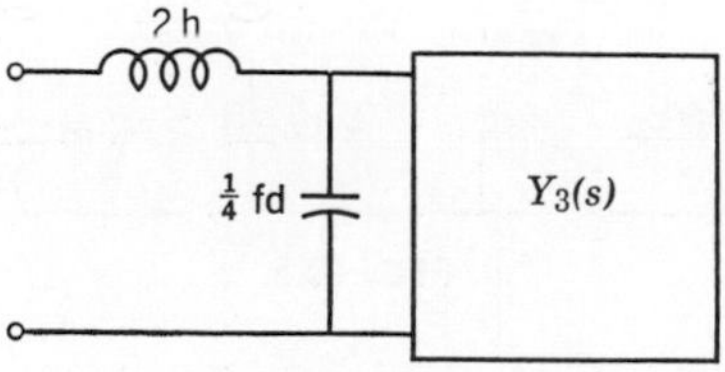

2 h

$\frac{1}{4}$ fd $Y_3(s)$

FIG. 10.9

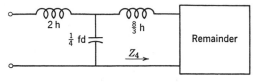

FIG. 10.10

Removing the pole at $s = \infty$ of $Z_3(s) = 1/Y_3(s)$, we obtain a series inductor of $\frac{8}{3}$ h and

$$Z_4(s) = Z_3(s) - \frac{8}{3}s = \frac{2s}{\frac{3}{2}s^2 + 3} \qquad (10.32)$$

as shown in Fig. 10.10. The admittance $Y_4(s) = 1/Z_4(s)$ has a pole at $s = \infty$, which we remove to give a capacitor of $\frac{3}{4}$ fd and a remainder $Y_5(s) = 3/2s$, which represents an inductor of $\frac{2}{3}$ h. Removing this inductor gives us zero remainder. Our synthesis is therefore complete and the final network is shown in Fig. 10.11.

Since we always remove a pole at $s = \infty$ by inverting the remainder and dividing, we conclude that we can synthesize an L-C ladder network by a continued fraction expansion. The quotients represent the poles at $s = \infty$, which we remove, and we invert the remainder successively until the remainder is zero. For the previous example, the continued fraction expansion is

$$s^4 + 4s^2 + 3\overline{)2s^5 + 12s^3 + 16s}(2s \leftrightarrow Z$$
$$\underline{2s^5 + 8s^3 + 6s}$$
$$4s^3 + 10s\overline{)s^4 + 4s^2 + 3}(\tfrac{1}{4}s \leftrightarrow Y$$
$$\underline{s^4 + \tfrac{5}{2}s^2}$$
$$\tfrac{3}{2}s^2 + 3\overline{)4s^3 + 10s}(\tfrac{8}{3}s \leftrightarrow Z$$
$$\underline{4s^3 + 8s}$$
$$2s\overline{)\tfrac{3}{2}s^2 + 3}(\tfrac{3}{4}s \leftrightarrow Y$$
$$\underline{\tfrac{3}{2}s^2}$$
$$3\overline{)2s}(\tfrac{2}{3}s \leftrightarrow Z$$
$$\underline{2s}$$

We see that the quotients of the continued fraction expansion give the elements of the ladder network. Because the continued fraction expansion

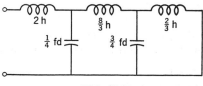

FIG. 10.11

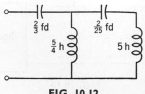

FIG. 10.12

always inverts each remainder and divides, the successive quotients alternate between Z and Y and then Z again, as shown in the expansion above. If the initial function is an impedance, the first quotient must necessarily be an impedance. When the first function is an admittance, the first quotient is an admittance.

Since the lowest degrees of numerator and denominator of an L-C admittance must differ by unity, it follows that there must be a zero or a pole at $s = 0$. If we follow the same procedure as above and remove successively poles at $s = 0$, we will have an alternate realization in a ladder structure. To do this by continued fractions, we arrange both numerator and denominator in *ascending* order and divide the lowest power of the denominator into the lowest power of the numerator; then we invert the remainder and divide again. For example, in the case of the impedance

$$Z(s) = \frac{(s^2 + 1)(s^2 + 3)}{s(s^2 + 2)} \tag{10.33}$$

the continued fraction expansion to give the alternate realization is

$$2s + s^3 \overline{)3 + 4s^2 + s^4}(3/2s \leftrightarrow Z$$
$$\underline{3 + \tfrac{3}{2}s^2}$$
$$\tfrac{5}{2}s^2 + s^4 \overline{)2s + }\ s^3(4/5s \leftrightarrow Y$$
$$\underline{2s + \tfrac{4}{5}s^3}$$
$$\tfrac{1}{5}s^3 \overline{)\tfrac{5}{2}s^2 + s^4}(25/2s \leftrightarrow Z$$
$$\underline{\tfrac{5}{2}s^2}$$
$$s^4 \overline{)\tfrac{1}{5}s^3}(1/5s \leftrightarrow Y$$
$$\underline{\underline{\tfrac{1}{5}s^3}}$$

The final synthesized network is shown in Fig. 10.12. The ladder networks realized are called *Cauer* ladder networks because W. Cauer* discovered the continued fraction method for synthesis of a passive network.

Note that for both the Foster and the Cauer form realizations, the number of elements is one greater than the number of internal critical frequencies, which we defined previously as being all the poles and zeros of the

---

* Wilhelm Cauer, "The Realization of Impedances with Prescribed Frequency Dependence," *Arch. Electrotech.*, **15** (1926), 355–388.

function excluding those at $s = 0$ and $s = \infty$. Without going into the proof of the statement, it can be said that both the Foster and the Cauer forms give the minimum number of elements for a specified L-C driving-point function. These realizations are sometimes known as *canonical* forms.

10.3 PROPERTIES OF R-C DRIVING-POINT IMPEDANCES

The properties of R-C driving-point impedances can be derived from known properties of L-C functions by a process of mapping the $j\omega$ axis on-to the $-\sigma$ axis.† We will not resort to this formalism here. Instead, we will assume that all driving-point functions which can be realized with two kinds of elements can be realized in a Foster form. Based upon this assumption we can derive all the pertinent properties of R-C or R-L driving-point functions. Let us consider first the properties of R-C driving-point impedance functions.

Referring to the series Foster form for an L-C impedance given in Fig. 10.3, we can obtain a Foster realization of an R-C impedance by simply replacing all the inductances by resistances so that a general R-C impedance could be represented as in Fig. 10.13. The R-C impedance, as seen from Fig. 10.13, is

$$Z(s) = \frac{K_0}{s} + K_\infty + \frac{K_1}{s + \sigma_1} + \frac{K_2}{s + \sigma_2} + \cdots \qquad (10.34)$$

where $C_0 = 1/K_0$, $R_\infty = K_\infty$, $C_1 = 1/K_1$, $R_1 = K_1/\sigma_1$, and so on. In order for the equation above to represent an R-C driving-point impedance, the constants K_i and σ_i must be positive and real. From this development, two major properties of R-C impedances are obtained, listed in the following:

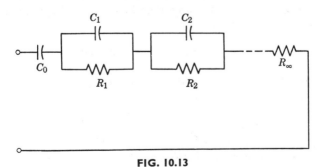

FIG. 10.13

---

† Van Valkenburg, *Modern Network Synthesis*, John Wiley & Sons, New York, 1960
140–145.

1. The poles of an R-C driving-point impedance are on the negative real $(-\sigma)$ axis. It can be shown from a parallel Foster form that the poles of an R-C admittance function are also on the axis. We can thus conclude that the zeros of an R-C impedance are also on the $-\sigma$ axis.

2. The residues of the poles, K_i, are real and positive. We shall see later that this property does not apply to R-C admittances.

Since the poles and zeros of R-C impedances are on the $-\sigma$ axis, let us examine the slope of $Z(\sigma)$ along the $-\sigma$ axis. To find the slope, $dZ(\sigma)/d\sigma$, we first let $s = \sigma$ in $Z(s)$, and then we take the derivative of $Z(\sigma)$ with respect to σ. Thus,

$$Z(\sigma) = \frac{K_0}{\sigma} + K_\infty + \frac{K_1}{\sigma + \sigma_1} + \frac{K_2}{\sigma + \sigma_2} + \cdots \qquad (10.35)$$

and

$$\frac{dZ(\sigma)}{d\sigma} = -\frac{K_0}{\sigma^2} + \frac{-K_1}{(\sigma + \sigma_1)^2} + \frac{-K_2}{(\sigma + \sigma_2)^2} + \cdots \qquad (10.36)$$

It is clear that

$$\frac{dZ(\sigma)}{d\sigma} \leq 0 \qquad (10.37)$$

Let us now look at the behavior of $Z(s)$ at the two points where the real axis and the imaginary axis intersect, namely, at $\sigma = \omega = 0$ and at $\sigma = \omega = \infty$. This is readily done by examining the general R-C network in Fig. 10.13 at these two frequencies. At $\sigma = 0$, (d-c), if the capacitor C_0 is in the circuit, it is an open circuit and there is a *pole* of $Z(s)$ at $\sigma = 0$. If C_0 is not in the circuit, then $Z(0)$ is simply the sum of all the resistances in the circuit,

$$Z(0) = R_1 + R_2 + \cdots + R_\infty, \qquad (10.38)$$

because all of the capacitors are open circuits at $\sigma = 0$.

At $\sigma = \infty$, all the capacitors are short circuits. Thus, if R_∞ is in the circuit, $Z(\infty) = R_\infty$. If R_∞ is missing, then $Z(\infty) = 0$. To summarize these last two statements, we have

$$Z(0) = \begin{cases} \infty, & C_0 \text{ present} \\ \sum_{i=1}^{m} R_i, & C_0 \text{ missing} \end{cases}$$

$$Z(\infty) = \begin{cases} 0, & R_\infty \text{ missing} \\ R_\infty, & R_\infty \text{ present} \end{cases}$$

If we examine the two cases for $Z(0)$ and $Z(\infty)$, we see that

$$Z(0) \geq Z(\infty) \qquad (10.39)$$

10.5   PROPERTIES OF R-L IMPEDANCES AND R-C ADMITTANCES

The immittance which represents a series Foster R-L impedance or a parallel Foster R-C admittance is given as

$$F(s) = K_\infty s + K_0 + \frac{K_i s}{s + \sigma_i} + \cdots \qquad (10.50)$$

The significant difference between an R-C impedance and an R-L impedance is that the partial fraction expansion term for the R-C "tank" circuit is

$$\frac{K_i}{s + \sigma_i}$$

whereas, for the R-L impedance, the corresponding term must be multiplied by an s in order to give an R-L tank circuit consisting of a resistor in parallel with an inductor.

The properties of R-L impedance or R-C admittance functions can be derived in much the same manner as the properties of R-C impedance functions. Without going into the derivation of the properties, the more significant ones are given in the following:

1. Poles and zeros of an R-L impedance or R-C admittance are located on the negative real axis, and they alternate.
2. The singularity nearest to the origin is a zero. The singularity nearest to $s = \infty$ must be a pole.
3. The residues of the poles must be real and *negative*.

Because of the third property, a partial fraction expansion of an R-L impedance function would yield terms as

$$- \frac{K_i}{s + \sigma_i} \qquad (10.51)$$

This does not present any trouble, however, because the term above does not represent an R-L impedance at all. To obtain the Foster form of an R-L impedance, we will resort to the following artifice. Let us first expand $Z(s)/s$ into partial fractions. If $Z(s)$ is an R-L impedance, we will state without proof here that the partial fraction expansion of $Z(s)/s$ yields positive residues.* Thus,

$$\frac{Z(s)}{s} = \frac{K_0}{s} + K_\infty + \frac{K_i}{s + \sigma_i} + \cdots \qquad (10.52)$$

---

* Actually, $Z_{RL}(s)/s$ has the properties of an R-C impedance; see Van Valkenburg, *loc. cit.*

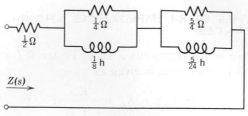

FIG. 10.20

where $K_0, K_1, \cdots, K_\infty \geq 0$. If we multiply both sides by s, we will obtain $Z(s)$ in the desired form for synthesis. Consider the following function,

$$F(s) = \frac{2(s + 1)(s + 3)}{(s + 2)(s + 6)} \tag{10.53}$$

$F(s)$ represents an R-L impedance or an R-C admittance because it satisfies the first two criteria cited. The partial fraction expansion of $F(s)$ is

$$F(s) = \frac{1}{2} - \frac{\frac{1}{2}}{s + 2} - \frac{5}{s + 6} \tag{10.54}$$

so we see that the residues are negative. The partial fraction expansion of $F(s)/s$, on the other hand, is

$$\frac{F(s)}{s} = \frac{2(s + 1)(s + 3)}{s(s + 2)(s + 6)} = \frac{\frac{1}{2}}{s} + \frac{\frac{1}{4}}{s + 2} + \frac{\frac{5}{4}}{s + 6} \tag{10.55}$$

If we multiply both sides by s, we obtain

$$F(s) = \frac{1}{2} + \frac{\frac{1}{4}s}{s + 2} + \frac{\frac{5}{4}s}{s + 6} \tag{10.56}$$

If $F(s)$ represents an impedance $Z(s)$, it is synthesized in series Foster form, giving the R-L network in Fig. 10.20. If $F(s)$ is an admittance $Y(s)$, then the resulting network is the R-C network shown in Fig. 10.21.

To synthesize an R-L impedance in ladder form, we make use of the fact that min Re $[Z(j\omega)] = Z(0)$. If we remove $Z(0)$ from $Z(s)$, the remainder

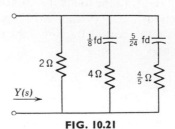

FIG. 10.21

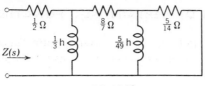

FIG. 10.22

function $Z_1(s)$ will have a zero at $s = 0$. After inverting $Z_1(s)$, we can then remove the pole at $s = 0$. Since the value $Z(0)$ is obtained by dividing the lowest power of the denominator into the lowest power term of the numerator, the synthesis could be carried out by a continued fraction expansion by arranging the numerator and denominator polynomials in ascending order and then dividing. For example, the following function is either an R-L impedance or an R-C admittance.

$$F(s) = \frac{2(s + 1)(s + 3)}{(s + 2)(s + 6)} = \frac{6 + 8s + 2s^2}{12 + 8s + s^2} \tag{10.57}$$

The continued fraction expansion of $F(s)$ is

$$12 + 8s + s^2 \overline{)6 + 8s + 2s^2}(\tfrac{1}{2}$$
$$\underline{6 + 4s + \tfrac{1}{2}s^2}$$
$$4s + \tfrac{3}{2}s^2 \overline{)12 + 8s + s^2}(3/s$$
$$\underline{12 + \tfrac{9}{2}s}$$
$$\tfrac{7}{2}s + s^2 \overline{)4s + \tfrac{3}{2}s^2}(\tfrac{8}{7}$$
$$\underline{4s + \tfrac{8}{7}s^2}$$
$$-\tfrac{5}{14}s^2 \overline{)\tfrac{7}{2}s + s^2}(49/5s$$
$$\underline{\tfrac{7}{2}s}$$
$$s^2 \overline{)\tfrac{5}{14}s^2}(\tfrac{5}{14}$$
$$\underline{\tfrac{5}{14}s^2}$$

If $F(s)$ is an impedance function, then the resulting network is the R-L network shown in Fig. 10.22. If, on the other hand, $F(s)$ is an R-C admittance, $Y(s)$, the network is synthesized as in Fig. 10.23.

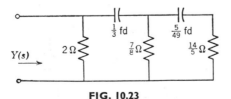

FIG. 10.23

10.6 SYNTHESIS OF CERTAIN *R-L-C* FUNCTIONS

Under certain conditions, R-L-C driving-point functions may be synthesized with the use of either partial fractions or continued fractions. For example, the function

$$Z(s) = \frac{s^2 + 2s + 2}{s^2 + s + 1} \tag{10.58}$$

is neither L-C, R-C, nor R-L. Nevertheless, the function can be synthesized by continued fractions as shown.

$$
s^2 + s + 1 \overline{\smash{\big)}\, s^2 + 2s + 2} \big(1 \leftarrow Z
$$
$$
\underline{s^2 +\ s + 1}
$$
$$
s + 1 \overline{\smash{\big)}\, s^2 + s + 1} \big(s \leftarrow Y
$$
$$
\underline{s^2 + s}
$$
$$
1 \overline{\smash{\big)}\, s + 1} \big(s + 1 \leftarrow Z
$$
$$
\underline{s + 1}
$$

The network derived from this expansion is given in Fig. 10.24.

In another case, the poles and zeros of the following admittance are all on the negative real axis, but they do not alternate.

$$Y(s) = \frac{(s + 2)(s + 3)}{(s + 1)(s + 4)} \tag{10.59}$$

The partial fraction expansion for $Y(s)$ is

$$Y(s) = 1 + \frac{\frac{2}{3}}{s + 1} + \frac{-\frac{2}{3}}{s + 4} \tag{10.60}$$

Since one of the residues is negative, we cannot use this expansion for synthesis. An alternate method would be to expand $Y(s)/s$ and then multiply the whole expansion by s.

$$\frac{Y(s)}{s} = \frac{\frac{3}{2}}{s} - \frac{\frac{2}{3}}{s + 1} + \frac{\frac{1}{6}}{s + 4} \tag{10.61}$$

When we multiply by s, we obtain,

$$Y(s) = \frac{3}{2} - \frac{\frac{2}{3}s}{s + 1} + \frac{\frac{1}{6}s}{s + 4} \tag{10.62}$$

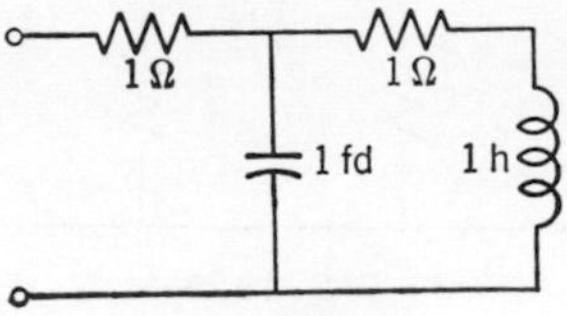

FIG. 10.24

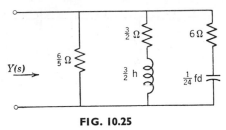

FIG. 10.25

Note that $Y(s)$ also has a negative term. If we divide the denominator of this negative term into the numerator, we can rid ourselves of any terms with negative signs.

$$Y(s) = \frac{3}{2} - \left(\frac{2}{3} - \frac{\frac{2}{3}}{s+1}\right) + \frac{\frac{1}{6}s}{s+4}$$

$$= \frac{5}{6} + \frac{\frac{2}{3}}{s+1} + \frac{\frac{1}{6}s}{s+4} \tag{10.63}$$

The network which is realized from the expanded function is given in Fig. 10.25.

If we try to expand $Y(s)$ by continued fractions, we see that negative quotients will result. However, we can expand $Z(s) = 1/Y(s)$ by continued fractions, although the expansion is not as simple or straightforward as in the case of an R-C function because we sometimes have to reverse the order of division to make the quotients all positive. The continued fraction expansion of $Z(s)$ is

$$6 + 5s + s^2 \overline{)4 + 5s + s^2}\left(\frac{2}{3}\right.$$
$$\underline{4 + \tfrac{10}{3}s + \tfrac{2}{3}s^2}$$
$$\tfrac{5}{3}s + \tfrac{1}{3}s^2\overline{)6 + 5s + s^2}(18/5s$$
$$\underline{6 + \tfrac{6}{5}s}$$
$$\tfrac{19}{5}s + s^2\overline{)\tfrac{1}{3}s^2 + \tfrac{5}{3}s}\left(\tfrac{1}{3}\right.$$
$$\underline{\tfrac{1}{3}s^2 + \tfrac{19}{15}s}$$
$$\tfrac{6}{15}s\overline{)\tfrac{19}{5}s + s^2}\left(\tfrac{19}{2}\right.$$
$$\underline{\tfrac{19}{5}s}$$
$$s^2\overline{)\tfrac{6}{15}s}(6/15s$$
$$\underline{\tfrac{6}{15}s}$$

As we see, the division process giving the quotient of 1/3 involves a reversal of the order of the polynomials involved. The resulting ladder network is given in Fig. 10.26.

In the beginning of this section, it was stated that only under special conditions can an R-L-C driving-point function be synthesized with the use of a ladder form or the Foster forms. These conditions will not be given here because they are rather involved. Instead, when a positive real

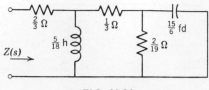

FIG. 10.26

function is given, and it is found that the function is not synthesizable by using two kinds of elements only, it is suggested that a continued fraction expansion or a partial fraction expansion be tried first.

Problems

10.1 (*a*) Which of the following functions are *L-C* driving point impedances? Why?

$$Z_1(s) = \frac{s(s^2 + 4)(s^2 + 16)}{(s^2 + 9)(s^2 + 25)}, \quad Z_2(s) = \frac{(s^2 + 1)(s^2 + 8)}{s(s^2 + 4)}$$

(*b*) Synthesize the realizable impedances in a Foster and a Cauer form.

10.2 Indicate the general *form* of the two Foster and the two Cauer networks which could be used to synthesize the following *L-C* impedance.

$$Z(s) = \frac{(s^2 + 1)(s^2 + 9)(s^2 + 25)}{s(s^2 + 4)(s^2 + 16)}$$

There is no need to calculate the element values of the four networks.

10.3 Synthesize the *L-C* driving-point impedance,

$$Z(s) = \frac{6s^4 + 42s^2 + 48}{s^5 + 18s^3 + 48s}$$

in the form shown in the figure; i.e., determine the element values of the network in henrys and farads.

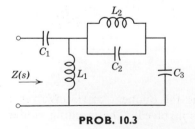

PROB. 10.3

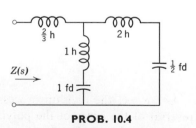

PROB. 10.4

10.4 There exists an *L-C* network with the same driving-point impedance as the network shown in the figure. This alternate network should contain only two elements. Find this network.

10.5 The input impedance for the network shown is

$$Z_{in} = \frac{2s^2 + 2}{s^3 + 2s^2 + 2s + 2}$$

If Z_0 is an *L-C* network:
(a) Find the expression for Z_0.
(b) Synthesize Z_0 in a Foster series form.

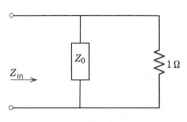

PROB. 10.5

10.6 Indicate which of the following functions are either *R-C*, *R-L*, or *L-C* *impedance* functions. Give reasons for each case.

(a)
$$Z(s) = \frac{s^3 + 2s}{s^4 + 4s^2 + 3}$$

(b)
$$Z(s) = \frac{s^2 + 6s + 8}{s^2 + 4s + 3}$$

(c)
$$Z(s) = \frac{s^2 + 4s + 3}{s^2 + 6s + 8}$$

(d)
$$Z(s) = \frac{s^2 + 5s + 6}{s^2 + s}$$

(e)
$$Z(s) = \frac{s^4 + 5s^2 + 6}{s^3 + s}$$

10.7 An impedance function has the pole-zero pattern shown in the figure.
If $Z(-2) = 3$, synthesize the impedance in a Foster form and a Cauer form.

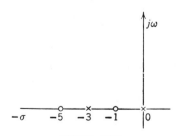

PROB. 10.7

10.8 From the following functions, pick out the ones which are R-C admittances and synthesized in one Foster and one Cauer form.

$$Y(s) = \frac{2(s + 1)(s + 3)}{(s + 2)(s + 4)} \qquad Y(s) = \frac{4(s + 1)(s + 3)}{s(s + 2)}$$

$$Y(s) = \frac{s(s + 4)(s + 8)}{(s + 1)(s + 6)} \qquad Y(s) = \frac{(s + 1)(s + 4)}{s(s + 2)}$$

10.9 Find the networks for the following functions. Both Foster and ladder forms are required.

(a)
$$Z(s) = \frac{(s + 1)(s + 4)}{s(s + 2)}$$

(b)
$$Z(s) = \frac{3(s + 1)(s + 4)}{(s + 3)}$$

10.10 For the network shown, find Y, when

$$\frac{V_2}{V_0} = \frac{1}{2 + Y}$$

$$= \frac{s(s^2 + 3)}{2s^3 + s^2 + 6s + 1}$$

Synthesize Y as an L-C admittance.

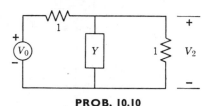

PROB. 10.10

10.11 Synthesize by continued fractions:

$$Y(s) = \frac{s^3 + 2s^2 + 3s + 1}{s^3 + s^2 + 2s + 1}$$

10.12 Find the networks for the following functions in one Foster and one Cauer form.

$$Y(s) = \frac{(s + 1)(s + 3)}{(s + 2)(s + 4)}$$

$$Z(s) = \frac{2(s + 0.5)(s + 4)}{s(s + 2)}$$

10.13 Synthesize the following functions in Cauer form.

$$Z(s) = \frac{s^3 + 2s^2 + s + 1}{s^3 + s^2 + s}$$

$$Z(s) = \frac{s^3 + s^2 + 2s + 1}{s^4 + s^3 + 3s^2 + s + 1}$$

$$Z(s) = \frac{4s^3 + 3s^2 + 4s + 2}{2s^2 + s}$$

10.14 Synthesize $Z(s) = \dfrac{(s + 2)(s + 4)}{(s + 1)(s + 5)}$ into the form shown in the figure.

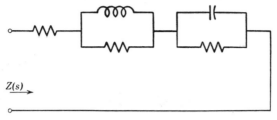

PROB. 10.14

10.15 Of the three pole-zero diagrams shown, pick out the diagram that represents an *R-L* impedance function and synthesize in a series Foster form.

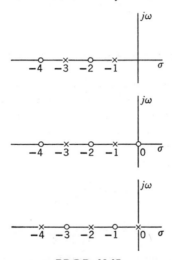

PROB. 10.15

10.16 Synthesize a driving-point impedance with the pole-zero pattern shown in the figure in any form you choose. (*Hint:* Use uniform loading concepts.)

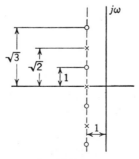

PROB. 10.16

chapter 11

Elements of transfer
function synthesis

11.1 PROPERTIES OF TRANSFER FUNCTIONS

A transfer function is a function which relates the current or voltage at one port to the current or voltage at another port. In Chapter 8, we discussed various descriptions of two-port networks in terms of the open-circuit parameters z_{ij} and the short-circuit parameters y_{ij}. Recall that for the two-port network given in Fig. 11.1, the open-circuit transfer impedances z_{12} and z_{21} were defined as

$$z_{12} = \frac{V_1}{I_2}\bigg|_{I_1=0}$$

$$z_{21} = \frac{V_2}{I_1}\bigg|_{I_2=0} \tag{11.1}$$

In terms of the open-circuit transfer impedances, the voltage-ratio transfer function is given as

$$\frac{V_2}{V_1} = \frac{z_{21}}{z_{11}} \tag{11.2}$$

In terms of the short-circuit parameters, the voltage ratio is shown to be as follows:

$$\frac{V_2}{V_1} = -\frac{y_{21}}{y_{22}} \tag{11.3}$$

When the network is terminated at port two by a resistor R as, shown in Fig. 11.2, the transfer impedance of the over-all network is

$$Z_{21} = \frac{V_2}{I_1} = \frac{z_{21}R}{z_{22} + R} \tag{11.4}$$

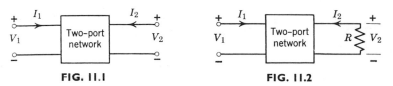

FIG. II.I   **FIG. II.2**

The transfer admittance of the over-all structure in Fig. 11.2 is

$$Y_{21} = \frac{I_2}{V_1} = \frac{y_{21}G}{y_{22} + G} \tag{11.5}$$

where $G = 1/R$. When both ports are terminated in resistors, as shown in Fig. 11.3, the voltage-ratio transfer function V_2/V_g is

$$\frac{V_2}{V_g} = \frac{z_{21}R_2}{(z_{11} + R_1)(z_{22} + R_2) - z_{21}z_{12}} \tag{11.6}$$

Other transfer functions such as current-ratio transfer functions can also be described in terms of the open- and short-circuit parameters. In Chapter 9 we discussed the various properties of driving-point impedances such as z_{11} and z_{22}. This chapter deals with the properties of the transfer immittances z_{21} and y_{21} for a passive reciprocal network. First, let us discuss certain properties which apply to all transfer functions of passive linear networks with lumped elements. We denote a transfer function as $T(s)$.

1. $T(s)$ is real for real s. This property is satisfied when $T(s)$ is a rational function with real coefficients.

2. $T(s)$ has no poles in the right-half plane and no multiple poles on the $j\omega$ axis. If $T(s)$ is given as

$$T(s) = \frac{P(s)}{Q(s)}$$

the degree of $P(s)$ cannot exceed the degree of $Q(s)$ by more than unity. In addition, $Q(s)$ must be a Hurwitz polynomial.

3. Suppose $P(s)$ and $Q(s)$ are given in terms of even and odd parts, i.e.,

$$T(s) = \frac{P(s)}{Q(s)} = \frac{M_1(s) + N_1(s)}{M_2(s) + N_2(s)} \tag{11.7}$$

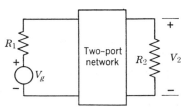

FIG. II.3

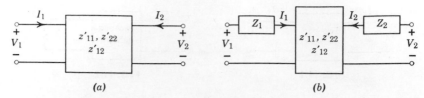

FIG. 11.4

where $M_i(s)$ is even and $N_i(s)$ is odd. Then $T(j\omega)$ is

$$T(j\omega) = \frac{M_1(j\omega) + N_1(j\omega)}{M_2(j\omega) + N_2(j\omega)} \qquad (11.8)$$

The amplitude response of $T(j\omega)$ is

$$|T(j\omega)| = \left[\frac{M_1^2(j\omega) + N_1^2(j\omega)}{M_2^2(j\omega) + N_2^2(j\omega)}\right]^{\frac{1}{2}} \qquad (11.9)$$

and is an even function in ω. The phase response is

$$\text{Arg } T(j\omega) = \arctan\left[\frac{N_1(\omega)}{M_1(\omega)}\right] - \arctan\left[\frac{N_2(\omega)}{M_2(\omega)}\right] \qquad (11.10)$$

If $\arg T(j0) = 0$, then we see that the phase response is an odd function in ω.

Now let us discuss some specific properties of the open-circuit and short-circuit parameters.

1. The poles of $z_{21}(s)$ are also the poles of $z_{11}(s)$ and $z_{22}(s)$. However, not *all* the poles of $z_{11}(s)$ and $z_{22}(s)$ are the poles of $z_{21}(s)$. Recall that, in Chapter 8, we defined the z parameters in terms of a set of node equations as

$$z_{11}(s) = \frac{\Delta_{11}}{\Delta} \qquad z_{22}(s) = \frac{\Delta_{22}}{\Delta}$$

$$z_{12} = z_{21} = \frac{\Delta_{12}}{\Delta}$$

If there is no cancellation between the numerator and denominator of z_{11}, z_{22}, and z_{12}, then the poles are the roots of the determinant Δ, and all three functions have the same poles. Consider the two-port network described by the black box in Fig. 11.4a. Let z'_{11}, z'_{22}, and z'_{12} be the z parameters of the network. Let us examine the case when we attach the impedances Z_1

and Z_2 to ports one and two, as shown in Fig. 11.4b. The z parameters for the two-port network in Fig. 11.4b are

$$z_{11} = z'_{11} + Z_1$$

$$z_{22} = z'_{22} + Z_2$$

$$z_{12} = z'_{12}$$

It is clear that the poles of z_{11} include the poles of Z_1; the poles of z_{22} include the poles of Z_2. However, the poles of z_{12} include neither the poles of Z_1 nor Z_2. Consequently, we see that all the poles of z_{12} are also poles of z_{11} and z_{22}. The reverse is not necessarily true.

2. The poles of $y_{12}(s)$ are also the poles of $y_{11}(s)$ and $y_{22}(s)$. However, not all of the poles of $y_{11}(s)$ and $y_{22}(s)$ are the poles of $y_{12}(s)$. This property is readily seen when we examine the two-port network in Fig. 11.5. The y parameters are

$$y_{11} = y'_{11} + Y_1$$

$$y_{22} = y'_{22} + Y_2$$

$$y_{12} = y'_{12}$$

Clearly, the poles of $y_{12}(s)$ do not include the poles of either Y_1 and Y_2. Consider the network in Fig. 11.6. The y parameters are

$$y_{11}(s) = \frac{2}{s} + 3s$$

$$y_{22}(s) = \frac{4}{s} + 3s$$

$$y_{12}(s) = -3s$$

Observe that $y_{11}(s)$ and $y_{22}(s)$ have poles at $s = 0$ and $s = \infty$, whereas $y_{12}(s)$ only has a pole at $s = \infty$.

3. Suppose $y_{11}(s)$, $y_{22}(s)$, and $y_{12}(s)$ all have poles at $s = s_1$. Let us denote by k_{11} the residue of the pole at s_1 of the function $y_{11}(s)$. The residue of the pole $s = s_1$ of $y_{22}(s)$ will be denoted as k_{22}, and the residue of the

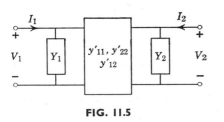

FIG. 11.5

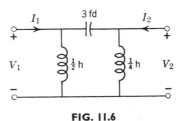

FIG. 11.6

same pole of $y_{12}(s)$ will be denoted as k_{12}. Without going into the proof,* a general property of L-C, R-C, or R-L two-port networks is that

$$k_{11}k_{22} - k_{12}{}^2 \geq 0 \qquad (11.11)$$

This equation is known as the residue condition. For example, for the L-C network in Fig. 11.6, the residue condition applied to the pole at $s = \infty$ gives

$$3 \times 3 - 3^2 = 0$$

whereas for the pole at $s = 0$, we have

$$2 \times 4 - 0^2 = 8 > 0$$

Thus we see that the residue condition is fulfilled for both poles.

11.2 ZEROS OF TRANSMISSION

A zero of transmission is a zero of a transfer function. At a zero of transmission, there is zero output for an input of the same frequency. For the network in Fig. 11.7, the capacitor is an open circuit at $s = 0$, so there is a zero of transmission at $s = 0$. For the networks in Figs. 11.8 and 11.9, the zero of transmission occurs at

$$s = \pm \frac{j}{\sqrt{LC}}$$

For the network in Fig. 11.10, the zero of transmission occurs at $s = -1/RC$.

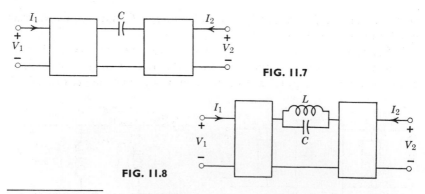

FIG. 11.7

FIG. 11.8

---

* For a general discussion, see M. E. Van Valkenburg, *Introduction to Modern Network Synthesis*, John Wiley & Sons, New York, 1960, pp. 305–313.

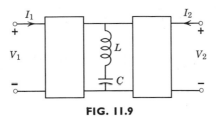

FIG. 11.9

In general, all the transfer functions of a given network have the same zeros of transmission, except in certain special cases. For example if $z_{12}(s)$ has a zero of transmission at $s = s_1$, then $y_{12}(s)$, $V_2(s)/V_1(s)$, etc., will also have a zero at $s = s_1$. This fact is clearly seen when we examine the relationships between the transfer functions. For example,

$$z_{21} = -\frac{y_{21}}{y_{11}y_{22} - y_{12}y_{21}} \tag{11.12}$$

and

$$y_{21} = -\frac{z_{21}}{z_{11}z_{22} - z_{12}z_{21}} \tag{11.13}$$

In addition, the voltage- and current-ratio transfer functions can be expressed in terms of the z and y parameters as:

$$\frac{V_2}{V_1} = \frac{z_{21}}{z_{11}}, \qquad \frac{I_2}{I_1} = \frac{y_{21}}{y_{11}} \tag{11.14}$$

In Chapter 7 we saw that transfer functions which have zeros of transmission only on the $j\omega$ axis or in the left-half plane are called *minimum phase* functions. If the function has one or more zeros in the right-half plane, then the function is *nonminimum phase*. It will be shown now that any transfer function of a passive reciprocal ladder network must be minimum phase. Consider the ladder network in Fig. 11.11. The zeros of transmission of the ladder occur at the poles of the series branch impedances or at the zeros of the shunt branch impedances. Since these branch impedances are themselves positive real, the poles and zeros of these impedances cannot be in the right-half plane. Consequently, the transfer

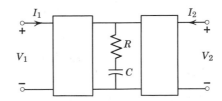

FIG. 11.10

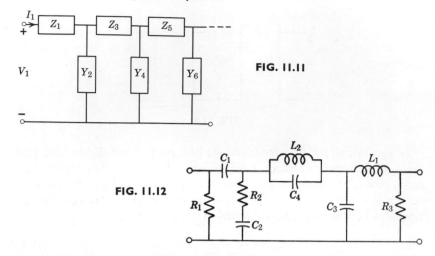

FIG. 11.11

FIG. 11.12

functions of ladder networks must be minimum phase. For the network in Fig. 11.12, a transfer function would have two zeros of transmission at $s = \infty$ due to the elements L_1 and C_3. It would also have a zero of transmission at $s = 0$ due to C_1, a zero at $s = -1/R_2C_2$ due to the parallel R-C branch, and a zero of transmission at $s = j/(L_2C_4)^{1/2}$ due to the L-C tank circuit. It is seen that none of the transmission zeros are in the right-half plane. We also see that a transfer function may possess multiple zeros on the $j\omega$ axis.

It will be shown in Section 11.4 that lattice and bridge circuits can easily be nonminimum phase. It can also be demonstrated that, when two ladder networks are connected in parallel, the resulting structure may have right-half-plane zeros.*

11.3 SYNTHESIS OF Y_{21} AND Z_{21} WITH A 1-Ω TERMINATION

In this section we will consider the synthesis of an L-C ladder network with a 1-Ω resistive termination to meet a specified transfer impedance Z_{21} or transfer admittance Y_{21}. In terms of the open- and short-circuit parameters of the L-C circuit, $Z_{21}(s)$ can be expressed as

$$Z_{21} = \frac{z_{21}}{z_{22} + 1} \qquad (11.15)$$

and $Y_{21}(s)$ is

$$Y_{21} = \frac{y_{21}}{y_{22} + 1} \qquad (11.16)$$

as depicted in Figs. 11.13 and 11.14.

---

* See Van Valkenburg, *loc. cit.*, Chapter 11.

Before we proceed with the actual details of the synthesis, it is necessary to discuss two important points. The first deals with the ratio of the odd to even or even to odd parts of a Hurwitz polynomial $Q(s)$. Suppose $Q(s)$ is given as

$$Q(s) = M(s) + N(s) \tag{11.17}$$

where $M(s)$ is the even part of $Q(s)$, and $N(s)$ is the odd part. We know that the continued fraction expansion of $M(s)/N(s)$ or $N(s)/M(s)$ should yield all positive quotients. These quotients can, in turn, be associated with reactances. Therefore, it is clear that the ratio of the even to odd or the odd to even parts of a Hurwitz polynomial is an L-C driving-point function.

The second point to be discussed is the fact that the open-circuit transfer impedance z_{21} or the short-circuit transfer admittance y_{21} of an L-C circuit is an odd function. To show this, we must remember that, in an L-C circuit, with steady-state input, the currents are 90° out of phase with the voltages. Thus the phase shifts between the input currents and output voltages or input voltages and output currents must be 90° out of phase, or

$$\text{Arctan} \frac{V_2(j\omega)}{I_1(j\omega)} = \pm \frac{\pi}{2} \text{ rad} \tag{11.18}$$

and

$$\text{Arctan} \frac{I_2(j\omega)}{V_1(j\omega)} = \pm \frac{\pi}{2} \text{ rad} \tag{11.19}$$

so that Re $z_{21}(j\omega) = 0 = $ Re $y_{21}(j\omega)$ for an L-C network. In order for the real parts to be equal to zero, the functions z_{21} and y_{21} of an L-C two-port network must be odd.

Suppose, now, that the transfer admittance Y_{21} is given as the quotient of two polynomials,

$$Y_{21} = \frac{P(s)}{Q(s)} = \frac{P(s)}{M(s) + N(s)} \tag{11.20}$$

where $P(s)$ is either even or odd. Now, how do we determine the short-circuit parameters y_{21} and y_{22} from the above equation to get it into the form

$$Y_{21} = \frac{y_{21}}{1 + y_{22}} \tag{11.21}$$

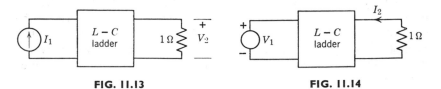

FIG. 11.13   FIG. 11.14

The answer is quite simple. We divide both the numerator $P(s)$ and the denominator $Q(s)$ by $M(s)$ or $N(s)$, the even or the odd part of $Q(s)$. Since y_{21} must be odd, if $P(s)$ is even, we divide by $N(s)$, so that

$$Y_{21} = \frac{P(s)/N(s)}{1 + [M(s)/N(s)]} \tag{11.22}$$

From this we obtain

$$y_{21} = \frac{P(s)}{N(s)}$$
$$\tag{11.23}$$
$$y_{22} = \frac{M(s)}{N(s)}$$

On the other hand, if $P(s)$ is odd, we divide by $M(s)$, so that

$$Y_{21} = \frac{P(s)/M(s)}{1 + [N(s)/M(s)]} \tag{11.24}$$

and

$$y_{21} = \frac{P(s)}{M(s)}$$
$$\tag{11.25}$$
$$y_{22} = \frac{N(s)}{M(s)}$$

We assume that $P(s)$, $M(s)$, and $N(s)$ do not possess common roots. For our purposes here, we will only consider the synthesis of Y_{21} or Z_{21} with zeros of transmission either at $s = 0$ or $s = \infty$. In a ladder network, a zero of transmission at $s = 0$ corresponds to a single capacitor in a series branch or a single inductor in a shunt branch. On the other hand, a zero of transmission at $s = \infty$ corresponds to an inductor in a series branch or a capacitor in a shunt branch. In terms of the transfer impedance

$$Z_{21}(s) = \frac{P(s)}{Q(s)} = \frac{K(s^n + a_{n-1}s^{n-1} + \cdots + a_1s + a_0)}{s^m + b_{m-1}s^{m-1} + \cdots + b_1s + b_0} \tag{11.26}$$

the presence of n zeros of $Z_{21}(s)$ at $s = 0$ implies that the coefficients a_{n-1}, $a_{n-2}, \cdots, a_1, a_0$ are all zero. The number of zeros of $Z_{21}(s)$ at $s = \infty$ is given by the difference between the highest powers of the denominator and the numerator, $m - n$. We know that n can exceed m by at most unity, while m can be greater than n by more than one. For example, if $m - n = 2$, and $n = 3$ with $a_{n-1}, \cdots a_1, a_0 = 0$, we know that the transfer function has three zeros of transmission at $s = 0$ and two zeros of transmission at $s = \infty$.

We can now proceed with the matter of synthesis. Consider the following example.

$$Z_{21}(s) = \frac{2}{s^3 + 3s^2 + 4s + 2} \qquad (11.27)$$

We see that all three zeros of transmission at $s = \infty$. Since the numerator $P(s)$ is a constant, it must be even, so we divide by the odd part of the denominator, $s^3 + 4s$. We then obtain

$$z_{21} = \frac{2}{s^3 + 4s}$$

$$z_{22} = \frac{3s^2 + 2}{s^3 + 4s} \qquad (11.28)$$

We see that both z_{21} and z_{22} have the same poles. Our task is thus simplified to the point where we must synthesize z_{22} so that the resulting network has the transmission zeros of z_{21}. This requires that we first examine the possible structures of the networks which have the required zeros of transmission and see if we can synthesize z_{22} in one of those forms. For the example that we are considering, a network which gives us three zeros of transmission at $s = \infty$ is shown in Fig. 11.15. We can synthesize z_{22} to give us this structure by the following continued fraction expansion of $1/z_{22}$.

$$3s^2 + 2 \overline{)s^3 + 4s} \left(\tfrac{1}{3}s \leftarrow Y\right)$$
$$\underline{s^3 + \tfrac{2}{3}s}$$
$$\tfrac{10}{3}s \overline{)3s^2 + 2} \left(\tfrac{9}{10}s \leftarrow Z\right)$$
$$\underline{3s^2}$$
$$2 \overline{)\tfrac{10}{3}s} \left(\tfrac{5}{3}s \leftarrow Y\right)$$
$$\underline{\tfrac{10}{3}s}$$

Since z_{22} is synthesized from the 1-Ω termination towards the input end, the final network takes the form shown in Fig. 11.16. Examining the network more closely, we see that it takes the form of a *low-pass* filter. Thus the specification of all zeros at $s = \infty$ is equivalent to the specification of a low-pass filter.

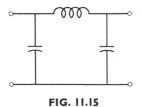

FIG. 11.15

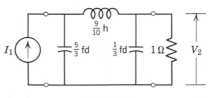

FIG. 11.16

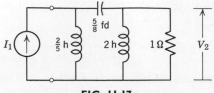

FIG. 11.17

As a second example, consider the transfer impedance,

$$Z_{21}(s) = \frac{s^3}{s^3 + 3s^2 + 4s + 2} \qquad (11.29)$$

Since the numerator of $Z_{21}(s)$ is an odd function, we have to divide both numerator and denominator by the even part of the denominator, so that

$$z_{21} = \frac{s^3}{3s^2 + 2} \qquad z_{22} = \frac{s^3 + 4s}{3s^2 + 2} \qquad (11.30)$$

The network which gives three zeros of transmission at $s = \infty$ is a high-pass structure which is realized by a continued fraction expansion of z_{22}. The final realization is shown in Fig. 11.17.

Finally, consider the transfer admittance

$$Y_{21}(s) = \frac{s^2}{s^3 + 3s^2 + 4s + 2} \qquad (11.31)$$

which has two zeros of transmission at $s = 0$, and one zero at $s = \infty$. Since the numerator is even, we divide by $s^3 + 4s$, so that

$$y_{22} = \frac{3s^2 + 2}{s^3 + 4s} \qquad (11.32)$$

The question remains as to how we synthesize y_{22} to give a zero of transmission at $s = \infty$ and two zeros at $s = 0$. First, remember that a parallel inductor gives us a zero of transmission at $s = 0$. We can remove this

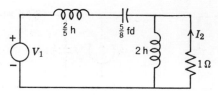

FIG. 11.18

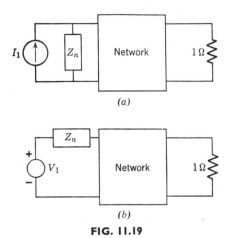

FIG. 11.19

parallel inductor by removing the pole at $s = 0$ of y_{22} to give

$$y_1 = y_{22} - \frac{1}{2s} = \frac{5s/2}{s^2 + 4} \qquad (11.33)$$

If we invert y_1, we see that we have a series L-C combination which gives us another transmission zero at $s = 0$, as represented by the $\frac{5}{8}$-fd capacitor, and we have the zero of transmission at $s = \infty$ also when we remove the inductor of $\frac{2}{5}$ h. The final realization is shown in Fig. 11.18.

An important point to note in this synthesis procedure is that we must place the last element in series with a voltage source or in parallel with a current source in order for the element to have any effect upon the transfer function. If the last element is denoted as Z_n, then the proper connection of Z_n should be as shown in Fig. 11.19.

11.4 SYNTHESIS OF CONSTANT-RESISTANCE NETWORKS

In this section we will consider the synthesis of *constant-resistance* two-port networks. They derive their name from the fact that the impedance looking in at either port is a constant resistance R when the other port is terminated in the same resistance R, as depicted in Fig. 11.20. Constant resistance networks are particularly useful in transfer function synthesis

FIG. 11.20. Constant-resistance network.

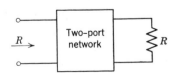

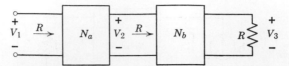

FIG. 11.21. Constant-resistance networks in tandem.

because, when two constant-resistance networks with the same R are connected in tandem, as shown in Fig. 11.21, neither network *loads down* the other. As a result, if the voltage-ratio transfer function of N_a is V_2/V_1 and that of N_b is V_3/V_2, the voltage-ratio transfer function of the total network is

$$\frac{V_3}{V_1} = \frac{V_2}{V_1}\frac{V_3}{V_2} \tag{11.34}$$

Equation 11.34 implies that, if a voltage-ratio transfer function is to be realized in terms of constant-resistance networks, the voltage ratio could be decomposed into a product of simpler voltage ratios, which could be realized as constant-resistance networks, and then connected in tandem. For example, suppose our objective is to realize

$$\frac{V_b}{V_a} = \frac{K(s - z_0)(s - z_1)(s - z_2)}{(s - p_0)(s - p_1)(s - p_2)} \tag{11.35}$$

in terms of constant-resistance networks. We can first synthesize the individual voltage ratios,

$$\frac{V_1}{V_a} = \frac{K_0(s - z_0)}{(s - p_0)}$$

$$\frac{V_2}{V_1} = \frac{K_1(s - z_1)}{(s - p_1)} \tag{11.36}$$

$$\frac{V_b}{V_2} = \frac{K_2(s - z_2)}{(s - p_2)}$$

as constant resistance networks and then connect the three networks in tandem to realize V_b/V_a.

Although there exist many different types of constant-resistance networks, we will restrict ourselves to networks of the bridge- and lattice-type structures as shown in Figs. 11.22a and 11.22b. These networks are *balanced* structures; i.e., the input and output ports do not possess common terminals. Upon a close examination, we see that the bridge and lattice circuits in Figs. 11.22 are identical circuits. The bridge circuit is

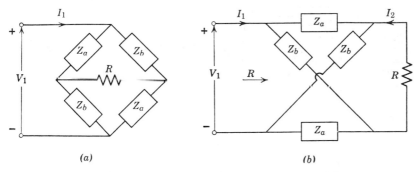

FIG. 11.22. (*a*) Bridge circuit. (*b*) Constant-resistance lattice.

merely the *unfolded* version of the lattice. Consider the open-circuit parameters of the bridge circuit in Fig. 11.23. First we determine the impedance z_{11} as

$$z_{11} = \frac{Z_a + Z_b}{2} \tag{11.37}$$

Next the transfer impedance z_{21}, which can be expressed as

$$z_{21} = \frac{V_2 - V_{2'}}{I_1} \tag{11.38}$$

is obtained as follows. We first obtain the current I' as

$$I' = \frac{V_1}{Z_a + Z_b} = \frac{I_1}{2} \tag{11.39}$$

Next we find that

$$V_2 - V_{2'} = (Z_b - Z_a)I'$$
$$= (Z_b - Z_a)\frac{I_1}{2} \tag{11.40}$$

FIG. 11.23. Analysis of bridge circuit.

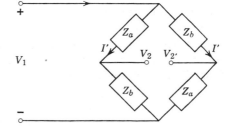

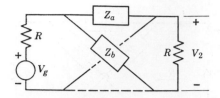

FIG. 11.24. Double-terminated lattice.

so that

$$z_{21} = \frac{Z_b - Z_a}{2} \tag{11.41}$$

From the lattice equivalent of the bridge circuit we note that $z_{22} = z_{11}$. Now let us consider the lattice circuit which is terminated in a resistance R, as shown in Fig. 11.22b. What are the conditions on the open-circuit parameters such that the lattice is a constant-resistance network? In other words, what are the conditions upon z_{11} and z_{21} such that the input impedance of the lattice terminated in the resistor R is also equal to R? In Chapter 8 we found that the input impedance could be expressed as

$$Z_{11} = z_{11} - \frac{z_{21}^2}{z_{22} + R} \tag{11.42}$$

Since $z_{22} = z_{11}$ for a symmetrical network, we have

$$Z_{11} = \frac{z_{11}R + z_{11}^2 - z_{21}^2}{z_{11} + R} \tag{11.43}$$

In order for $Z_{11} = R$, the following condition must hold:

$$z_{11}^2 - z_{21}^2 = R^2 \tag{11.44}$$

For the lattice network, we then have

$$\tfrac{1}{4}[(Z_a + Z_b)^2 - (Z_a - Z_b)^2] = R^2 \tag{11.45}$$

which simplifies to give

$$Z_a Z_b = R^2 \tag{11.46}$$

Therefore, in order for a lattice to be a constant-resistance network, Eq. 11.46 must hold.

Next, let us examine the voltage ratio V_2/V_g of a constant-resistance lattice whose source and load impedances are equal to R (Fig. 11.24). From Chapter 8 we can write

$$\frac{V_2}{V_g} = \frac{z_{21}R}{(z_{11} + R)(z_{22} + R) - z_{21}z_{12}} \tag{11.47}$$

which simplifies to

$$\frac{V_2}{V_g} = \frac{z_{21}R}{(z_{11} + R)^2 - z_{21}{}^2}$$

$$= \frac{z_{21}R}{2Rz_{11} + 2R^2} \tag{11.48}$$

In terms of the element values of the lattice, we have

$$\frac{V_2}{V_g} = \frac{\frac{1}{2}(Z_b - Z_a)R}{R(Z_b + Z_a) + 2R^2} \tag{11.49}$$

From the constant-resistance condition in Eq. 11.46, we obtain

$$\frac{V_2}{V_g} = \frac{\frac{1}{2}[Z_b - (R^2/Z_b)]R}{R[Z_b + (R^2/Z_b)] + 2R^2}$$

$$= \frac{\frac{1}{2}(Z_b{}^2 - R^2)}{(Z_b{}^2 + R^2) + 2RZ_b}$$

$$= \frac{\frac{1}{2}(Z_b{}^2 - R^2)}{(Z_b + R)^2}$$

$$= \frac{\frac{1}{2}(Z_b - R)}{(Z_b + R)} \tag{11.50}$$

In Eq. 11.50, the constant multiplier ½ comes about from the fact that the source resistance R acts as a voltage divider. If we let

$$G(s) \triangleq \frac{2V_2}{V_g} \tag{11.51}$$

we can express Z_b in Eq. 11.50 in terms of G as

$$Z_b = \frac{R[1 + G(s)]}{1 - G(s)} \tag{11.52}$$

In terms of Z_a, the voltage ratio can be given as

$$\frac{V_2}{V_g} = \frac{1}{2}\frac{(R - Z_a)}{(R + Z_a)} \tag{11.53}$$

In the following examples, we will usually let R be normalized to unity.

Example 11.1. The voltage ratio is given as

$$\frac{V_2}{V_g} = \frac{1}{2}\left(\frac{s - 1}{s + 1}\right) \tag{11.54}$$

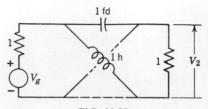

FIG. 11.25

which, as we recall, is an all-pass transfer function. By associating Eq. 11.54 with Eq. 11.50, we have

$$Z_b = s, \qquad R = 1 \qquad (11.55)$$

Since $Z_b Z_a = 1$, we then obtain

$$Z_a = \frac{1}{s} \qquad (11.56)$$

We see that Z_b is a 1-h inductor and Z_a is a 1-fd capacitor. The final network is shown in Fig. 11.25.

Example 11.2.   Let us synthesize the all-pass function,

$$\frac{V_2}{V_g} = \frac{1}{2} \frac{(s-1)}{(s+1)} \cdot \frac{(s^2 - 2s + 2)}{(s^2 + 2s + 2)} \qquad (11.57)$$

whose pole-zero diagram is shown in Fig. 11.26. Since the portion

$$\frac{V_a}{V_g} = \frac{1}{2} \frac{(s-1)}{(s+1)}$$

has already been synthesized, let us concentrate on synthesizing the function

$$\frac{V_2}{V_a} = \frac{s^2 - 2s + 2}{s^2 + 2s + 2} \qquad (11.58)$$

First, we will separate the numerator and denominator function into odd and even parts. Thus we have

$$\frac{V_2}{V_a} = \frac{(s^2 + 2) - 2s}{(s^2 + 2) + 2s} \qquad (11.59)$$

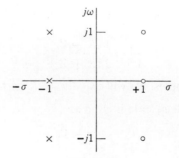

FIG. 11.26

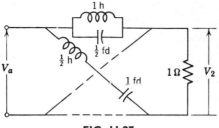

FIG. 11.27

If we divide both numerator and denominator by the odd part $2s$, we obtain

$$\frac{V_2}{V_a} = \frac{[(s^2 + 2)/2s] - 1}{[(s^2 + 2)/2s] + 1} \tag{11.60}$$

We then see that

$$Z_b = \frac{s^2 + 2}{2s}$$

$$= \frac{s}{2} + \frac{1}{s} \tag{11.61}$$

which consists of a $\frac{1}{2}$-h inductor in series with a 1-fd capacitor. The impedance Z_a is then

$$Z_a = \frac{2s}{s^2 + 2} \tag{11.62}$$

and is recognized as a $\frac{1}{2}$-fd capacitor in parallel with a 1-h inductor. The voltage ratio V_2/V_a is thus realized as shown in Fig. 11.27. The structure which realizes the transfer function V_2/V_g in Eq. 11.57 is formed by connecting the networks in Figs. 11.25 and 11.27 in tandem, as shown in Fig. 11.28. Finally, it should be pointed out that constant-resistance lattices can be used to realize other than all-pass networks.

Next, let us consider the constant-resistance bridged-T network in Fig. 11.29. If the resistances in the network are all equal to R ohms, the network is constant-resistant if

$$Z_a Z_b = R^2 \tag{11.63}$$

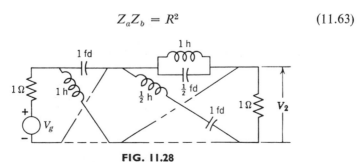

FIG. 11.28

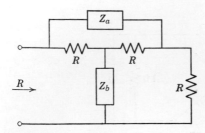

FIG. 11.29. Constant-resistance bridged-T circuit.

Under the constant-resistance assumption, the voltage-ratio transfer function can be given as

$$\frac{V_2}{V_1} = \frac{R}{R + Z_a} = \frac{Z_b}{Z_b + R} \tag{11.64}$$

Example 11.3.   Let us synthesize the voltage ratio

$$\frac{V_2}{V_1} = \frac{s^2 + 1}{s^2 + 2s + 1} \tag{11.65}$$

as a constant-resistance bridged-T network terminated in a 1-Ω resistor. First let us write V_2/V_1 as

$$\frac{V_2}{V_1} = \frac{1}{1 + [2s/(s^2 + 1)]} \tag{11.66}$$

so that

$$Z_a = \frac{2s}{s^2 + 1} \tag{11.67}$$

and

$$Z_b = \frac{s^2 + 1}{2s} \tag{11.68}$$

We recognize Z_a as a parallel L-C tank circuit and Z_b as a series L-C tank circuit. The final network is shown in Fig. 11.30.

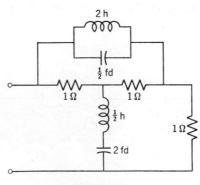

FIG. 11.30

Example 11.4.   Let us synthesize the voltage ratio

$$\frac{V_2}{V_1} = \frac{(s+2)(s+4)}{(s+3)(3s+4)} \tag{11.69}$$

in terms of two constant-resistance bridged-T circuits connected in tandem. At first, we will break up the voltage ratio in Eq. 11.69 into two separate voltage ratios,

$$\frac{V_a}{V_1} = \frac{s+2}{s+3} \tag{11.70}$$

and

$$\frac{V_2}{V_a} = \frac{s+4}{3s+4} \tag{11.71}$$

For the voltage ratio V_a/V_1, we have

$$\frac{s+2}{s+3} = \frac{Z_{b1}}{Z_{b1}+1} \tag{11.72}$$

so that $Z_{b1} = s + 2$ and

$$Z_{a1} = \frac{1}{s+2} \tag{11.73}$$

For the voltage ratio V_2/V_a we have

$$\frac{s+4}{3s+4} = \frac{1}{1+Z_{a2}} \tag{11.74}$$

from which we find

$$Z_{a2} = \frac{2s}{s+4} \tag{11.75}$$

and

$$Z_{b2} = \frac{s+4}{2s} \tag{11.76}$$

The final synthesized network is shown in Fig. 11.31.

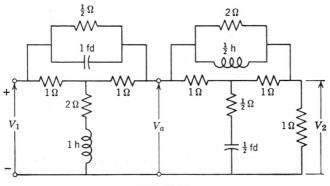

FIG. 11.31

Problems

11.1 Give an example of a network where: (*a*) a transfer function has multiple zeros on the $j\omega$ axis; (*b*) the residue of a pole of a transfer function on the $j\omega$ axis is negative.

11.2 Show that the residue condition holds for the networks shown in the figure.

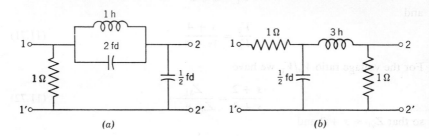

(*a*)   (*b*)

PROB. 11.2

11.3 For the network shown, find by inspection the zeros of transmission and plot on a complex plane.

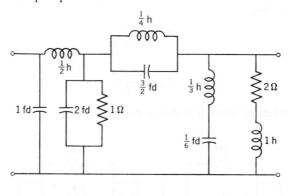

PROB. 11.3

11.4 The networks in the figure show that the driving point impedances Z_{in} are equal to R when $Z_a Z_b = R^2$.

11.5 For the networks in Prob. 11.4, find the voltage-ratio transfer functions V_2/V_1.

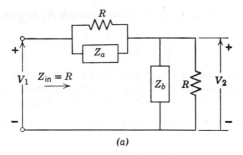

(a)

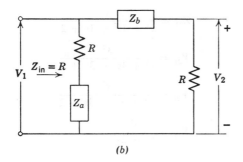

(b)

PROB. 11.4

11.6 Synthesize the following voltage ratios in one of the forms of the networks in Prob. 11.4.

(a)
$$\frac{V_2}{V_1} = \frac{s+2}{s+3}$$

(b)
$$\frac{V_2}{V_1} = \frac{2(s^2+3)}{2s^2+2s+6}$$

(c)
$$\frac{V_2}{V_1} = \frac{3(s+0.5)}{4s+1.5}$$

11.7 Synthesize N_a with termination resistors $R_2 = 4\,\Omega$, $R_1 = 1\,\Omega$ to give

$$\frac{V_2}{V_g} = \frac{12s^2}{15s^2+7s+2}$$

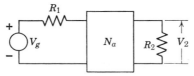

PROB. 11.7

11.8 For the network in Prob. 7, realize network N_a to give

$$\frac{V_2}{V_g} = \frac{1}{2}\left(\frac{1}{2p+3}\right)$$

(a) Synthesize N_a as a constant-resistance lattice. $(R = 1\,\Omega.)$
(b) Synthesize N_a as a constant-resistance ladder as in Prob. 11.4. $(R = 1\,\Omega.)$
(c) Synthesize N_a as a constant-resistance bridged-T circuit. $(R = 1\,\Omega.)$

11.9 Synthesize the following functions into the form shown in the figure

(a)
$$Z_{21} = \frac{1}{s^3 + 3s^2 + 3s + 2}$$

(b)
$$Z_{21} = \frac{s}{s^3 + 3s^2 + 3s + 2}$$

(c)
$$Y_{21} = \frac{s^2}{s^3 + 3s^2 + 3s + 2}$$

(d)
$$Y_{21} = \frac{s^3}{s^3 + 3s^2 + 3s + 2}$$

(e)
$$Y_{21} = \frac{s^2}{(s+2)^4}$$

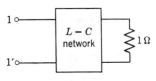

PROB. II.9

11.10 Synthesize as a constant-resistance lattice terminated in a 1-Ω resistor.

(a)
$$\frac{V_2}{V_1} = \frac{s^2 - s + 1}{s^2 + s + 1}$$

(b)
$$\frac{I_2}{V_1} = \frac{s^2 - 3s + 2}{s^2 + 3s + 2}$$

(c)
$$\frac{V_2(s)}{V_1(s)} = \frac{s^3 - 20s^2 + 5s - 20}{s^3 + 20s^2 + 5s + 20}$$

11.11 Synthesize the functions in Prob. 11.6 as constant-resistance bridged-T circuits.

chapter 12
Some problems in filter design

12.1 THE FILTER DESIGN PROBLEM

In the previous chapters we examined different methods for synthesizing a driving point or transfer function $H(s)$. Most problems have as their initial specification an amplitude or phase characteristic, or an impulse response characteristic, instead of the system function $H(s)$. Our problem is to obtain a realizable system function from the given amplitude or phase characteristic. For example, a typical design problem might be to synthesize a network to meet a given low-pass filter characteristic. The specifications might consist of the cutoff frequency ω_C, the maximum allowed deviation from a prescribed amplitude within the pass band, and the rate of "fall-off" in the stop band. We must then construct the system function from the amplitude specification. After we obtain $H(s)$, we proceed with the actual synthesis as described in the previous chapter. Another problem might consist of designing a low-pass filter with a linear phase characteristic within the pass band. Here, both amplitude and phase are specified. We must construct $H(s)$ to meet both specifications. Problems of this nature fall within the domain of *approximation* theory. In this chapter we will consider selected topics in approximation theory and then present examples of filter design where both the approximation and the synthesis problems must be solved.

In Chapter 9 we saw that the ideal low-pass filter in Fig. 12.1 is not realizable because its associated impulse response is not zero for $t < 0$. However, if we use a rational function approximation to this low-pass filter characteristic, the Paley-Wiener criterion will be automatically satisfied. We will therefore restrict ourselves to rational function approximations.

327

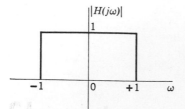

FIG. 12.1. Ideal low-pass filter characteristic.

In low-pass filter design, if we assume that all the zeros of the system function are at infinity, the magnitude function takes the general form,

$$M(\omega) = \frac{K_0}{[1 + f(\omega^2)]^{1/2}} \qquad (12.1)$$

where K_0 is the dc gain constant and $f(\omega^2)$ is the polynomial to be selected to give the desired amplitude response. For example, if

$$f(\omega^2) = \omega^{2n} \qquad (12.2)$$

then the amplitude function can be written as

$$M(\omega) = \frac{K_0}{(1 + \omega^{2n})^{1/2}} \qquad (12.3)$$

We see that $M(0) = K_0$, and that $M(\omega)$ is monotonically decreasing with ω. In addition, the 0.707 or 3-db point is at $\omega = 1$ for all n, i.e.,

$$M(1) = \frac{K_0}{\sqrt{2}} \qquad \text{all } n \qquad (12.4)$$

The cutoff frequency is thus seen to be $\omega = 1$. The parameter n controls the closeness of approximation in both the pass band and the stop band. Curves of $M(\omega)$ for different n are shown in Fig. 12.2. Observe that the higher n is, the better the approximation. The amplitude approximation of the type in Eq. 12.3 is called a *Butterworth* or *maximally flat* response. The reason for the term "maximally flat" is that, when we expand $M(\omega)$ in a power series about $\omega = 0$, we have

$$M(\omega) = K_0\left(1 - \frac{\omega^{2n}}{2} + \frac{3}{8}\omega^{4n} - \frac{5}{16}\omega^{6n} + \frac{35}{128}\omega^{8n} + \cdots\right) \qquad (12.5)$$

We see that the first $(2n - 1)$ derivatives of $M(\omega)$ are equal to zero at $\omega = 0$. For $\omega \gg 1$, the amplitude response of a Butterworth function can be written as (with K_0 normalized to be unity)

$$M(\omega) \simeq \frac{1}{\omega^n} \qquad \omega \gg 1 \qquad (12.6)$$

We observe that, asymptotically, $M(\omega)$ falls off as ω^{-n} for a Butterworth response. In terms of decibels, the asymptotic slope is obtained as

$$20 \log M(\omega) = -20n \log \omega \qquad (12.7)$$

Consequently, the amplitude response falls asymptotically at a rate of $6n$ db/octave or $20n$ db/decade.

One question remains. How do we obtain a transfer function $H(s)$ from only the amplitude characteristics $M(\omega)$? The procedure is as follows. We first note that the amplitude response $M(\omega)$ and the complex system function $H(j\omega)$ are related by

$$M^2(\omega) = H(j\omega)\, H(-j\omega) \qquad (12.8)$$

If we define a new function $h(s^2)$ such that

$$h(s^2) = H(s)\, H(-s) \qquad (12.9)$$

we see that

$$M^2(\omega) = h(-\omega^2) \qquad (12.10)$$

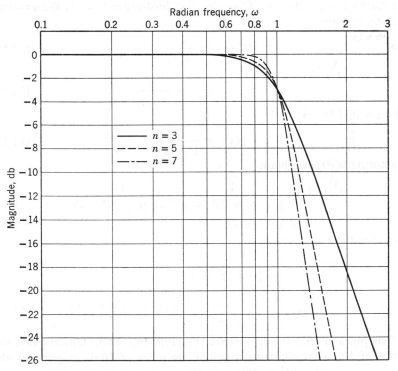

FIG. 12.2. Amplitude response of Butterworth low-pass filters.

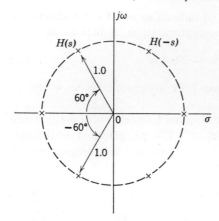

FIG. 12.3. Poles of $H(s)\,H(-s)$ for an $n = 3$ Butterworth filter.

From $h(-\omega^2)$ all we need do is to substitute $s^2 = -\omega^2$ to give $h(s^2)$. Then we factor $h(s^2)$ into the product $H(s)\,H(-s)$. Since the poles and zeros of $H(s)$ are the mirror images of the poles and zeros of $H(-s)$, we simply choose the Hurwitz factors of $h(s^2)$ as $H(s)$. An example will serve to clarify this discussion. Consider the third-order ($n = 3$) Butterworth response given by

$$M^2(\omega) = \frac{1}{1 + \omega^6} \tag{12.11}$$

$$= \frac{1}{1 - (-\omega^2)^3} \tag{12.12}$$

We see that $h(s^2)$ is

$$h(s^2) = \frac{1}{1 - (s^2)^3} \tag{12.13}$$

Factoring $h(s^2)$, we obtain

$$h(s^2) = \frac{1}{1 + 2s + 2s^2 + s^3} \frac{1}{1 - 2s + 2s^2 - s^3}$$

$$= H(s)\,H(-s) \tag{12.14}$$

We then have

$$H(s) = \frac{1}{s^3 + 2s^2 + 2s + 1}$$

$$= \frac{1}{(s + 1)(s + \tfrac{1}{2} + j\sqrt{3}/2)(s + \tfrac{1}{2} - j\sqrt{3}/2)} \tag{12.15}$$

The poles of $H(s)$ and $H(-s)$ are shown in Fig. 12.3. Observe that the poles of $H(-s)$ are mirror images of the poles of $H(s)$, as given by the theorem on Hurwitz polynomials in the previous chapter.

For a Butterworth response, the poles of $H(s)\, H(-s)$ are the roots of

$$(-1)^n s^{2n} = -1$$

$$= e^{j(2k-1)\pi} \qquad k = 0, 1, 2, \cdots, 2n \qquad (12.16)$$

The poles s_k are then given by

$$s_k = e^{j[(2k-1)/2n]\pi} \qquad n \text{ even} \tag{12.17}$$

$$= e^{j(k/n)\pi} \qquad n \text{ odd}$$

or simply

$$s_k = e^{j[(2k+n-1)/2n]\pi} \qquad k = 0, 1, 2, \cdots, 2n \qquad (12.18)$$

Expressing s_k as $s_k = \sigma_k + j\omega_k$, the real and imaginary parts are given by

$$\sigma_k = \cos \frac{(2k+n-1)}{2n}\pi = \sin \left(\frac{2k-1}{n}\right)\frac{\pi}{2}$$

$$(12.19)$$

$$\omega_k = \sin \frac{(2k+n-1)}{2n}\pi = \cos \left(\frac{2k-1}{n}\right)\frac{\pi}{2}$$

It is seen from Eqs. 12.17 and 12.18 that all the poles of $H(s)\, H(-s)$ are located on the unit circle in the s-plane, and are symmetrical about both the σ and the $j\omega$ axes. To satisfy realizability conditions, we associate the poles in the right-half plane with $H(-s)$, and the poles in the left-half plane with $H(s)$.

As an example, consider the construction of an $H(s)$ that gives an $n = 4$ Butterworth response. From Eq. 12.18, it is seen that the poles are given by

$$s_k = e^{j[(2k+3)/8]\pi} \tag{12.20}$$

$H(s)$ is then given as

$$H(s) = \frac{1}{(s + e^{j(5/8)\pi})(s + e^{j(7/8)\pi})(s + e^{j(9/8)\pi})(s + e^{j(11/8)\pi})} \tag{12.21}$$

If we express s_k in complex form and expand, we obtain

$$H(s) = \frac{1}{(s^2 + 0.76536s + 1)(s^2 + 1.84776s + 1)} \tag{12.22}$$

To simplify the use of Butterworth functions, $H(s)$ is given in Tables 12.1 and 12.2 for $n = 1$ to $n = 8$, in factored form as in Eq. 12.22 or multiplied out as

$$H(s) = \frac{1}{a_n s^n + a_{n-1} s^{n-1} + \cdots + a_1 s + 1} \tag{12.23}$$

TABLE 12.1.   BUTTERWORTH POLYNOMIALS (FACTORED FORM)

n	
1	$(s + 1)$
2	$(s^2 + \sqrt{2}s + 1)$
3	$(s^2 + s + 1)(s + 1)$
4	$(s^2 + 0.76536s + 1)(s^2 + 1.84776s + 1)$
5	$(s + 1)(s^2 + 0.6180s + 1)(s^2 + 1.6180s + 1)$
6	$(s^2 + 0.5176s + 1)(s^2 + \sqrt{2}s + 1)(s^2 + 1.9318s + 1)$
7	$(s + 1)(s^2 + 0.4450s + 1)(s^2 + 1.2465s + 1)(s^2 + 1.8022s + 1)$
8	$(s^2 + 0.3896s + 1)(s^2 + 1.1110s + 1)(s^2 + 1.6630s + 1)(s^2 + 1.9622s + 1)$

TABLE 12.2.   BUTTERWORTH POLYNOMIALS *

n	a_1	a_2	a_3	a_4	a_5	a_6	a_7	a_8
1	1							
2	$\sqrt{2}$	1						
3	2	2	1					
4	2.613	3.414	2.613	1				
5	3.236	5.236	5.236	3.236	1			
6	3.864	7.464	9.141	7.464	3.864	1		
7	4.494	10.103	14.606	14.606	10.103	4.494	1	
8	5.126	13.138	21.848	25.691	21.848	13.138	5.126	1

Note: * $a_0 = 1$.

12.2   OTHER LOW-PASS FILTER APPROXIMATIONS

In the previous section, we examined the maximally flat approximation to a low-pass filter characteristic. We will consider other low-pass filter approximants in this section.

The Chebyshev or equal-ripple approximation

We have seen that the maximally flat approximation to the ideal low-pass filter is best at $\omega = 0$, whereas, as we approach the cutoff frequency $\omega = 1$, the approximation becomes progressively poorer. We will now consider an approximation which "ripples" about unity in the pass band and falls off rapidly beyond the cutoff $\omega = 1$. The approximation is equally good at $\omega = 0$ and $\omega = 1$ and, as a result, is called an "equal-ripple" approximation. The equal-ripple property is brought about by the use of

Chebyshev cosine polynomials defined as

$$C_n(\omega) = \cos(n \cos^{-1} \omega) \qquad |\omega| \le 1$$
$$= \cosh(n \cosh^{-1} \omega) \qquad |\omega| > 1 \tag{12.24}$$

For $n = 0$ we see that

$$C_0(\omega) = 1 \tag{12.25}$$

and for $n = 1$, we have

$$C_1(\omega) = \omega \tag{12.26}$$

Higher order Chebyshev polynomials are obtained through the recursive formula,

$$C_n(\omega) = 2\omega C_{n-1}(\omega) - C_{n-2}(\omega) \tag{12.27}$$

Thus for $n = 2$, we obtain $C_2(\omega)$ as

$$C_2(\omega) = 2\omega(\omega) - 1$$
$$= 2\omega^2 - 1 \tag{12.28}$$

TABLE 12.3

n	Chebyshev polynomials $C_n(\omega) = \cos(n \cos^{-1} \omega)$
0	1
1	ω
2	$2\omega^2 - 1$
3	$4\omega^3 - 3\omega$
4	$8\omega^4 - 8\omega^2 + 1$
5	$16\omega^5 - 20\omega^3 + 5\omega$
6	$32\omega^6 - 48\omega^4 + 18\omega^2 - 1$
7	$64\omega^7 - 112\omega^5 + 56\omega^3 - 7\omega$
8	$128\omega^8 - 256\omega^6 + 160\omega^4 - 32\omega^2 + 1$
9	$256\omega^9 - 576\omega^7 + 432\omega^5 - 120\omega^3 + 9\omega$
10	$512\omega^{10} - 1280\omega^8 + 1120\omega^6 - 400\omega^4 + 50\omega^2 - 1$

In Table 12.3, Chebyshev polynomials of orders up to $n = 10$ are given. The pertinent properties of Chebyshev polynomials which are used in the low-pass filter approximation are:

1. The zeros of the polynomials are located in the interval $|\omega| \le 1$, as seen by the plots of $C_3(\omega)$ and $C_4(\omega)$ in Fig. 12.4.
2. Within the interval $|\omega| \le 1$, the absolute value of $C_n(\omega)$ never exceeds unity; i.e.,

$$|C_n(\omega)| \le 1 \quad \text{for} \quad |\omega| \le 1$$

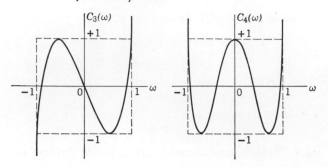

FIG. 12.4. $C_3(\omega)$ and $C_4(\omega)$ Chebyshev polynomials.

3. Beyond the interval $|\omega| \leq 1$, $C_n(\omega)$ increases rapidly for increasing values of $|\omega|$.

Now, how do we apply the Chebyshev polynomials to the low-pass filter approximation? Consider the function $\epsilon^2 \, C_n{}^2(\omega)$, where ϵ is real and small compared to 1. It is clear that $\epsilon^2 \, C_n{}^2(\omega)$ will vary between 0 and ϵ^2 in the interval $|\omega| \leq 1$. Now we add 1 to this function making it $1 + \epsilon^2 \, C_n{}^2(\omega)$. This new function varies between 1 and $1 + \epsilon^2$, a quantity slightly greater than unity, for $|\omega| \leq 1$. Inverting this function, we obtain the function which we will associate with $|H(j\omega)|^2$; thus,

$$|H(j\omega)|^2 = \frac{1}{1 + \epsilon^2 \, C_n{}^2(\omega)} \tag{12.29}$$

Within the interval $|\omega| \leq 1$, $|H(j\omega)|^2$ oscillates about unity such that the maximum value is 1 and the minimum is $1/(1 + \epsilon^2)$. Outside this interval, $C_n{}^2(\omega)$ becomes very large so that, as ω increases, a point will be reached where $\epsilon^2 \, C_n{}^2(\omega) \gg 1$ and $|H(j\omega)|^2$ approaches zero very rapidly with further increase in ω. Thus, we see that $|H(j\omega)|^2$ in Eq. 12.29 is indeed a suitable approximant for the ideal low-pass filter characteristic.

Figure 12.5 shows a Chebyshev approximation to the ideal low-pass filter. We see that, within the pass band, $0 \leq \omega \leq 1$, $|H(j\omega)|$ ripples between the value 1 and $(1 + \epsilon^2)^{-1/2}$. The *ripple height* or distance between maximum and minimum in the pass band is given as

$$\text{Ripple} = 1 - \frac{1}{(1 + \epsilon^2)^{1/2}} \tag{12.30}$$

At $\omega = 1$, $|H(j\omega)|$ is

$$|H(j1)| = \frac{1}{(1 + \epsilon^2)^{1/2}} \tag{12.31}$$

because $C_n{}^2(1) = 1$.

In the stop band, i.e., for $|\omega| \geq 1$, as ω increases, we reach a point ω_k, where $\epsilon^2 C_n^2(\omega) \gg 1$, so that

$$|H(j\omega)| \cong \frac{1}{\epsilon \, C_n(\omega)} \qquad \omega > \omega_k \qquad (12.32)$$

The loss in decibels is given as

$$\text{Loss} = -20 \log_{10} |H(j\omega)|$$
$$\cong 20 \log \epsilon + 20 \log C_n(\omega) \qquad (12.33)$$

But for large ω, $C_n(\omega)$ can be approximated by its leading term $2^{n-1}\omega^n$, so that

$$\text{Loss} = 20 \log \epsilon + 20 \log 2^{n-1} \, \omega^n$$
$$= 20 \log \epsilon + 6(n-1) + 20n \log \omega \qquad (12.34)$$

We see that the Chebyshev response also falls off at the rate of $20n$ db/ decade after an initial drop of $20 \log \epsilon + 6(n-1)$ db. However, in most applications, ϵ is a very small number so that the $20 \log \epsilon$ term is actually negative. It is necessary, therefore, to compensate for this decrease in loss in the stop band by choosing a sufficiently large n.

From the above discussion, we see that a Chebyshev approximation depends upon two variables, ϵ and n, which can be determined from the specifications directly. The maximum permissible ripple puts a bound on ϵ. Once ϵ is determined, any desired value of attenuation in the stop band fixes n.

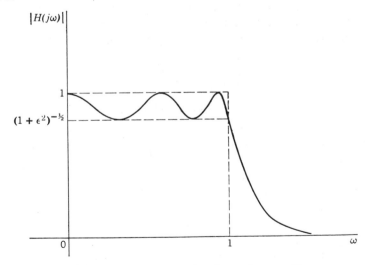

FIG. I2.5. Chebyshev approximation to low-pass filter.

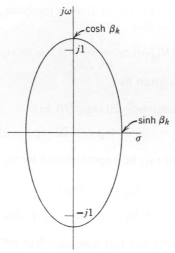

FIG. 12.6. Locus of poles of Chebyshev filter.

The derivation for the system function $H(s)$ from a Chebyshev amplitude approximation $|H(j\omega)|$ is somewhat involved and will not be given here.* Instead, we will simply give the results of such a derivation. First we introduce a design parameter.

$$\beta_k = \frac{1}{n}\sinh^{-1}\frac{1}{\epsilon} \qquad (12.35)$$

where n is the degree of the Chebyshev polynomial and ϵ is the factor controlling ripple width. The poles, $s_k = \sigma_k + j\omega_k$, of the equal-ripple approximant $H(s)$ are located on an *ellipse* in the s-plane, given by

$$\frac{\sigma_k^2}{\sinh^2 \beta_k} + \frac{\omega_k^2}{\cosh^2 \beta_k} = 1 \qquad (12.36)$$

The major semiaxis of the ellipse is on the $j\omega$ axis and has a value $\omega = \pm \cosh \beta_k$. The minor semiaxis has a value $\sigma = \pm \sinh \beta_k$, and the foci are at $\omega = \pm 1$ (Fig. 12.6). The half-power point of the equal-ripple amplitude response occurs at the point where the ellipse intersects the $j\omega$ axis, i.e., at $\omega = \cosh \beta_k$. Recall that, for the Butterworth response, the half-power point occurs at $\omega = 1$. Let us normalize the Chebyshev poles s_k such that the half-power point also falls at $\omega = 1$ instead of at $\omega = \cosh \beta_k$; i.e., let us choose a normalizing factor, $\cosh \beta_k$, such that the

---

* Interested parties are referred to M. E. Van Valkenburg, *Introduction to Modern Network Synthesis*, John Wiley & Sons, New York, 1960, Chapter 13.

normalized pole locations s'_k are given by

$$s'_k = \frac{s_k}{\cosh \beta_k}$$

$$= \frac{\sigma_k}{\cosh \beta_k} + \frac{j\omega_k}{\cosh \beta_k} \qquad (12.37)$$

$$\triangleq \sigma'_k + j\omega'_k$$

The normalized pole locations can be derived as

$$\sigma'_k = \tanh \beta_k \sin \left(\frac{2k-1}{n}\right)\frac{\pi}{2}$$

$$\omega'_k = \cos \left(\frac{2k-1}{n}\right)\frac{\pi}{2} \qquad (12.38)$$

Comparing the normalized Chebyshev pole locations with the Butterworth pole locations in Eq. 12.19, we see that the imaginary parts are the same while the real part σ'_k of the Chebyshev pole location is equal to the real part of the Butterworth poles times the factor $\tanh \beta_k$. For example, with $n = 3$ and $\tanh \beta_k = 0.444$, the Butterworth poles are

$$s_1 = -1 + j0$$
$$s_{2,3} = -0.5 \pm j0.866$$

so that the normalized Chebyshev poles are given by

$$s_1 = -1(0.444) + j0$$
$$= -0.444 + j0$$
$$s_{2,3} = -0.5(0.444) \pm j0.866$$
$$= -0.222 \pm j0.866$$

Finally, to obtain the denormalized Chebyshev poles, we simply multiply s'_k by $\cosh \beta'_k$, i.e.,

$$s_k = (\sigma'_k + j\omega'_k) \cosh \beta_k \qquad (12.39)$$

There is an easier geometrical method to obtain the Chebyshev poles, given only the semiaxis information and the degree n. First we draw two circles, the smaller of radius $\sinh \beta_k$ and the larger of radius $\cosh \beta_k$, as shown in Fig. 12.7. Next, we draw radial lines according to the angles of the Butterworth poles (Eq. 12.17) as shown. Finally, we draw vertical dashed lines from the intersections of the smaller circle and the radial lines, and horizontal dashed lines from the intersections of the large circle and the radial lines. The Chebyshev poles are located at the intersection of the vertical and horizontal dashed lines, as shown in Fig. 12.7.

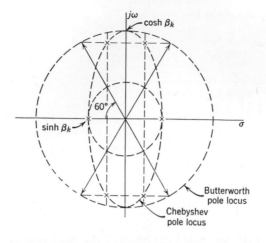

FIG. 12.7. $n = 3$ Chebyshev filter poles.

Consider the following example. We would like to obtain a system function $H(s)$ that exhibits a Chebyshev characteristic with not more than 1-db ripple in the pass band and is down at least 20 db at $\omega = 2$.

When we design for 1 db ripple, we know that, at $\omega = 1$, $|H(j1)|$ is down 1 db so that

$$20 \log |H(j1)| = 20 \log \frac{1}{(1 + \epsilon^2)^{\frac{1}{2}}} = -1 \qquad (12.40)$$

We then obtain

$$\frac{1}{(1 + \epsilon^2)^{\frac{1}{2}}} = 0.893 \qquad (12.41)$$

and

$$\epsilon = 0.505 \qquad (12.42)$$

Our next task is to find n from the 20 db at $\omega = 2$ specification. From Eq. 12.34 the loss can be given as approximately

$$20 \cong 20 \log 0.505 + 6(n - 1) + 20n \log 2. \qquad (12.43)$$

Solving for n, we obtain $n = 2.69$. Since n must be an integer, we let $n = 3$.

With the specification of n and ϵ, the pole locations are completely specified. Our next task is to determine these pole locations. First we must find β_k. From Eq. 12.35 we have

$$\beta_k = \frac{1}{n} \sinh^{-1} \frac{1}{\epsilon}$$

$$= \tfrac{1}{3} \sinh^{-1} 1.98 = 0.478 \qquad (12.44)$$

In order to find the normalized Chebyshev pole from the Butterworth poles, we must first determine tanh β_k. Here

$$\tanh \beta_k = \tanh 0.478 = 0.444 \qquad (12.45)$$

From Table 12.2, the $n = 3$ Butterworth poles are

$$s_1 = -1.0, \qquad s_{2,3} = -0.5 \pm j0.866 \qquad (12.46)$$

Multiplying the real parts of these poles by 0.444, we obtain the normalized Chebyshev poles.

$$s'_1 = -0.444, \quad s'_{2,3} = -0.222 \pm j0.866$$

Finally, the denormalized Chebyshev poles are obtained by multiplying the normalized ones by $\cosh \beta_k = 1.12247$ so that the denormalized poles are

$$s_1 = -0.509 \quad \text{and} \quad s_{2,3} = -0.255 + j0.972.$$

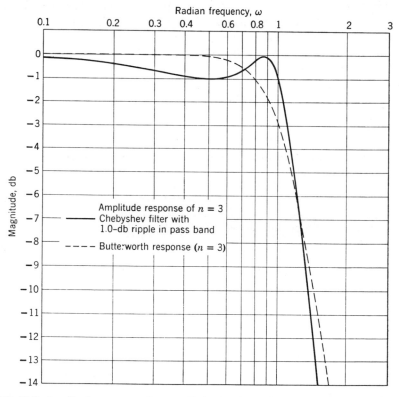

FIG. 12.8. Amplitude response of $n = 3$ Chebyshev filter with 1.0-db ripple in pass band and Butterworth response ($n = 3$).

$H(s)$ is then

$$H(s) = \frac{k}{(s + 0.509)(s + 0.255 - j0.972)(s + 0.255 + j0.972)}$$

$$= \frac{k}{s^3 + 1.02s^2 + 1.267s + 0.514} \qquad (12.47)$$

In Fig. 12.8, the amplitude responses of the Chebyshev and an $n = 3$ Butterworth filter are shown.

Monotonic filters with optimum cutoff

In comparing Butterworth filters with Chebyshev filters, the following can be said. The Butterworth response is a maximally flat, monotonic response, whereas the Chebyshev response is equal ripple in the pass band. In the stop band, the Chebyshev response falls off more rapidly than the Butterworth (except when ϵ is very, very small). In this respect, the Chebyshev filter is a better filter than the Butterworth. However, as we shall see in the following section, the transient response of the Chebyshev filter is very poor. If we require sharp cutoff characteristics for a given degree n, however, the Butterworth filter is quite unsatisfactory. In 1958, Papoulis* proposed a class of filters called *Optimum* or "L" filters which have the following properties:

1. The amplitude response is monotonic.
2. The falloff rate at ω cutoff is the greatest possible, if monotonicity is assumed.
3. The zeros of the system function of the L filter are all at infinity.

Recall that the magnitude response of a low-pass filter with all zeros at infinity can be expressed as

$$M(\omega) = \frac{K_0}{[1 + f(\omega^2)]^{\frac{1}{2}}} \qquad (12.48)$$

Let us denote the polynomial generating the L filter by

$$f(\omega^2) = L_n(\omega^2) \qquad (12.49)$$

The polynomial $L_n(\omega^2)$ has the following properties:

(a) $$L_n(0) = 0$$

(b) $$L_n(1) = 1$$

(c) $$\frac{dL_n(\omega^2)}{d\omega} \geq 0$$

(d) $$\frac{dL_n(\omega^2)}{d\omega}\bigg|_{\omega=1} = M \qquad (M \text{ maximum})$$

---

* A. Papoulis, "Optimum Filters with Monotonic Response," *Proc. IRE*, **46**, No. 3 (Mar. 1958).

Properties *a* and *b* are the same as for the Butterworth generating polynomial, $f(\omega^2) = \omega^{2n}$. Property *c* insures that the response $M(\omega)$ is monotonic and property *d* requires that the slope of $L_n(\omega^2)$ at $\omega = 1$ be the steepest to ensure sharpest cutoff.

Papoulis originally derived the generating equation for the polynomials L_n (for *n* odd) to be

$$L_n(\omega^2) = \int_{-1}^{2\omega^2 - 1} \left[\sum_{i=0}^{k} a_i\, P_i(x) \right]^2 dx \qquad (12.50)$$

where $n = 2k + 1$ and the $P_i(x)$ are the Legendre polynomials of the first kind,*

$$P_0(x) = 1$$
$$P_1(x) = x$$
$$P_2(x) = \tfrac{1}{2}(3x^2 - 1)$$
$$P_3(x) = \tfrac{1}{2}(5x^3 - 3x)$$
$$\cdot$$
$$\cdot$$
$$\cdot \qquad (12.51)$$

and the constants a_i are given by

$$a_0 = \frac{a_1}{3} = \frac{a_2}{5} = \cdots = \frac{a_k}{2k + 1} = \frac{1}{\sqrt{2(k + 1)}} \qquad (12.52)$$

Later Papoulis† and, independently, Fukada,‡ showed that the even-ordered L_n polynomials can be given by

$$L_{2k+2}(\omega^2) = \int_{-1}^{2\omega^2 - 1} (x + 1) \left[\sum_{i=0}^{k} a_i\, P_i(x) \right]^2 dx \qquad (12.53)$$

$$n = 2k + 2$$

where the constants a_i are given by:

Case 1 (*k* even):

$$a_0 = \frac{a_2}{5} = \cdots = \frac{a_k}{2k + 1} = \frac{1}{\sqrt{(k + 1)(k + 2)}}$$

$$\qquad (12.54)$$

$$a_1 = a_3 = \cdots = a_{k-1} = 0$$

---

* E. Jahnke and F. Emde, *Tables of Functions*, Dover Publications, New York, 1945.
† A. Papoulis, "On Monotonic Response Filters," *Proc. IRE*, **47** (Feb. 1959), 332–333.
‡ M. Fukada, "Optimum Filters of Even Orders with Monotonic Response," *Trans. IRE*, **CT-6**, No. 3 (Sept. 1959), 277–281.

Case 2 (*k* odd):

$$\frac{a_1}{3} = \frac{a_3}{7} = \cdots = \frac{a_k}{2k+1} = \frac{1}{\sqrt{(k+1)(k+2)}}$$

$$a_0 = a_2 = \cdots = a_{k-1} = 0$$

(12.55)

Fukada tabulated the $L_n(\omega^2)$ polynomials up to $n = 7$ together with $dL_n(\omega^2)/d\omega$ evaluated at $\omega = 1$ to give an indication of the steepness of the cutoff. This is shown in Table 12.4.

TABLE 12.4. $L_n(\omega^2)$ POLYNOMIALS

n	$L_n(\omega^2)$	$\dfrac{dL_n(1)}{d\omega}$
2	ω^4	4
3	$3\omega^6 - 3\omega^4 + \omega^2$	8
4	$6\omega^8 - 8\omega^6 + 3\omega^4$	12
5	$20\omega^{10} - 40\omega^8 + 28\omega^6 - 8\omega^4 + \omega^2$	18
6	$50\omega^{12} - 120\omega^{10} + 105\omega^8 - 40\omega^6 + 6\omega^4$	24
7	$175\omega^{14} - 525\omega^{12} + 615\omega^{10} - 355\omega^8 + 105\omega^6 - 15\omega^4 + \omega^2$	32

To obtain the system function $H(s)$ for the L filter, we must factor the equation for $h(s^2)$ and choose the Hurwitz factors as $H(s)$.

$$h(s^2) = H(s)\,H(-s) = \frac{1}{1 + L_n(-s^2)}$$

(12.56)

For example, for $n = 3$, the magnitude response squared is

$$M^2(\omega) = \frac{1}{1 + L_3(\omega^2)}$$

$$= \frac{1}{1 + \omega^2 - 3\omega^4 + 3\omega^6}$$

(12.57)

Substituting $-\omega^2 = s^2$, we obtain

$$h(s^2) = H(s)\,H(-s) = \frac{1}{1 - s^2 - 3s^4 - 3s^6}$$

(12.58)

After we factor $h(s^2)$, we obtain

$$H(s) = \frac{0.577}{s^3 + 1.31s^2 + 1.359s + 0.577}$$

(12.59)

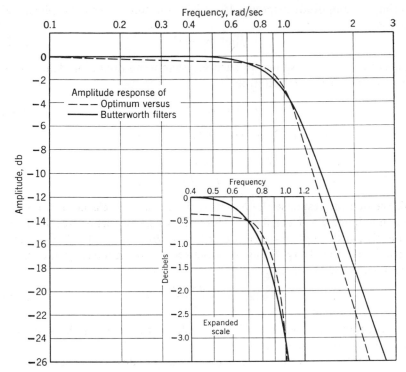

FIG. 12.9. Amplitude response of optimum versus Butterworth filters.

where the numerator factor, 0.577, is chosen to let the d-c gain be unity. The poles of $H(s)$ are

$$s_1 = -0.62$$
$$s_{2,3} = -0.345 \pm j0.901$$

The amplitude response of third-order Optimum (L) and Butterworth filters are compared in Fig. 12.9. Note that the amplitude response of the Optimum filter is not maximally flat, although still monotonic. However, the cutoff characteristic of the Optimum filter is sharper than the cutoff of the Butterworth filter.

Linear phase filters

Suppose a system function is given by

$$H(s) = Ke^{-sT} \tag{12.60}$$

where K is a positive real constant. Then the frequency response of the system can be expressed as

$$H(j\omega) = Ke^{-j\omega T} \tag{12.61}$$

so that the amplitude response $M(\omega)$ is a constant K, and the phase response

$$\phi(\omega) = -\omega T \tag{12.62}$$

is *linear* in ω. The response of such a system to an excitation denoted by the transform pair $\{e(t), E(s)\}$ is

$$R(s) = K E(s)e^{-sT} \tag{12.63}$$

so that the inverse transform $r(t)$ can be written as,

$$\begin{aligned} r(t) &= \mathcal{L}^{-1}[R(s)] \\ &= K e(t - T)\,ut(-T) \end{aligned} \tag{12.64}$$

We see that the response $r(t)$ is simply the excitation delayed by a time T, and multiplied by a constant. Thus, no signal distortion results from transmission through a system described by $H(s)$ in Eq. 12.60. We note further that the delay T can be obtained by differentiating the phase response, $\phi(\omega)$, by ω; i.e.,

$$\text{Delay} = -\frac{d\phi(\omega)}{d\omega} = T \tag{12.65}$$

Consequently, in a system with linear phase, the delay of the system is obtained by differentiating the phase response $\phi(\omega)$.

A system with linear phase and constant amplitude is obviously desirable from a pulse transmission viewpoint. However, the system function $H(s)$ in Eq. 12.60 is only realizable in terms of a lossless transmission line called a *delay line*. If we require that the transmission network be made up of lumped elements, then we must approximate $H(s) = Ke^{-sT}$ by a rational function in s. The approximation method we shall describe here is due to Storch.* We can write $H(s)$ as

$$\begin{aligned} H(s) &= \frac{K_0}{e^{sT}} \\ &= \frac{K_0}{\sinh sT + \cosh sT} \end{aligned} \tag{12.66}$$

where K_0 is chosen such that $H(0) = 1$. Let the delay T be normalized to unity and let us divide both numerator and denominator of $H(s)$ by $\sinh s$ to obtain

$$H(s) = \frac{K_0/\sinh s}{\coth s + 1} \tag{12.67}$$

---

* L. Storch, "Synthesis of Constant Time Delay Ladder Networks Using Bessel Polynomials," *Proc. IRE*, **42** (Nov. 1954), 1666–1676.

If sinh s and cosh s are expanded in power series, we have

$$\cosh s = 1 + \frac{s^2}{2!} + \frac{s^4}{4!} + \frac{s^6}{6!} + \cdots$$

$$\sinh s = s + \frac{s^3}{3!} + \frac{s^5}{5!} + \frac{s^7}{7!} + \cdots$$

(12.68)

From these series expansions, we then obtain a continued fraction expansion of coth s as

$$\coth s = \frac{1}{s} + \cfrac{1}{\dfrac{3}{s} + \cfrac{1}{\dfrac{5}{s} + \cfrac{1}{\dfrac{7}{s} + \cdots}}}$$

(12.69)

If the continued fraction is terminated in n terms, then $H(s)$ can be written as

$$H(s) = \frac{K_0}{B_n(s)}$$

(12.70)

where $B_n(s)$ are *Bessel* polynomials defined by the formulas,

$$B_0 = 1,$$
$$B_1 = s + 1,$$

.

.

.

$$B_n = (2n - 1)B_{n-1} + s^2 B_{n-2}$$

(12.71)

From these formulas, we obtain

$$B_2 = s^2 + 3s + 3,$$
$$B_3 = s^3 + 6s^2 + 15s + 15$$

(12.72)

Higher order Bessel polynomials are given in Table 12.5 and the roots of Bessel polynomials are given in Table 12.6. Note that the roots are all in the left-half plane.

The amplitude and phase response of a system function employing a third-order Bessel polynomial,

$$H(s) = \frac{15}{s^3 + 6s^2 + 15s + 15}$$

(12.73)

is given by the solid lines in Figs. 12.10 and 12.11. These are compared

TABLE 12.5.   COEFFICIENTS OF BESSEL POLYNOMIALS

$$B(s) = b_0 + b_1 s + b_2 s + \cdots + b_n s^n$$

n	b_0	b_1	b_2	b_3	b_4	b_5	b_6	b_7
0	1							
1	1	1						
2	3	3	1					
3	15	15	6	1				
4	105	105	45	10	1			
5	945	945	420	105	15	1		
6	10,395	10,395	4,725	1,260	210	21	1	
7	135,135	135,135	62,370	17,325	3,150	378	28	1

TABLE 12.6.   ROOTS OF BESSEL POLYNOMIALS

n	Roots of Bessel Polynomials
1	$-1.0 + j0$
2	$-1.5 \pm j0.866667$
3	$\begin{cases} -2.32219 + j0 \\ -1.83891 \pm j1.75438 \end{cases}$
4	$\begin{cases} -2.89621 \pm j0.867234 \\ -2.10379 \pm j2.65742 \end{cases}$
5	$\begin{cases} -3.64674 + j0 \\ -3.35196 \pm j1.74266 \\ -2.32467 \pm j3.57102 \end{cases}$
6	$\begin{cases} -4.24836 \pm j0.86751 \\ -3.73571 \pm j2.62627 \\ -2.5159 \pm j4.49267 \end{cases}$
7	$\begin{cases} -4.97181 + j0 \\ -4.75827 \pm j1.73928 \\ -4.07014 \pm j3.51718 \\ -2.68568 \pm j5.42069 \end{cases}$

with the amplitude and phase of a third-order Butterworth function given by the dotted lines. Note that the phase response of the constant-delay function is more linear than the phase of the Butterworth function. Also, the amplitude cutoff of the constant-delay curve is more gradual than that of the Butterworth. It is a general rule that linearity in the phase response implies a gentle cutoff characteristic for the amplitude response. In

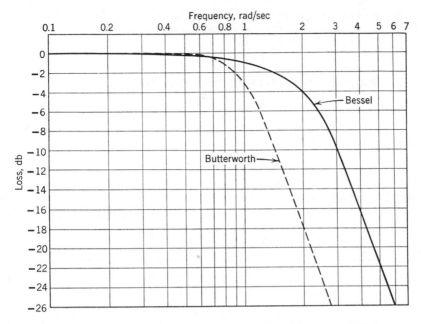

FIG. 12.10. Amplitude response of $n = 3$ Bessel and Butterworth filters.

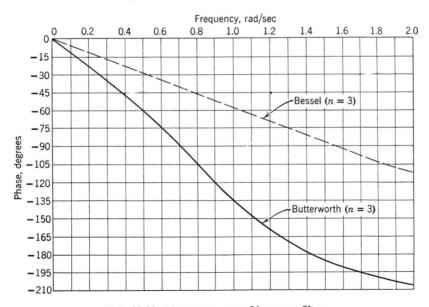

FIG. 12.11. Phase responses of low-pass filters.

addition, we can show that the higher the degree of the Bessel polynomial, the more linear the phase and the more gentle the cutoff for the amplitude in the pass band.

12.3 TRANSIENT RESPONSE OF LOW-PASS FILTERS

In this section, we will compare the transient response of the filters discussed in the previous sections. In particular, we will compare the step response of the filters according to the following figures of merit:

1. *Rise Time.* The rise time of the step response is defined here as the time required for the step response to rise from 10% to 90% of its final value, as depicted in Fig. 12.12.

2. *Overshoot.* The overshoot of the step response is defined as the difference between the peak value and the final value of the step response expressed as a percentage of the final value.

3. *Settling Time.* The settling time is that time t_s, measured from the first peak, beyond which the step response does not differ from the final value by more than $\pm 2\%$, as depicted in Fig. 12.12.

First, the step responses of the $n = 3$, $n = 7$, and $n = 10$ Butterworth filters are shown in Fig. 12.13. Note that, as n increases, the rise time, overshoot, and settling time also increase. In many cases, it can be said

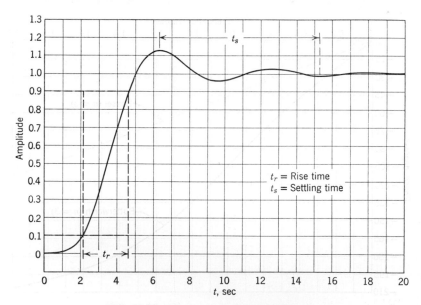

FIG. 12.12. Measures of transient response.

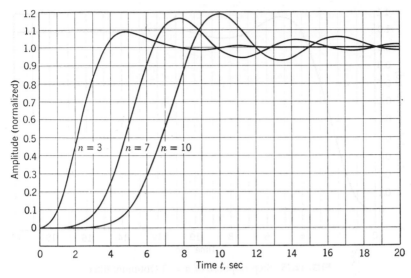

FIG. 12.13. Step response of normalized Butterworth low-pass filters.

that, as the sharpness of cutoff of the amplitude response is increased while maintaining the same cutoff frequency, the overshoot, rise time, and settling time are also increased.

Next, consider the step response of the $n = 3$ constant-delay filter in Fig. 12.14. We see that there is no overshoot and the rise time is quite small. This is a general characteristic of linear-phase low-pass filters.

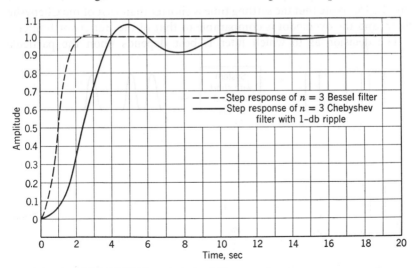

FIG. 12.14. Comparison of filter transient responses.

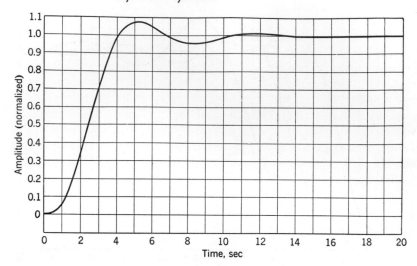

FIG. 12.15. Step response of $n = 3$ Optimum filter.

The step response of the Chebyshev filter taken from the example in the previous section is also shown in Fig. 12.14. Note that the settling time is quite long as compared to the step responses of the $n = 3$ Butterworth and constant-delay sections. Although phase does play a role in determining settling time, it has been observed that ripples in the amplitude response usually give rise to prolonged ringing in the step response.

Finally, the step response of the $n = 3$ Optimum (L) filter is given in Fig. 12.15. Note that the settling time is shorter than that of the Chebyshev filter, and the overshoot is comparable to that of the Butterworth filter.

The decision as to which filter is best depends upon the particular

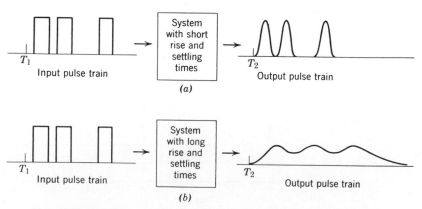

FIG. 12.16. Smearing of pulses in systems with long rise and settling times.

application. In certain applications, such as for transmission of music, phase is not important. In these cases, the sharpness of cutoff is the important factor, so that the Chebyshev or the Optimum filter is better than the others. Suppose we were dealing with a pulse transmission system with the requirement that the output sequence of pulses have the same pulse shape and separation as the input sequence, except for a time delay $T = T_2 - T_1$, as shown in Fig. 12.16a. It is clear that a filter with a long rise time is not suitable because the pulses would "smear" over each other, as seen in Fig. 12.16b. The same can be said for long settling times. Obviously, the best filter for the pulse transmission system is the constant-delay filter with small rise time and settling time.

12.4 SYNTHESIS OF LOW-PASS FILTERS

Given the system function of the low-pass filter as derived by the methods described in the previous section, we can proceed with the synthesis of the filter network. If we consider the class of filters terminated in a 1-Ω load, and if we let the system function be a transfer impedance,

$$Z_{21}(s) = \frac{z_{21}}{1 + z_{22}} \tag{12.74}$$

or a transfer admittance

$$Y_{21}(s) = \frac{y_{21}}{1 + y_{22}} \tag{12.75}$$

we can synthesize the low-pass filter according to methods given in Chapter 11. For example, consider the $n = 3$ Optimum (L) filter function given as a transfer impedance,

$$Z_{21}(s) = \frac{0.577}{s^3 + 1.31s^2 + 1.359s + 0.577} \tag{12.76}$$

We see that the zeros of transmission are all at infinity. Since the numerator of Z_{21} is even, we divide both numerator and denominator by the odd part of the denominator, $s^3 + 1.359s$. Thus,

$$z_{21} = \frac{0.577}{s^3 + 1.359s}$$
$$z_{22} = \frac{1.31s^2 + 0.577}{s^3 + 1.359s} \tag{12.77}$$

The structure of the low-pass filter with three zeros of transmission at infinity is given in Chapter 11. We must synthesize z_{22} to give the π reactance

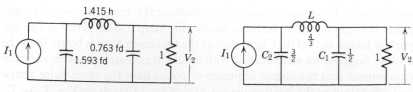

FIG. 12.17. Optimum filter.   **FIG. 12.18.** Butterworth filter.

structure. This we accomplish through the following continued fraction expansion of $1/z_{22}$:

$$
\begin{array}{r}
0.763s \\
1.31s^2 + 0.577 \overline{)\, s^3 + 1.359s\,} \\
s^3 + 0.440s \\
\hline
1.415s \\
0.919s \overline{)\, 1.31s^2 + 0.577\,} \\
1.31s^2 \\
\hline
1.593s \\
0.577 \overline{)\, 0.919s\,} \\
0.919s \\
\hline
\end{array}
$$

The final filter structure is shown in Fig. 12.17. For the $n = 3$ Butterworth filter given by the transfer admittance,

$$
Z_{21}(s) = \frac{1}{s^3 + 2s^2 + 2s + 1}, \tag{12.78}
$$

we have

$$
z_{21}(s) = \frac{1}{s^3 + 2s}
$$

$$
z_{22}(s) = \frac{2s^2 + 1}{s^3 + 2s} \tag{12.79}
$$

We then synthesize $z_{22}(s)$ by a continued fraction expansion to give the filter shown in Fig. 12.18.

In the next chapter, we will consider some example of synthesis of double terminated filters. To stimulate the curiosity of the reader, note that the voltage-ratio transfer function V_2/V_0 of the network in Fig. 12.19 is precisely the $n = 3$ Butterworth function.

Recall that, in the previous chapter, when we cascaded two constant-resistance networks, the over-all system function $H_0(s)$ was the product of

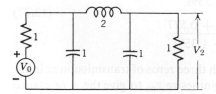

FIG. 12.19. $N = 3$ double-terminated Butterworth filter.

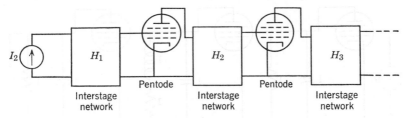

FIG. 12.20. Pentodes used as isolation amplifiers.

the individual system functions, $H_1(s)$ $H_2(s)$. We can apply this property to networks which are not constant-resistance if we place an isolation amplifier between the networks, as shown in Fig. 12.20. Since pentodes provide the necessary isolation, our task is simplified to the design of the individual structures $H_1(s), H_2(s), \cdots, H_n(s)$, which we call *interstage* networks.

Some common interstage structures are shown in Fig. 12.21. In Fig. 12.21a a structure known as the *shunt-peaked* network is shown. The transfer impedance of the shunt-peaked network is

$$Z_{21}(s) = \frac{1}{C}\left[\frac{s + R/L}{s^2 + sR/L + (1/LC)}\right] \qquad (12.80)$$

We see that $Z_{21}(s)$ has a real zero and a pair of poles which may be complex depending upon the values of R, L, and C. In Fig. 12.21b. a simple $R\text{-}C$ interstage is shown whose transfer impedance is

$$Z_{21}(s) = \frac{1}{C}\frac{1}{s + 1/RC} \qquad (12.81)$$

Observe that all of the filter transfer functions considered up to this point are made up of pairs of conjugate poles and simple poles on the $-\sigma$ axis. It is clear that, if we cascade shunt-peaked stages and $R\text{-}C$ stages, we can adjust the R, L, and C, elements to give the desired response characteristic. The only problem is to cancel the finite zero of the shunt-peaked stage. For example, if we wish to design an amplifier with an $n = 3$ low-pass

FIG. 12.21. (*a*) Shunt-peaked interstage. (*b*) $R\text{-}C$ interstage.

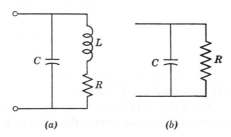

(*a*)   (*b*)

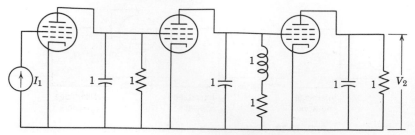

FIG. 12.22. Butterworth amplifier.

Butterworth characteristic, we first break up the system function into complex pole pairs and real pole terms, as given by

$$Z_{21}(s) = \frac{1}{(s^2 + s + 1)(s + 1)}$$

$$= \frac{(s + 1)}{(s^2 + s + 1)} \frac{1}{(s + 1)} \frac{1}{(s + 1)} \tag{12.82}$$

We then associate the individual factors with shunt-peaked or simple R-C stages and solve for the element values. The $n = 3$ Butterworth amplifier is given in Fig. 12.22.

12.5 MAGNITUDE AND FREQUENCY NORMALIZATION

In the previous section, we discussed the synthesis of low-pass filters with a cutoff frequency of 1 rad/sec and a load impedance of 1 Ω. Filters designed with these restrictions are considered to be *normalized* in both cutoff frequency and impedance level. We will now discuss methods whereby the normalized filters can be converted into filters which meet arbitrary cutoff frequency and impedance level specifications. Let us denote by a subscript n the normalized frequency variable s_n and the normalized element values L_n, R_n, and C_n. The normalized frequency variable s_n is related to the actual frequency s by the relation,

$$s_n = \frac{s}{\omega_0} \tag{12.83}$$

where ω_0, the normalizing constant, is dimensionless and is often taken to be the actual cutoff frequency.

Since the impedance of an element remains invariant under frequency normalization, we obtain the actual element values from the normalized values by setting the impedances in the two cases equal to each other. For example, for an inductor, we have

$$s_n L_n = sL = \omega_0 s_n L \qquad (12.84)$$

From this equation we then obtain the denormalized value of inductance as

$$L = \frac{L_n}{\omega_0} \qquad (12.85)$$

Similarly, from the impedance $1/s_n C_n$ of a frequency normalized capacitor C_n we obtain the denormalized value of capacitance through the equation,

$$\frac{1}{s_n C_n} = \frac{1}{sC} \qquad (12.86)$$

so that the actual value of the capacitance is

$$C = \frac{C_n}{\omega_0} \qquad (12.87)$$

Since resistances, ideally, are independent of frequency, they are unaffected by frequency normalization.

Consider, next, impedance denormalization. Suppose the actual impedance level should be R_0 ohms instead of $1\,\Omega$. Then a denormalized impedance Z is related to a normalized impedance Z_n by

$$Z = R_0 Z_n, \qquad (12.88)$$

where R_0 is taken to be dimensionless here. Thus, for a normalized resistor R_n, the denormalized (actual) resistance is

$$R = R_0 R_n \qquad (12.89)$$

For an inductance, the corresponding relationship is

$$sL = R_0(sL_n) \qquad (12.90)$$

so that the actual inductance value is

$$L = R_0 L_n \qquad (12.91)$$

Similarly for a capacitor we have

$$\frac{1}{sC} = \frac{R_0}{sC_n} \qquad (12.92)$$

so that the actual capacitance is

$$C = \frac{C_n}{R_0} \qquad (12.93)$$

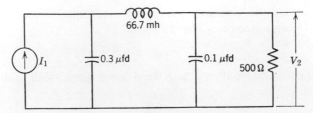

FIG. 12.23. Denormalized low-pass filter.

For combined frequency and magnitude denormalization, we simply combine the two sets of equations to give,

$$R = R_0 R_n$$

$$C = \frac{C_n}{R_0 \omega_0}$$

$$L = \frac{R_0 L_n}{\omega_0}$$

(12.94)

Let us consider an actual example in design. In the previous section, we synthesized a transfer impedance Z_{21} with an $n = 3$ Butterworth amplitude characteristic with a cutoff frequency of 1 rad/sec and a load impedance of 1 Ω. Let us redesign this filter for a cutoff frequency of 10^4 rad/sec to work into a load of 500 Ω. From the original network in Fig. 12.18, we take the element values and denormalize with the normalizing factors, $\omega_0 = 10^4$ and $R_0 = 500$.

Then the denormalized element values are

$$R = 500 R_L = 500$$

$$C_1 = \frac{\frac{1}{2}}{500(10^4)} = 0.1 \ \mu\text{fd}$$

$$L = \frac{\frac{4}{3}(500)}{10,000} = 0.0667 \ \text{h}$$

(12.95)

$$C_2 = \frac{\frac{3}{2}}{500(10^4)} = 0.3 \ \mu\text{fd}$$

The final design is shown in Fig. 12.23.

12.6 FREQUENCY TRANSFORMATIONS

Up to this point, we have only discussed the design of low-pass filters while neglecting the equally important designs of high-pass, band-pass, and band-elimination filters. We will remedy this situation here, not by introducing new design procedures but through a technique known as a *frequency transformation* whereby, beginning from a normalized low-pass filter, we can *generate* any other form of filter. Using frequency transformations, the elements of the normalized low-pass filter are changed into elements of a high-pass, band-pass, or band-elimination filter.

Analytically, a frequency transformation simply changes one *L-C* driving point function into another *L-C* driving-point function. Therefore, the transformation equations must be *L-C* functions themselves. Also, since we proceed from normalized low-pass filters, the transformation equations include built-in frequency denormalization factors so that the resulting networks need only be scaled for impedance level. Consider the simplest transformation equation, that of low-pass to high-pass, which is

$$s = \frac{\omega_0}{s_n} \tag{12.96}$$

where s_n represents the normalized low-pass frequency variable, s is the regular frequency variable, and ω_0 is the cutoff frequency of the high-pass filter. In terms of real and imaginary parts, we have,

$$\sigma + j\omega = \frac{\omega_0}{\sigma_n + j\omega_n}$$
$$= \frac{\omega_0(\sigma_n - j\omega_n)}{\sigma_n^2 + \omega_n^2} \tag{12.97}$$

Since we are interested principally in how the $j\omega_n$ axis maps into the $j\omega$ axis, we let $\sigma_n = 0$ so that

$$\omega = -\frac{\omega_0}{\omega_n} \tag{12.98}$$

is the equation that transforms normalized low-pass filters to denormalized high-pass filters. From Eq. 12.98 we see that the point $\omega_n = \pm 1$ corresponds to the point $\omega = \pm\omega_0$. It is also clear that the transformation maps the segment $|\omega_n| \leq 1$ on to the segments defined by $\omega_0 \leq |\omega| \leq \infty$, as shown in Fig. 12.24.

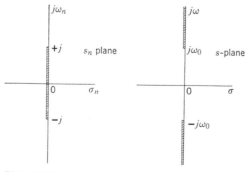

FIG. 12.24. Low-pass to high-pass transformation.

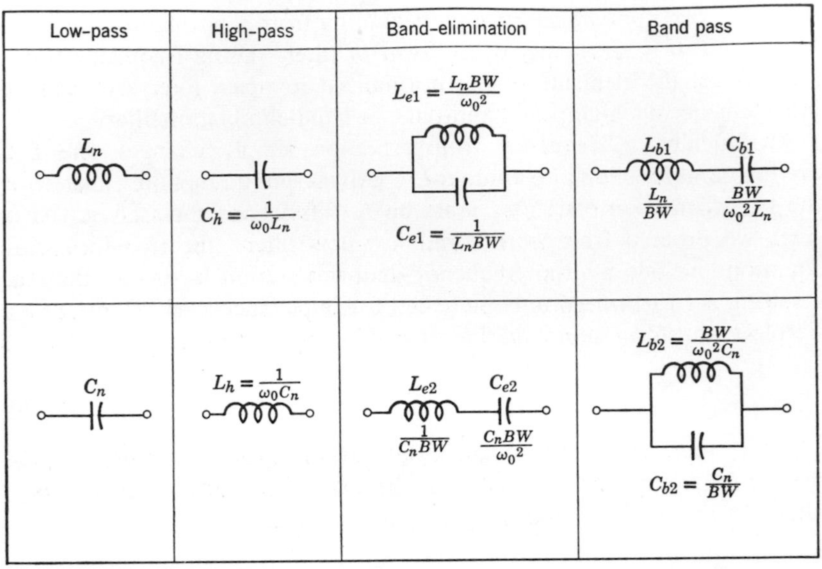

Low-pass	High-pass	Band-elimination	Band pass

FIG. 12.25. Element changes resulting from frequency transformations.

Now let us see how the frequency transformations change the network elements. For convenience, let us denote the normalized low-pass network elements with a subscript n, the high-pass elements with a subscript h, the band-pass elements with a subscript b, and the band-elimination elements with a subscript e. For the low-pass to high-pass case, let us first consider the changes for the capacitor C_n. The transformation is given by the equation

$$\frac{1}{C_n s_n} = \frac{s}{\omega_0 C_n} \triangleq L_h s \qquad (12.99)$$

For the inductor L_n, we have

$$L_n s_n = L_n \frac{\omega_0}{s} \triangleq \frac{1}{C_h s} \qquad (12.100)$$

We observe that a capacitor changes into an inductor and an inductor changes into a capacitor in a low-pass to high-pass transformation (Fig. 12.25). The element values of the high-pass filter are given in terms of the normalized low-pass filter elements as

$$L_h = \frac{1}{\omega_0 C_n} \qquad (12.101)$$

and

$$C_h = \frac{1}{\omega_0 L_n} \qquad (12.102)$$

Consider the following example. From the normalized third-order Butterworth filter given in Fig. 12.18, let us design a corresponding high-pass filter with its cutoff frequency $\omega_0 = 10^6$ rad/sec and the impedance level of 500 Ω. From the low-pass filter, we can draw by inspection the high-pass-filter circuit shown in Fig. 12.26. Its element values are:

$$R_L = 500 \ \Omega$$

$$L_{1h} = \frac{500}{10^6(\frac{1}{2})} = 10^{-3} \ h$$

$$C_h = \frac{1}{(500)10^6(\frac{4}{3})} = 1.5 \times 10^{-9} \ \text{fd} \tag{12.103}$$

$$L_{2h} = \frac{500}{10^6(\frac{3}{2})} = 0.333 \times 10^{-3} \ h$$

Next, let us examine the low-pass to band-pass transformation (also an L-C function):

$$s_n = \frac{\omega_0}{BW}\left(\frac{s}{\omega_0} + \frac{\omega_0}{s}\right) \tag{12.104}$$

where, if ω_{C2} and ω_{C1} denote the upper and lower cutoff frequencies of the band-pass filter, BW is the bandwidth

$$BW = \omega_{C2} - \omega_{C1} \tag{12-105}$$

and ω_0 is the geometric mean of ω_{C2} and ω_{C1},

$$\omega_0 = \sqrt{\omega_{C2}\omega_{C1}} \tag{12.106}$$

The low-pass to band-pass transformation maps the segment $|\omega_n| \leq 1$ to the segments $|\omega_{C2}| \geq |\omega| \geq |\omega_{C1}|$, shown in Fig. 12.27. The normalized low-pass elements are then modified according to the following equations:

$$L_n s_n = \frac{L_n}{BW} s + \frac{\omega_0^2 L_n}{BW s}$$

$$\overset{\Delta}{=} L_{b1} s + \frac{1}{C_{b1} s} \tag{12.107}$$

FIG. 12.26. Transformation of low-pass filter in Fig. 12.18 into high-pass filter.

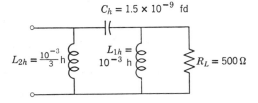

$$C_h = 1.5 \times 10^{-9} \ \text{fd}$$

$$L_{2h} = \frac{10^{-3}}{3} h \qquad L_{1h} = 10^{-3} \ h \qquad R_L = 500 \ \Omega$$

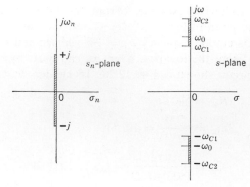

FIG. 12.27. Low-pass to band-pass transformation.

We note that the inductor L_n is transformed into a series-tuned tank, shown in Fig. 12.25, whose elements are given as

$$L_{b1} = \frac{L_n}{BW}$$

$$C_{b1} = \frac{BW}{\omega_0^2 L_n}$$

(12.108)

The capacitor C_n is transformed into a parallel-tuned tank (Fig. 12.25), whose elements are

$$L_{b2} = \frac{BW}{\omega_0^2 C_n}$$

$$C_{b2} = \frac{C_n}{BW}$$

(12.109)

Let us transform the third-order Butterworth low-pass filter in Fig. 12.18 into a band-pass filter with a 1-Ω impedance level whose bandwidth is

$$BW = 6 \times 10^4 \text{ rad/sec}$$

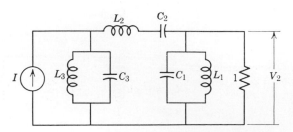

FIG. 12.28. Band-pass filter transformed from low-pass filter in Fig. 12.18.

and its band-pass is "centered" at

$$\omega_0 = 4 \times 10^4 \text{ rad/sec}$$

We draw the band-pass filter shown in Fig. 12.28 by the rules given above. The element values of the band-pass filter are given in the following equations:

$$L_1 = \frac{6 \times 10^4}{(4 \times 10^4)^2(\frac{1}{2})} = 0.75 \times 10^{-4} \text{ h}$$

$$C_1 = \frac{\frac{1}{2}}{6 \times 10^4} = \frac{1}{12} \times 10^{-4} \text{ fd}$$

$$L_2 = \frac{\frac{4}{3}}{6 \times 10^4} = \frac{2}{9} \times 10^{-4} \text{ h}$$

$$C_2 = \frac{6 \times 10^4}{(4 \times 10^4)^2(\frac{4}{3})} = \frac{9}{32} \times 10^{-4} \text{ fd} \tag{12.110}$$

$$L_3 = \frac{6 \times 10^4}{(4 \times 10^4)^2(\frac{3}{2})} = 0.25 \times 10^{-4} \text{ h}$$

$$C_3 = \frac{\frac{3}{2}}{6 \times 10^4} = 0.25 \times 10^{-4} \text{ fd}$$

Finally, the band-elimination filter is obtained through the transformation,

$$s_n = \frac{BW}{\omega_0\left(\dfrac{s}{\omega_0} + \dfrac{\omega_0}{s}\right)} \tag{12.111}$$

where BW and ω_0 are defined in similar manner as for the band-pass filter. The transformation maps the segment of the $j\omega_n$ axis in Fig. 12.29a onto the segments shown on the $j\omega$ axis in Fig. 12.29b. For the low-pass to band-elimination transformation, we, therefore, have the following element changes:

$$L_n s_n = \frac{1}{(s/L_n BW) + (\omega_0{}^2/L_n BW s)}$$

$$\overset{\Delta}{=} \frac{1}{C_{e1}s + (1/L_{e1}s)}$$

$$\frac{1}{C_n s_n} = \frac{\omega_0}{C_n BW}\left(\frac{s}{\omega_0} + \frac{\omega_0}{s}\right)$$

$$\overset{\Delta}{=} L_{e2}s + \frac{1}{C_{e2}s} \tag{12.112}$$

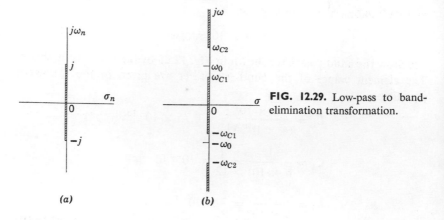

FIG. 12.29. Low-pass to band-elimination transformation.

Observe that the normalized low-pass inductor goes into a parallel-tuned circuit and the capacitor C_n goes into a series-tuned circuit, as shown in Fig. 12.25. In Table 12.7, we have a composite summary of the various transformations.

TABLE 12.7.   TABLE OF VARIOUS FREQUENCY TRANSFORMATIONS

Transformation Low-Pass to	Equation
High-pass	$s_n = \dfrac{\omega_0}{s}$
Band-pass	$s_n = \dfrac{\omega_0}{BW}\left(\dfrac{s}{\omega_0} + \dfrac{\omega_0}{s}\right)$
Band elimination	$s_n = \dfrac{BW}{\omega_0\left(\dfrac{s}{\omega_0} + \dfrac{\omega_0}{s}\right)}$

Problems

12.1 Find the transfer impedance $Z_{21} = V_2/I_1$ for the filter shown in the figure. What should L be in order for $|Z_{21}(j\omega)|$ to be maximally flat?

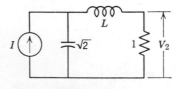

PROB. 12.1

12.2 Find the poles of system functions with $n = 3$, $n = 4$, and $n = 5$ Butterworth characteristics. (Do not use the tables.)

12.3 Show that the half-power point of a Chebyshev low-pass amplitude response is at $\omega = \cosh \beta_k$ for $\epsilon \ll 1$.

12.4 Determine the system function for the following filter specifications:
(a) Ripple of $\frac{1}{2}$ db in band $|\omega| \leq 1$;
(b) at $\omega = 3$, amplitude is down 30 db.

12.5 Compare the slopes at $\omega = 1$ of the following polynomials (for $n = 3$):

(a) $$f(\omega^2) = \omega^{2n}$$
(b) $$f(\omega^2) = \tfrac{1}{2}C_n(2\omega^2 - 1) + \tfrac{1}{2} = C_n{}^2(\omega)$$
(c) $$f(\omega^2) = L_n(\omega^2)$$

12.6 Determine the polynomials $L_4(\omega^2)$ and $L_5(\omega^2)$.

12.7 Expand $\cosh s$ and $\sinh s$ into power series and find the first four terms of the continued fraction expansion of $\cosh s/\sinh s$. Truncate the expansion at $n = 4$ and show that $H(s) = K_0/B_4(s)$.

12.8 Synthesize the $n = 3$ linear phase filter as a transfer impedance terminated in a 1-Ω load.

12.9 Synthesize the low-pass filter which, when terminated in a 1-Ω resistor, will have a transfer admittance whose poles are shown in the figure.

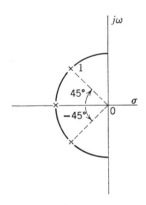

PROB. 12.9

12.10 Determine the asymptotic rate of falloff in the stop band of: (a) optimum filters; (b) linear phase filters.

12.11 Synthesize the $n = 3$ and $n = 4$ Butterworth responses as transfer impedances terminated in a load of 600 Ω with a cutoff frequency of 10^6 rad/sec.

12.12 Synthesize a Chebyshev low-pass filter to meet the following specifications:
(a) Load resistor, $R_L = 600$ Ω;
(b) $\frac{1}{2}$-db ripple within pass band;
(c) cutoff frequency $= 5 \times 10^5$ rad/sec;
(d) at 1.5×10^6 rad/sec, the magnitude must be down 30 db.

12.13 Synthesize $n = 3$ optimum and linear phase filters to meet the following specifications:
(a) Load resistor $= 10^3 \, \Omega$;
(b) cutoff frequency $= 10^6$ rad/sec.

12.14 Design an $n = 4$ Butterworth amplifier with the following specifications:
(a) Impedance level $= 500 \, \Omega$;
(b) cutoff frequency $= 10^3$ rad/sec.

12.15 Synthesize a high-pass filter for a given transfer admittance terminated in a 10^3-Ω load whose amplitude characteristic is optimum (L) with a cutoff frequency of $\omega_0 = 10^4$ rad/sec.

12.16 Synthesize: (a) a band-pass filter; (b) a band-elimination filter, with maximally flat ($n = 4$) amplitude response with $\omega_{C2} = 8 \times 10^4$ and $\omega_{C1} = 2 \times 10^4$.

chapter 13
The scattering matrix

13.1 INCIDENT AND REFLECTED POWER FLOW

In this chapter, we will devote our attention to certain *power* relationships in one- and two-port networks. The characterization of a network in terms of power instead of the conventional voltage-current description is a helpful analytical tool used by transmission engineers. It is especially important in microwave transmission problems where circuits can no longer be given in terms of lumped R, L, and C elements. In the power-flow description, we are concerned with the power into the network which we call the *incident* power and the power reflected back from the load which is the *reflected* power. A convenient description of the network in terms of incident and reflected power is given by the scattering matrix, which is the main topic of discussion in this chapter.

It is convenient to think of incident and reflected power when dealing with transmission lines. Therefore, we will briefly review some concepts in transmission line theory. For a more comprehensive treatment of transmission lines, the reader is referred to any standard text on wave propagation.* Consider the transmission line shown in Fig. 13.1. The voltage

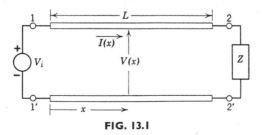

FIG. 13.1

---

* See, for example, E. C. Jordan, *Electromagnetic Waves and Radiating Systems*, Prentice-Hall, Englewood Cliffs, N.J., 1950.

365

at any point down the line is a function of x, the distance from the source. The parameters which describe the transmission line are given in the following:

R = resistance per unit length;
G = conductance per unit length;
L = inductance per unit length;
C = capacitance per unit length.

Given these parameters, we can now define the impedance per unit length as

$$Z = R + j\omega L, \tag{13.1}$$

and the admittance per unit length as

$$Y = G + j\omega C \tag{13.2}$$

The *characteristic impedance* Z_0 of the line is given in terms of Z and Y as

$$Z_0 = \sqrt{\frac{Z}{Y}} \tag{13.3}$$

and the *propagation constant* is

$$\gamma = \sqrt{ZY} \tag{13.4}$$

With these definitions in mind, let us turn to the general equations for the current and voltage at any point x down the line,

$$V(x) = V_i e^{-\gamma x} + V_r e^{\gamma x}$$
$$I(x) = I_i e^{-\gamma x} - I_r e^{\gamma x}$$
$$= \frac{V_i}{Z_0} e^{-\gamma x} - \frac{V_r}{Z_0} e^{\gamma x} \tag{13.5}$$

The terms with the subscript i refer to the incident wave at point x and the terms with subscript r refer to the reflected wave at x. Solving Eqs. 13.5 simultaneously, we obtain explicit expressions for the incident and reflected waves,

$$V_i e^{-\gamma x} = \tfrac{1}{2}[V(x) + Z_0 I(x)]$$
$$V_r e^{\gamma x} = \tfrac{1}{2}[V(x) - Z_0 I(x)] \tag{13.6}$$

Consider the case when a transmission line of length L is terminated in its characteristic impedance, i.e.,

$$\frac{V(L)}{I(L)} = Z_0 \tag{13.7}$$

Then we see that the reflected wave is zero,

$$V_r e^{\gamma L} = 0 \qquad (13.8)$$

Since $e^{\gamma L}$ cannot be zero, we see that the coefficient V_r is identically zero for this case. As a result, the reflected wave at any point x is zero. Also, the impedance at any point x down the line is equal to Z_0 as seen from Eq. 13.5 with $V_r = 0$. With these brief thoughts of transmission lines in mind, let us turn our attention to the main topic of this chapter, namely, the *scattering parameters*.

13.2 THE SCATTERING PARAMETERS FOR A ONE-PORT NETWORK

For the one-port network shown in Fig. 13.2a, consider the following definitions. The *incident parameter a* is defined as

$$a = \frac{1}{2}\left(\frac{V}{\sqrt{R_0}} + \sqrt{R_0}I\right) \qquad (13.9)$$

and the *reflected parameter b*, is defined as

$$b = \frac{1}{2}\left(\frac{V}{\sqrt{R_0}} - \sqrt{R_0}I\right) \qquad (13.10)$$

where R_0 is an arbitrary, positive, dimensionless constant called the *reference impedance* factor. For the transmission line described in the previous section, if the characteristic impedance $Z_0 = R_0$, then we can describe the incident parameter in terms of the incident voltage as

$$a = \frac{V_i e^{-\gamma x}}{\sqrt{Z_0}} \qquad (13.11)$$

Similarly, b can be expressed in terms of the reflected wave as

$$b = \frac{V_r e^{\gamma x}}{\sqrt{Z_0}} \qquad (13.12)$$

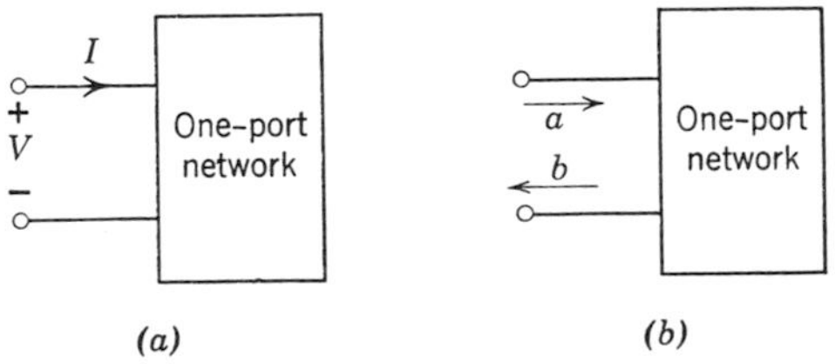

(a)   (b)

FIG. 13.2

When we choose the reference impedance to be equal to the source resistance, i.e., when $R_0 = R_g$, then $S = 0$ and

$$P_A = \frac{|a|^2}{2} = \frac{|V_g|^2}{8R_g} \tag{13.27}$$

where P_A represents the *available gain* or *available power* of a voltage source V_g with a source resistance R_g. For the case of a one-port network, the available gain is defined as the power dissipated in the one-port network when the impedance of the network Z is equal to the resistance of the source R_g. As a result of this definition, we see that, for the one-port network shown in Fig. 13.4, the power dissipated in Z for $Z = R_g$ is

$$P_A = \frac{|V_g|^2}{8R_g} \tag{13.28}$$

The available gain thus represents the *maximum available power* at the terminals of the voltage source.

From this discussion, it is apparent that the value of the reference impedance R_0 should be chosen equal to the source impedance R_g. A standard procedure is to assume a 1-Ω source impedance and denormalize when necessary, i.e., let

$$S = \frac{z - 1}{z + 1} \tag{13.29}$$

where

$$z = \frac{Z}{R_0} \tag{13.30}$$

Next, let us briefly consider some of the important properties of the scattering parameter S for a one-port network.

1. The magnitude of S along the $j\omega$ axis is always less or equal to unity for a passive network, i.e.,

$$|S(j\omega)| \leq 1 \tag{13.31}$$

This property follows from the fact that the power dissipated in a passive network is always greater or equal to zero. Since the power can be expressed as

$$P = \frac{|a|^2}{2}(1 - |S|^2) \geq 0 \tag{13.32}$$

we see that

$$|S(j\omega)|^2 \leq 1 \tag{13.33}$$

2. For a reactive network, $|S(j\omega)| = 1$. This property follows from the fact that the power dissipated in a purely reactive network is zero.

3. For an open circuit, $S = 1$, and for a short circuit, $S = -1$. This is shown to be true from the equation,

$$S = \frac{z - 1}{z + 1} \qquad (13.34)$$

For an open circuit, $z = \infty$, so that $S = 1$. For a short circuit, $z = 0$; therefore $S = -1$.

Before we proceed to the next property, let us consider the following definition.

DEFINITION. A *bounded real function* $F(s)$ is defined by the conditions:

(a) $|F(s)| \leq K$ for   Re $s \geq 0$;

(b) $F(s)$ is real when s is real.

In (a), K denotes any positive real constant.

4. If $z = Z/R_0$ is a positive real function, then S is a bounded real function.

The proof follows from the equation,

$$S = \frac{z - 1}{z + 1}$$

From the positive real condition:

(a)   Re $z(s) \geq 0$, when Re $s \geq 0$, we see that

$$S = \frac{j \operatorname{Im} z(s) - [1 - \operatorname{Re} z(s)]}{j \operatorname{Im} z(s) + [1 + \operatorname{Re} z(s)]} \qquad (13.35)$$

so that

$$|S(s)| = \left\{ \frac{\operatorname{Im}^2 z(s) + [1 - \operatorname{Re} z(s)]^2}{\operatorname{Im}^2 z(s) + [1 + \operatorname{Re} z(s)]^2} \right\}^{\frac{1}{2}} \leq 1 \qquad (13.36)$$

when Re $s \geq 0$.

(b) Where s is real, $z(s)$ is real. Then

$$S = \frac{z - 1}{z + 1}$$

must be real. Thus the scattering parameter for a passive network is a bounded real function.

13.3 THE SCATTERING MATRIX FOR A TWO-PORT NETWORK

In this section, we will extend the concepts developed for one-port networks in the previous section to two-port networks. In the two-port

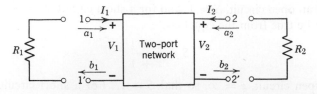

FIG. 13.5

network shown in Fig. 13.5, we are concerned with two sets of incident and reflected parameters, $\{a_1, b_1\}$ at the 1–1′ port, and $\{a_2, b_2\}$ at the 2–2′ port. These parameters are defined in similar manner as for the one-port network, i.e.,

$$a_1 = \frac{1}{2}\left(\frac{V_1}{\sqrt{R_{01}}} + \sqrt{R_{01}}I_1\right)$$

$$b_1 = \frac{1}{2}\left(\frac{V_1}{\sqrt{R_{01}}} - \sqrt{R_{01}}I_1\right)$$

$$a_2 = \frac{1}{2}\left(\frac{V_2}{\sqrt{R_{02}}} + \sqrt{R_{02}}I_2\right)$$

$$b_2 = \frac{1}{2}\left(\frac{V_2}{\sqrt{R_{02}}} - \sqrt{R_{02}}I_2\right) \tag{13.37}$$

where R_{01} and R_{02} are the reference impedances at the input and output ports respectively.

The *scattering parameters* S_{ij} for the two-port network are given by the equations,

$$b_1 = S_{11}a_1 + S_{12}a_2$$
$$b_2 = S_{21}a_1 + S_{22}a_2 \tag{13.38}$$

In matrix form the above set of equations becomes

$$\begin{bmatrix} b_1 \\ b_2 \end{bmatrix} = \begin{bmatrix} S_{11} & S_{12} \\ S_{21} & S_{22} \end{bmatrix} \begin{bmatrix} a_1 \\ a_2 \end{bmatrix} \tag{13.39}$$

where the matrix

$$[S] = \begin{bmatrix} S_{11} & S_{12} \\ S_{21} & S_{22} \end{bmatrix} \tag{13.40}$$

is called the *scattering matrix* of the two-port network. From Eqs. 13.38, we see that the scattering parameters of the two-port network can be expressed in terms of the incident and reflected parameters as

$$S_{11} = \frac{b_1}{a_1}\bigg|_{a_2=0} \qquad S_{12} = \frac{b_1}{a_2}\bigg|_{a_1=0}$$

$$S_{21} = \frac{b_2}{a_1}\bigg|_{a_2=0} \qquad S_{22} = \frac{b_2}{a_2}\bigg|_{a_1=0}$$

(13.41)

In Eqs. 13.41, the parameter S_{11} is called the *input reflection coefficient*, S_{21} is the *forward transmission coefficient*, S_{12} is the *reverse transmission coefficient*, and S_{22} is the *output reflection coefficient*. Observe that all four scattering parameters are expressed as ratios of reflected to incident parameters.

Now let us examine the physical meaning of these scattering parameters. First, consider the implications of setting the incident parameters a_1 and a_2 to zero in the defining relations in Eqs. 13.41. Let us see what the condition $a_2 = 0$ implies in the definition for the forward reflection coefficient,

$$S_{11} = \frac{b_1}{a_1}\bigg|_{a_2=0}$$

Figure 13.6 shows the terminating section of the two-port network of Fig. 13.5 with the parameters a_2 and b_2 of the 2–2' port shown. If we treat the load resistor R_2 as a one-port network with scattering parameter

$$S_2 = \frac{R_2 - R_{02}}{R_2 + R_{02}} \tag{13.42}$$

where R_{02} is the reference impedance of port 2, then a_2 and b_2 are related by*

$$a_2 = S_2 b_2 \tag{13.43}$$

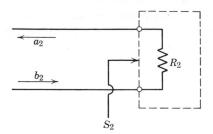

FIG. 13.6.

---

* From the viewpoint of the load resistor R_2, the incident parameter is b_2 and the reflected parameter is a_2.

When the reference impedance R_{02} is set equal to the load impedance R_2, then S_2 becomes

$$S_2 = \frac{R_{02} - R_{02}}{R_{02} + R_{02}} = 0 \tag{13.44}$$

so that $a_2 = 0$ under this condition. Similarly, we can show that, when $a_1 = 0$, the reference impedance of port 1 is equal to the terminating impedance, i.e., $R_{01} = R_1$. We see as a result of this discussion that the conditions $a_1 = 0$ and $a_2 = 0$ merely imply that the reference impedances R_{01} and R_{02} are chosen to be equal to the terminating resistors R_1 and R_2 respectively.

Next, let us consider the relationship between the driving-point impedances at ports 1 and 2 and the reflection coefficients S_{11} and S_{22}. Let us denote the driving-point impedances at ports 1 and 2 as

$$Z_1 = \frac{V_1}{I_1} \qquad Z_2 = \frac{V_2}{I_2} \tag{13.45}$$

From the equation

$$S_{11} = \frac{b_1}{a_1}\bigg|_{a_2=0} \tag{13.46}$$

We can write

$$S_{11} = \frac{\frac{1}{2}[(V_1/\sqrt{R_{01}}) - \sqrt{R_{01}}I_1]}{\frac{1}{2}[(V_1/\sqrt{R_{01}}) + \sqrt{R_{01}}I_1]} \tag{13.47}$$

which reduces easily to

$$S_{11} = \frac{Z_1 - R_{01}}{Z_1 + R_{01}}\bigg|_{R_2=R_{02}} \tag{13.48}$$

Similarly, we have

$$S_{22} = \frac{Z_2 - R_{02}}{Z_2 + R_{02}}\bigg|_{R_1=R_{01}} \tag{13.49}$$

These expressions tell us if we choose the reference impedance at a given port to equal the driving-point impedance at that port, the reflection coefficient of that port will be zero, provided the other port is terminated in its reference impedance.

Next, let us derive some physically meaningful expressions for the forward and reverse transmission coefficients S_{21} and S_{12}. Consider the definition for S_{21},

$$S_{21} = \frac{b_2}{a_1}\bigg|_{a_2=0} \tag{13.50}$$

As we have just seen, the condition $a_2 = 0$ implies that the reference impedance R_{02} is set equal to the load impedance R_2, as seen in Fig. 13.7. If we connect a voltage source V_{g1} with source impedance $R_{01} = R_1$, then we can express a_1 as

$$a_1 = \frac{V_{g1}}{2\sqrt{R_1}} \tag{13.51}$$

Since $a_2 = 0$, we have the equation

$$a_2 = 0 = \frac{1}{2}\left(\frac{V_2}{\sqrt{R_2}} + \sqrt{R_2}I_2\right) \tag{13.52}$$

from which we obtain

$$\frac{V_2}{\sqrt{R_2}} = -\sqrt{R_2}I_2 \tag{13.53}$$

Consequently,

$$b_2 = \frac{1}{2}\left(\frac{V_2}{\sqrt{R_2}} - \sqrt{R_2}I_2\right)$$

$$= \frac{V_2}{\sqrt{R_2}} \tag{13.54}$$

Finally, we can express the forward transmission coefficient as

$$S_{21} = \frac{V_2/\sqrt{R_2}}{V_{g1}/(2\sqrt{R_1})}$$

$$= \frac{2V_2}{V_{g1}}\sqrt{\frac{R_1}{R_2}}\Bigg|_{R_2=R_{02}, R_1=R_{01}} \tag{13.55}$$

In similar fashion, we find that when port 1 is terminated in $R_{01} = R_1$ and when a voltage source V_{g2} with source impedance R_2 is connected to port 2, then

$$S_{12} = \frac{2V_1}{V_{g2}}\sqrt{\frac{R_2}{R_1}}\Bigg|_{R_1=R_{01}, R_2=R_{02}} \tag{13.56}$$

We see that both S_{12} and S_{21} have the dimensions of a voltage-ratio transfer function. Indeed, if $R_{01} = R_{02}$, then S_{12} and S_{21} are simple voltage ratios. It is seen that, for a passive reciprocal network, $S_{21} = S_{12}$.

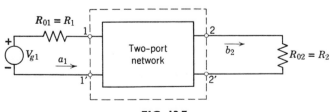

FIG. 13.7

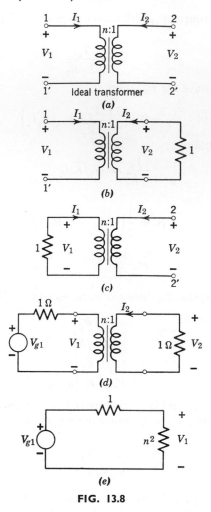

FIG. 13.8

Now, let us consider as an example the scattering matrix of the $n{:}1$ ratio ideal transformer in Fig. 13.8a. Recall that, for an ideal transformer,

$$V_1 = nV_2, \qquad I_1 = -\frac{1}{n}I_2 \qquad (13.57)$$

Assuming first that $R_{01} = R_{02} = 1$, let us find S_{11} by terminating the 2–2' port in a 1-Ω resistor, as shown in Fig. 13.8b. Then

$$\frac{V_2}{-I_2} = 1 \qquad (13.58)$$

so that

$$Z_1 = \frac{V_1}{I_1} = n^2 \tag{13.59}$$

From Eq. 13.48, we have

$$S_{11} = \frac{n^2 - 1}{n^2 + 1} \tag{13.60}$$

Next we terminate the 1–1′ port in a 1-Ω resistor (Fig. 13.8c). In similar fashion as for S_{11} we obtain

$$S_{22} = \frac{(1/n^2) - 1}{(1/n^2) + 1} = \frac{1 - n^2}{1 + n^2} \tag{13.61}$$

We obtain S_{21} by connecting a voltage source V_{g1} with a source impedance $R_{01} = 1\ \Omega$ at the 1–1′ port and terminating the 2–2′ port with a resistance $R_{02} = 1\ \Omega$, as seen in Fig. 13.8d. Since

$$\frac{V_1}{I_1} = n^2$$

the equivalent circuit of the ideal transformer as seen from the voltage source is a 1-Ω impedance in series with an n^2-ohm resistance (Fig. 13.8e). Then V_1 can be expressed in terms of V_{g1}, as

$$V_1 = \frac{V_{g1} n^2}{n^2 + 1} \tag{13.62}$$

Since $V_2 = V_1/n$, we have

$$V_2 = \frac{V_{g1} n}{n^2 + 1} \tag{13.63}$$

Since $R_{01} = R_{02} = 1\ \Omega$, S_{21} is

$$S_{21} = \frac{2V_2}{V_{g1}} = \frac{2n}{n^2 + 1} \tag{13.64}$$

We can show in similar fashion that

$$S_{12} = \frac{2n}{n^2 + 1} \tag{13.65}$$

Therefore the scattering matrix for the ideal transformer is given as

$$S = \begin{bmatrix} \dfrac{n^2 - 1}{n^2 + 1} & \dfrac{2n}{n^2 + 1} \\[2mm] \dfrac{2n}{n^2 + 1} & \dfrac{1 - n^2}{n^2 + 1} \end{bmatrix} \tag{13.66}$$

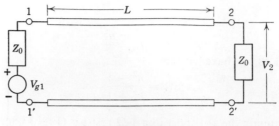

FIG. 13.9

As a second example, let us find the scattering matrix for a lossless transmission line of length L terminated in its characteristic impedance, as shown in Fig. 13.9. If we assume that $R_{01} = R_{02} = Z_0$, then the reflection coefficients are

$$S_{11} = \frac{Z_0 - Z_0}{Z_0 + Z_0} = 0 = S_{22} \tag{13.67}$$

This result is not implausible because a transmission line terminated in its characteristic impedance has zero reflected energy. To determine S_{21}, we terminate the line in Z_0 at both ends and connect at the 1–1′ port a voltage source V_{g1}, as depicted in Fig. 13.9. Since the transmission line has zero reflected energy, i.e.,

$$b_1 = a_2 = 0$$

then

$$V_2 = V_{g1}e^{-\gamma L} \tag{13.68}$$

From the equation,

$$S_{21} = 2\sqrt{\frac{R_{01}}{R_{02}}}\frac{V_2}{V_{g1}} \tag{13.69}$$

we obtain

$$S_{21} = 2e^{-\gamma L} \tag{13.70}$$

In similar fashion, we find that

$$S_{12} = 2e^{-\gamma L} \tag{13.71}$$

Therefore the scattering matrix for the lossless transmission line is

$$S = \begin{bmatrix} 0 & 2e^{-\gamma L} \\ 2e^{-\gamma L} & 0 \end{bmatrix} \tag{13.72}$$

13.4 PROPERTIES OF THE SCATTERING MATRIX

Having defined the scattering matrix of a two-port network in the previous section, let us consider some important properties of the scattering matrix. From the general restriction for a passive network that the net power delivered to all ports must be positive, we obtain the condition,

$$P = \tfrac{1}{2}(a_1 a_1^* + a_2 a_2^* - b_1 b_1^* - b_2 b_2^*) \geq 0 \tag{13.73}$$

Equation 13.73 follows from the fact that the power delivered to the 1–1' port is

$$P_1 = \tfrac{1}{2}(a_1 a_1^* - b_1 b_1^*) \tag{13.74}$$

and the power delivered to the 2–2' port is

$$P_2 = \tfrac{1}{2}(a_2 a_2^* - b_2 b_2^*) \tag{13.75}$$

The total power delivered to the network is then

$$P = P_1 + P_2 \tag{13.76}$$

which is exactly the expression in Eq. 13.73. In matrix notation, the power delivered to the network is

$$P = \tfrac{1}{2}\{[a^*]^T[a] - [b^*]^T[b]\} \geq 0 \tag{13.77}$$

where T denotes the transpose operation, and

$$[a] = \begin{bmatrix} a_1 \\ a_2 \end{bmatrix}$$
$$[b] = \begin{bmatrix} b_1 \\ b_2 \end{bmatrix} \tag{13.78}$$

Since $[b] = [S][a]$, then

$$[b^*]^T = [a^*]^T[S^*]^T \tag{13.79}$$

Equation 13.77 can now be rewritten as

$$2P = \{[a^*]^T[a] - [a^*]^T[S^*]^T[S][a]\}$$
$$= [a^*]^T[[u] - [S^*]^T[S]^T][a] \geq 0 \tag{13.80}$$

This then implies that the determinant of the matrix,

$$[[u] - [S^*]^T[S]]$$

must be greater or equal to zero, i.e.,

$$\text{Det } [[u] - [S^*]^T[S]] \geq 0 \tag{13.81}$$

Consider the special but, nevertheless, important case of a lossless network. In this case $P = 0$, so that

$$[S^*]^T[S] = [u] \tag{13.82}$$

A matrix satisfying the condition in Eq. (13.82) is *unitary*. For lossless two-port network,

$$[S^*]^T[S] = \begin{bmatrix} S_{11}^* & S_{21}^* \\ S_{12}^* & S_{22}^* \end{bmatrix} \begin{bmatrix} S_{11} & S_{12} \\ S_{21} & S_{22} \end{bmatrix} = \begin{bmatrix} 1 & 0 \\ 0 & 1 \end{bmatrix} \tag{13.83}$$

From this equation, we have the following conditions for the scattering matrix

$$S_{11}^*S_{11} + S_{21}^*S_{21} = 1 \tag{13.84}$$

$$S_{12}^*S_{11} + S_{22}^*S_{21} = 0 \tag{13.85}$$

$$S_{11}^*S_{12} + S_{21}^*S_{22} = 0 \tag{13.86}$$

$$S_{12}^*S_{12} + S_{22}^*S_{22} = 1 \tag{13.87}$$

Note that Eqs. 13.85 and 13.86 are conjugates of each other. If the network is reciprocal, then $S_{21} = S_{12}$ and

$$|S_{11}(j\omega)|^2 + |S_{21}(j\omega)|^2 = 1$$
$$|S_{22}(j\omega)|^2 + |S_{21}(j\omega)|^2 = 1 \tag{13.88}$$

from which it follows that, for a lossless reciprocal network,

$$|S_{11}(j\omega)| = |S_{22}(j\omega)| \le 1 \quad \text{and} \quad |S_{21}(j\omega)| \le 1$$

Also it is clear that when $|S_{21}(j\omega)| = 0$ (i.e., when there is a zero of transmission), then $|S_{11}(j\omega)| = 1$. This condition states that all the power that has been delivered to the network from port 1–1' is reflected back to port 1–1'.

At this point, it might be profitable to discuss the question–why scattering matrices? What are the advantages of the scattering description over conventional descriptions? Let us discuss three major reasons for the scattering formalism.

1. Many networks do not possess an impedance or admittance matrix. For example, an ideal transformer has no Z or Y matrix because its elements are not finite. However, as we have seen, the ideal transformer can be described by a scattering matrix. Carlin states† that all passive networks possess scattering matrices.

2. At high frequencies, incident and reflected parameters play dominant roles in problems of transmission, while voltage-current descriptions are relegated to the background. Then the scattering matrix is necessarily the

---

† H. J. Carlin, "The Scattering Matrix in Network Theory," *Trans. IRE*, **CT-3**, No. 2 (June 1956), 88–96; see his extensive bibliography.

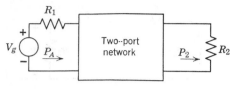

FIG. 13.10

more powerful description of the system. Note that the voltage standing-wave ratio ($VSWR$) is given in terms of a reflection coefficient S as

$$VSWR = \frac{1 + |S|}{1 - |S|} \tag{13.89}$$

3. In networks where power flow is a prime consideration (e.g., filters), the scattering matrix is very useful. For example, in the network given in Fig. 13.10, if P_A represents the available power from the generator and P_2 is the power dissipated in the load R_2, then we can show that the magnitude-squared forward transmission coefficient is

$$|S_{21}(j\omega)|^2 = \frac{P_2}{P_A} \tag{13.90}$$

We will discuss this point in more detail in the next section.

13.5 INSERTION LOSS

In the previous section, we described the forward and reverse transmission coefficients in terms of voltage ratios. Perhaps a more appropriate description of a transmission coefficient is in terms of a power ratio rather than a voltage ratio. In this section we will show that $|S_{21}(j\omega)|^2$ and $|S_{12}(j\omega)|^2$ can be expressed in terms of power ratios. We will then introduce the very important concept of insertion loss and finally relate $|S_{21}(j\omega)|^2$ to the *insertion power ratio*.

Consider the equation for S_{21} in the two-port network shown in Fig. 13.5,

$$S_{21} = \frac{2V_2}{V_{g1}} \sqrt{\frac{R_1}{R_2}} \tag{13.91}$$

From the equation

$$|S_{21}(j\omega)|^2 = S_{21}(j\omega)S_{21}^*(j\omega) \tag{13.92}$$

we obtain

$$|S_{21}(j\omega)|^2 = \frac{|V_2(j\omega)|^2/2R_2}{|V_{g1}(j\omega)|^2/8R_1} \tag{13.93}$$

$$= \frac{P_2}{P_{A1}}$$

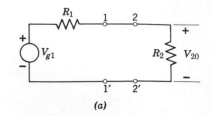

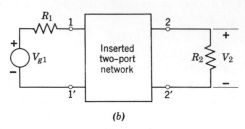

FIG. 13.11

where P_2 is the power dissipated by the load R_2, and P_{A1} is the available gain of the generator V_{g1}. Similarly,

$$|S_{12}(j\omega)|^2 = \frac{P_1}{P_{A2}} \tag{13.94}$$

We see that both $|S_{21}(j\omega)|^2$ and $|S_{12}(j\omega)|^2$ are power transfer ratios which relate the power dissipated at a given port to the available power in the other port.

Now let us examine the idea of *insertion loss*. Consider the network shown in Fig. 13.11a. Between the terminals 1–1' and 2–2' we will insert a two-port network, as shown in Fig. 13.11b. Let us denote by V_{20} the voltage across the load resistor R_2 before inserting the two-port network, and by V_2 the voltage across R_2 after inserting the two-port network. A measure of the effect of inserting the two-port network is given by the insertion voltage ratio IVR, which is defined as

$$IVR \triangleq \frac{V_{20}}{V_2} \tag{13.95}$$

Another method of gaging the effect of inserting the two-port network is to measure the power dissipated at the load before and after inserting the two-port network. If P_{20} is the power dissipated at the load before the two-port network is inserted, and if P_2 is the power dissipated after insertion, then the *insertion power ratio* of the two-port network is defined as

$$e^{2\alpha} \triangleq \frac{P_{20}}{P_2} \tag{13.96}$$

If we take the logarithm of both sides, we obtain

$$\alpha = 10 \log \frac{P_{20}}{P_2} \tag{13.97}$$

where α is the *insertion loss* of the two-port network. In terms of the circuit given in Fig. 13.11, we can calculate P_{20} from the relation,

$$V_{20} = \left(\frac{V_{g1}}{R_1 + R_2}\right) R_2 \tag{13.98}$$

Then P_{20} is

$$P_{20} = \frac{|V_{20}|^2}{2R_2}$$

$$= \frac{R_2 |V_{g1}|^2}{2(R_1 + R_2)^2} \tag{13.99}$$

The power dissipated by the load after inserting the two-port network is given by

$$P_2 = \frac{|V_2|^2}{2R_2} \tag{13.100}$$

The insertion power ratio can then be expressed as

$$e^{2\alpha} = \frac{P_{20}}{P_2} = \frac{|V_{g1}|^2}{|V_2|^2} \frac{(R_2)^2}{(R_1 + R_2)^2} \tag{13.101}$$

In the special case when the source and load impedances are equal, that is,

$$R_1 = R_2 = R_{01} = R_{02} \tag{13.102}$$

the reciprocal of the squared magnitude of the forward transmission coefficient in Eq. 13.93 is equal to the insertion power ratio,

$$\frac{1}{|S_{21}(j\omega)|^2} = \frac{P_{20}}{P_2} \tag{13.103}$$

When $R_1 \neq R_2$, then

$$\frac{P_{20}}{P_2} = \frac{4R_1 R_2}{(R_1 + R_2)^2} \frac{1}{|S_{21}(j\omega)|^2} \tag{13.104}$$

In any event, we see that the magnitude-squared transmission coefficients $|S_{21}(j\omega)|^2$ and $|S_{12}(j\omega)|^2$ can be regarded physically as equivalent insertion power ratios. In the next section, we will use this relationship in the synthesis of double-terminated filter networks.

13.6 DARLINGTON'S INSERTION LOSS FILTER SYNTHESIS

In this section, we will consider a filter synthesis procedure first proposed by Darlington in a classic paper in 1939.* We will use scattering matrix notation to describe the essence of Darlington's original work. Our coverage will be restricted to the class of low-pass filters which are terminated in equal source and load impedances, $R_{01} = R_{02} = R_0$, as shown in Fig. 13.12. For normalizing purposes we will let R_0 be equal to 1 Ω.

Recall that, when the source and load impedances are equal, then the insertion power ratio is equal to the reciprocal of $|S_{21}(j\omega)|^2$, i.e.,

$$\frac{P_{20}}{P_2} = \frac{1}{|S_{21}(j\omega)|^2} \tag{13.105}$$

Expressed as a loss function, the insertion power ratio is

$$A = 10 \log \frac{P_{20}}{P_2}$$
$$= -10 \log |S_{21}(j\omega)|^2 \quad \text{decibels} \tag{13.106}$$

In circuit design, the specification of an insertion loss A (Fig. 13.13a) is equivalent to the specification of the amplitude-squared transmission coefficient shown in Fig. 13.13b. One of the most ingenious techniques given in Darlington's synthesis procedure is the reduction of insertion loss synthesis to an equivalent L-C driving-point synthesis problem. This technique can be developed in terms of scattering parameters. Our initial specification is in terms of $|S_{21}(j\omega)|$. For an L-C two-port network,

$$|S_{11}(j\omega)|^2 = 1 - |S_{21}(j\omega)|^2 \tag{13.107}$$

Next, $S_{11}(s)$ is obtained from the magnitude-squared function,

$$S_{11}(s) S_{11}(-s) = 1 - |S_{21}(j\omega)|^2|_{j\omega=s} \tag{13.108}$$

Then from the equation

$$S_{11} = \frac{Z_1 - R_0}{Z_1 + R_0} \tag{13.109}$$

we obtain the driving-point impedance,

$$Z_1(s) = R_0 \frac{1 + S_{11}(s)}{1 - S_{11}(s)} \tag{13.110}$$

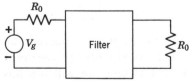

FIG. 13-12

* S. Darlington, "Synthesis of Reactance 4-Poles which Produce Prescribed Insertion Loss Characteristics," *J. Math. Phys.*, **18** (1939), 257–353.

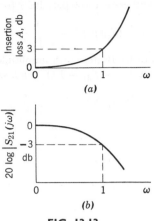

FIG. 13.13

shown in Fig. 13.14. We then synthesize the network from $Z_1(s)$.

We will restrict our discussion here to low-pass filters given by the loss-less ladder structure terminated at both ports by $1\,\Omega$ resistors in Fig. 13.15. These low-pass filters can take the form of a Butterworth or Chebyshev specification for $|S_{21}(j\omega)|^2$, i.e.,

$$|S_{21}(j\omega)|^2 = \frac{1}{1 + \omega^{2n}} \qquad (13.111)$$

or

$$|S_{21}(j\omega)|^2 = \frac{1}{1 + \epsilon^2 C_n^{\;2}(\omega)} \qquad (13.112)$$

where $C_n(\omega)$ represents an nth order Chebyshev polynomial.

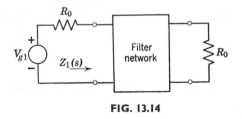

FIG. 13.14

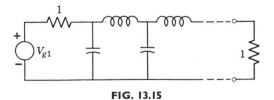

FIG. 13.15

Example 13.1.   Let us synthesize a low-pass filter for the specification

$$|S_{21}(j\omega)|^2 = \frac{1}{1 + \omega^6} \qquad (13.113)$$

which represents a third-order Butterworth amplitude characteristic. The load and source impedances are $R_{02} = R_{01} = 1\ \Omega$. First we find $|S_{11}(j\omega)|^2$ as

$$|S_{11}(j\omega)|^2 = 1 - \frac{1}{1 + \omega^6}$$

$$= \frac{\omega^6}{1 + \omega^6} \qquad (13.114)$$

Letting $j\omega = s$ in $|S_{11}(j\omega)|^2$, we obtain

$$S_{11}(s)\,S_{11}(-s) = -\frac{s^6}{1 - s^6} \qquad (13.115)$$

which factors into

$$S_{11}(s)\,S_{11}(-s) = \frac{s^3(-s^3)}{(1 + 2s + 2s^2 + s^3)(1 - 2s + 2s^2 - s^3)} \qquad (13.116)$$

so that $S_{11}(s)$ is

$$S_{11}(s) = \frac{s^3}{s^3 + 2s^2 + 2s + 1} \qquad (13.117)$$

Next, $Z_1(s)$ is obtained from the equation,

$$Z_1(s) = \frac{1 + S_{11}(s)}{1 - S_{11}(s)}$$

$$= \frac{2s^2 + 2s + 1}{2s^3 + 2s^2 + 2s + 1} \qquad (13.118)$$

We next perform a Cauer ladder expansion for $Z_1(s)$.

$$2s^2 + 2s + 1\overline{)2s^3 + 2s^2 + 2s + 1}(s$$
$$\underline{2s^3 + 2s^2 + s}$$
$$s + 1\overline{)2s^2 + 2s + 1}(2s$$
$$\underline{2s^2 + 2s}$$
$$1\overline{)s + 1}(s$$
$$\underline{s}$$
$$1\overline{)1}(1$$
$$\underline{1}$$
$$=$$

The low-pass filter is thus synthesized in the structure shown in Fig. 13.16.

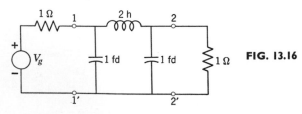

FIG. 13.16

Problems

13.1 Determine the reflection coefficient S for the one-port networks shown in the figure.

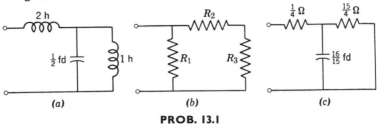

PROB. 13.1

13.2 For the one-port network in Fig. 13.3, let $R_0 = R_g$. If the incident parameter is $a = V_g/2\sqrt{R_0}$, find the reflected parameter b.

13.3 For the network in Prob. 13.1, determine $|S(j\omega)|$. Show that the scattering elements S for the networks in Prob. 13.1 are bounded real functions.

13.4 For each of the networks shown, find the scattering matrix for $R_{01} = R_{02} = 1$.

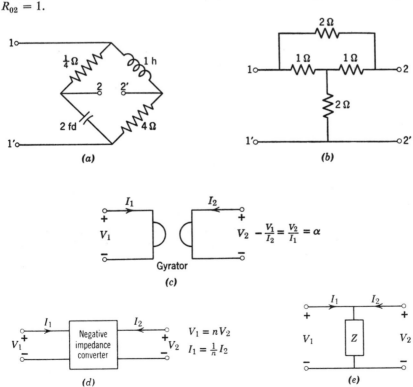

PROB. 13.4

13.5 Find the insertion voltage ratio and insertion power ratios for each of the networks shown. These networks are to be inserted between a source impedance $R_g = 2\,\Omega$ and a load impedance $R_L = 1\,\Omega$. From the insertion power ratios, find $|S_{21}(j\omega)|^2$.

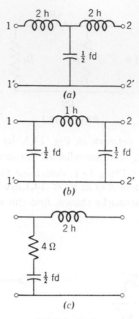

PROB. 13.5

13.6 Synthesize low-pass filters for the specifications,

(a)
$$|S_{21}(j\omega)|^2 = \frac{1}{1 + \omega^4}$$

(b)
$$|S_{21}(j\omega)|^2 = \frac{1}{1 + \omega^8}$$

13.7 Synthesize an equal-ripple low-pass filter such that $20 \log |S_{21}(j\omega)|$ has at most ½-db ripple in the pass band and an asymptotic falloff of 12 db/octave in the stop band.

appendix A

Elements of complex variables

A.I ELEMENTARY DEFINITIONS AND OPERATIONS

A complex variable z is a pair of real variables (x, y) written as

$$z = x + jy \qquad (A.1)$$

where j can be thought of as $\sqrt{-1}$.

The variable x is called the real part of z, and y is the imaginary part of z. Written in simpler notation, we have

$$x = \text{Re}(z), \qquad y = \text{Im}(z) \qquad (A.2)$$

The variable z can be plotted on a pair of rectangular coordinates. The abscissa represents the x or real axis, and the ordinate represents the y or imaginary axis. The plane upon which x and y are plotted is called the *complex* plane. Any point on the complex plane such as $z = 3 + j2$ can be represented in terms of its real and imaginary parts, as shown in Fig. A.1. From the origin of the complex plane, let us draw a vector to any point z.

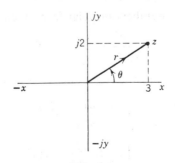

FIG. A.I

The distance from the origin to z is given by

$$|z| = (x^2 + y^2)^{\frac{1}{2}} \tag{A.3}$$

and is known as the *modulus* of z. The angle which the vector subtends is known as the *argument* of z or

$$\arg z = \tan^{-1} \frac{y}{x} \tag{A.4}$$

Letting $\theta = \arg z$ and $r = |z|$, we can represent z in polar coordinates as

$$z = re^{j\theta} \tag{A.5}$$

Expanding this last equation by Euler's formula, we obtain

$$z = r \cos \theta + jr \sin \theta, \tag{A.6}$$

so that

$$x = r \cos \theta$$
$$y = r \sin \theta \tag{A.7}$$

The rule for addition for two complex numbers is given as

$$(a + jb) + (c + jd) = (a + c) + j(b + d) \tag{A.8}$$

When two complex numbers are multiplied, we have,

$$(a + jb)(c + jd) = (ac - bd) + j(ad + bc) \tag{A.9}$$

where $j^2 = -1$. If we express the complex numbers in polar form, we obtain

$$(a + jb) = r_1 e^{j\theta_1} \tag{A.10}$$

and

$$(c + jd) = r_2 e^{j\theta_2} \tag{A.11}$$

When we multiply the two numbers in polar form, then

$$r_1 e^{j\theta_1} r_2 e^{j\theta_2} = r_1 r_2 e^{j(\theta_1 + \theta_2)} \tag{A.12}$$

If we divide these two numbers in polar form, then

$$\frac{r_1 e^{j\theta_1}}{r_2 e^{j\theta_2}} = \frac{r_1}{r_2} e^{j(\theta_1 - \theta_2)} \tag{A.13}$$

In rectangular coordinates, the operation of division can be expressed as

$$\frac{a + jb}{c + jd} = \frac{(a + jb)(c - jd)}{(c + jd)(c - jd)}$$
$$= \left(\frac{ac + bd}{c^2 + d^2}\right) + j\left(\frac{bc - ad}{c^2 + d^2}\right) \tag{A.14}$$

In connection with the modulus of a complex number, it is useful to note the following rules:

$$|z_1 z_2| = |z_1| \cdot |z_2|$$

$$|z_1 z_1^*| = |z_1| \cdot |z_1^*| = |z_1|^2 \qquad \text{(A.15)}$$

$$z \cdot z^* = |z|^2$$

where z^* is the complex conjugate of z and is defined as

$$z^* = \overline{x + jy} = x - jy \qquad \text{(A.16)}$$

The following rules deal with operations involving the conjugate definition:

$$\overline{z_1 + z_2} = z_1^* + z_2^*$$

$$\overline{z_1 z_2} = z_1^* \cdot z_2^* \qquad \text{(A.17)}$$

$$\overline{z_1/z_2} = z_1^*/z_2^*$$

Finally, if z has a modulus of unity, then

$$z = \frac{1}{z^*} \qquad \text{(A.18)}$$

The operations of raising a complex number to the nth power, or taking the nth root of a complex number, can be dealt with most readily by using the polar form of the number. Thus,

$$z^n = (re^{j\theta})^n = r^n e^{jn\theta}$$

and

$$z^{1/n} = r^{1/n} e^{j[(\theta + 2k\pi)/n]}, \qquad k, 0, 1, \cdots, n - 1 \qquad \text{(A.19)}$$

A.2 ANALYSIS

If to each $z = x + jy$, we assign a complex number $w = u + jv$, then w is a function of z or

$$w = f(z) \qquad \text{(A.20)}$$

The following are examples of complex functions, i.e., functions of a complex variable:

$$w = 2z$$
$$w = \log_e z$$
$$w = 1/z$$
$$w = z^2 + 4$$
$$w = |z| \qquad \text{(A.21)}$$

We see that w may be complex, pure real, or pure imaginary, depending upon the particular relationship with z. In general, the real and imaginary parts of w are both functions of x and y. i.e., if we let $w = u + jv$, then

$$u = f(x, y) \quad \text{and} \quad v = f(x, y) \tag{A.22}$$

As an example, let us find u and v for the function $w = z^2 + 4$.

$$w = z^2 + 4 = (x + jy)^2 + 4 \tag{A.23}$$

Simplifying, we obtain,

$$w = (x^2 - y^2 + j2xy) + 4 \tag{A.24}$$

so that

$$u = x^2 - y^2 + 4 \quad \text{and} \quad v = 2xy \tag{A.25}$$

The derivative of a complex function $f(z)$ is defined as

$$f'(z) = \lim_{\Delta z \to 0} \frac{f(z + \Delta z) - f(z)}{\Delta z} \tag{A.26}$$

If one restricts the direction or path along which Δz approaches zero, then we have what is known as a "directional derivative." However, if a complex function is to possess a derivative at all, the derivative must be the same at any point regardless of the direction in which Δz approaches zero. In other words, in order for $f(z)$ to be differentiable at $z = z_0$,

$$\left. \frac{df(z)}{dz} \right|_{z=z_0} = \text{constant} \tag{A.27}$$

for all directions of approach of Δz.

Consider the two directions in which Δz approaches zero in Figs. A.2 and A.3. For path 1,

$$f'(z) = \lim_{\Delta x \to 0} \lim_{\Delta y \to 0} \frac{f(z + \Delta z) - f(z)}{\Delta z} \tag{A.28}$$

Substituting

$$\Delta z = \Delta x + j\,\Delta y \tag{A.29}$$

into the last equation, we obtain,

$$f'(z) = \lim_{\Delta x \to 0} \lim_{\Delta y \to 0} \frac{f[x + \Delta x + j(y + \Delta y)] - f(x + jy)}{\Delta x + j\,\Delta y} \tag{A.30}$$

Since

$$f(z) = u + jv \tag{A.31}$$

and

$$f(z + \Delta z) = u + \Delta u + j(v + \Delta v) \tag{A.32}$$

we finally arrive at

$$f'(z) = \lim_{\Delta x \to 0} \lim_{\Delta y \to 0} \frac{\Delta u + j\,\Delta v}{\Delta x + j\,\Delta y}$$

$$= \lim_{\Delta x \to 0} \frac{\Delta u + j\,\Delta v}{\Delta x} = \frac{\partial u}{\partial x} + j\frac{\partial v}{\partial x} \qquad \text{(A.33)}$$

For path 2,

$$f'(z) = \lim_{\Delta y \to 0} \lim_{\Delta x \to 0} \frac{\Delta u + j\,\Delta v}{\Delta x + j\,\Delta y}$$

$$= \lim_{\Delta y \to 0} \frac{\Delta u + j\,\Delta v}{j\,\Delta y} \qquad \text{(A.34)}$$

$$= \frac{\partial v}{\partial y} - j\frac{\partial u}{\partial y}$$

Since we assume that the function $f(z)$ is differentiable, the derivatives must be independent of path. Thus,

$$\frac{\partial v}{\partial y} - j\frac{\partial u}{\partial y} = \frac{\partial u}{\partial x} + j\frac{\partial v}{\partial x} \qquad \text{(A.35)}$$

From this last equation, we obtain the *Cauchy-Riemann* equations,

$$\frac{\partial v}{\partial y} = \frac{\partial u}{\partial x}$$

$$\frac{\partial u}{\partial y} = -\frac{\partial v}{\partial x} \qquad \text{(A.36)}$$

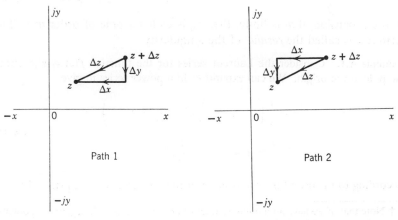

Path 1   Path 2

FIG. A.2   **FIG. A.3**

We have just seen that, in order for a function to have a derivative, the *Cauchy-Riemann* equations must hold. A function which is single-valued and possesses a unique derivative is called an *analytic* function. A set of sufficient conditions for analyticity is that the Cauchy-Riemann equations are obeyed. For example, consider the function,

$$f(z) = z^2 + 4 \tag{A.37}$$

$f(z)$ is analytic because

$$\frac{\partial v}{\partial y} = 2x = \frac{\partial u}{\partial x}$$

$$\frac{\partial u}{\partial y} = -2y = -\frac{\partial v}{\partial x} \tag{A.38}$$

On the other hand, $f(z) = z^*$ is not analytic because

$$u = x \qquad \text{and} \qquad v = -y$$

$$\frac{\partial u}{\partial x} = +1 \qquad \text{and} \qquad \frac{\partial v}{\partial y} = -1 \tag{A.39}$$

A.3 SINGULARITIES AND RESIDUES

If $f(z)$ is analytic within a region or *domain* in the complex plane except at a point z_0, then $f(z)$ has an *isolated singularity* at z_0. Suppose $f(z)$ has a singularity at z_0, then we can expand $f(z)$ about z_0 in a *Laurent* series

$$f(z) = \frac{a_{-n}}{(z - z_0)^n} + \cdots + \frac{a_{-1}}{z - z_0} + a_0(z - z_0)^0 + a_1(z - z_0) + \cdots$$

$$+ a_m(z - z_0)^m + \cdots \tag{A.40}$$

In the expansion, if m is finite, then z_0 is called a pole of order m.† The term a_{-1} is called the *residue* of the singularity.

Example A.1.   Consider the Laurent series for the function $f(z) = e^z/z$ about the pole at the origin. We can expand e^z in a power series to give

$$\frac{e^z}{z} = \frac{1}{z}\left(1 + z + \frac{1}{2!}z^2 + \frac{1}{3!}z^3 + \cdots\right)$$

$$= \frac{1}{z} + 1 + \frac{1}{2!}z + \frac{1}{3!}z^2 + \cdots. \tag{A.41}$$

According to the definition, the residue of the pole at $z = 0$ is equal to 1.

---

† Note that, if we have an infinite number of nonzero terms with negative exponents, then z_0 is an *essential singularity*.

Example A.2. Expand the function $f(z) = 1/z(z - 1)^2$ about the pole at $z = 1$ and find the residue of the pole at $z = 1$.

$$\frac{1}{z(z - 1)^2} = \frac{1}{(z - 1)^2} \frac{1}{1 + (z - 1)}$$

$$= \frac{1}{(z - 1)^2} [1 - (z - 1) + (z - 1)^2 - (z - 1)^3 + \cdots]$$

$$= \frac{1}{(z - 1)^2} - \frac{1}{(z - 1)} + 1 - (z - 1) + (z - 1)^2 + \cdots$$

$$\text{(A.42)}$$

for $0 < |z - 1| < 1$. Here, the residue of the pole at $z = 1$ is equal to -1.

Example A.3. Find the residues of the poles at $s = 0$ and $s = -1$ of the function,

$$f(s) = \frac{s + 2}{s^2(s + 1)^2} \tag{A.43}$$

To find the residues, we simply perform a partial fraction expansion,

$$f(s) = \frac{2}{s^2} - \frac{3}{s} + \frac{1}{(s + 1)^2} + \frac{3}{(s + 1)} \tag{A.44}$$

Thus the residue of the pole at $s = 0$ is -3, and the residue of the pole at $s = -1$ is $+3$.

A.4 CONTOUR INTEGRATION

In complex integration the integral is taken over a piecewise smooth path C and is defined as the limit of an infinite summation

$$\int_C f(z) \, dz = \lim_{n \to \infty} \sum_{j=1}^{n} f(z_j) \, \Delta z_j \tag{A.45}$$

where z_j lies on C. Unlike the process of differentiation, the path along which we take the integral makes a difference as to the ultimate value of the integral. Thus the integral

$$\int_{z_1}^{z_2} f(z) \, dz \tag{A.46}$$

in general, has different values depending upon whether we choose to integrate along path C_1 or path C_2, as shown in Fig. A.4. If we integrate along a *closed* path, say from a to b and then to a again, we are integrating along a *closed contour*. The path shown in Fig. A.5 is an example of a closed contour. The following theorem, known as *Cauchy's residue theorem* gives a method for rapid evaluation of integrals on closed paths.

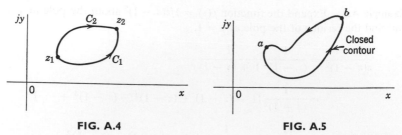

FIG. A.4   FIG. A.5

Theorem A.1.   If C is a simple closed curve in a domain D, within which $f(z)$ is analytic except for isolated singularities at $z_1, z_2, \cdots, z_n$, then the integral along the closed path C is

$$\oint_C f(z)\, dz = 2\pi j(K_1 + K_2 + \cdots + K_n) \tag{A.47}$$

where K_i represents the residue of the singularity z_i.

Example A.4.   Consider the integral

$$\oint \frac{s+2}{s^2(s+1)^2}\, ds \tag{A.48}$$

along the circle $|s| = 2$, as given in Fig. A.6. Since there are two singularities within the circle, at $s = 0$ and at $s = -1$, whose residues are respectively -3 and $+3$, then the integral along the circle is

$$\oint \frac{s+2}{s^2(s+1)^2}\, ds = 2\pi j(-3 + 3) = 0 \tag{A.49}$$

Example A.5.   Find the integral of $f(s)$ along the closed contour shown in Fig. A.7. The function $f(s)$ is given as

$$f(s) = \frac{3s+5}{(s+1)(s+2)} \tag{A.50}$$

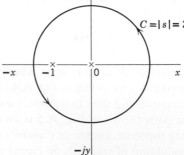

FIG A.6

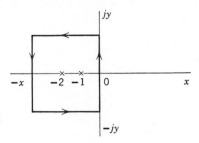

FIG. A.7

A partial fraction expansion of $f(s)$ shows that

$$f(s) = \frac{1}{s+1} + \frac{2}{s+2}$$ (A.51)

so that the residues are 1 and 2. The value of the integral along the closed path within which both the singularities lie is then

$$\oint_C f(s)\, ds = 2\pi j(1+2) = 6\pi j$$ (A.52)

If $f(z)$ is analytic in a domain with no singularities, then the integral along any closed path is zero, i.e.,

$$\oint_C f(z)\, dz = 0$$ (A.53)

This result is known as Cauchy's integral theorem.

Introduction to matrix algebra

B.I DEFINITION

A matrix of *order* (*mn*) is a rectangular *array* of m rows and n columns as given symbolically by

$$[a_{ij}]_{mn} = \begin{bmatrix} a_{11} & a_{12} & \cdots & a_{1n} \\ a_{21} & a_{22} & \cdots & \cdot \\ \cdot & \cdot & \cdots & \cdot \\ a_{m1} & a_{m2} & \cdots & a_{mn} \end{bmatrix} \tag{B.1}$$

The *elements* of the matrix are the individual quantities a_{ij}. In this discussion, we will denote a matrix by a pair of square brackets, as shown in Eq. B.1. The first subscript of an element denotes the row orientation and the second subscript denotes the column orientation.

B.2 ELEMENTARY CONCEPTS

Square matrix

A square matrix has the same number of rows as columns, i.e., a matrix of order (*nn*). The $[y]$ matrix is an example of a square matrix.

$$[y]_{22} = \begin{bmatrix} y_{11} & y_{12} \\ y_{21} & y_{22} \end{bmatrix} \tag{B.2}$$

The subscripts (2 2) of the $[y]$ matrix in Eq. B.2 indicate the order of the matrix.

Diagonal matrix

A diagonal matrix is a square matrix whose elements off the main diagonal are zero, i.e., one in which $a_{ij} = 0$ for $i \neq j$. The following matrix is diagonal.

$$\begin{bmatrix} 1 & 0 & 0 \\ 0 & -2 & 0 \\ 0 & 0 & 3 \end{bmatrix} \tag{B.3}$$

Unit matrix

A unit matrix is a diagonal matrix for which $a_{ij} = 1$ for $i = j$, and is denoted as $[u]_n$. For example, $[u]_3$ is

$$[u]_3 = \begin{bmatrix} 1 & 0 & 0 \\ 0 & 1 & 0 \\ 0 & 0 & 1 \end{bmatrix} \tag{B.4}$$

Equality

Two matrices are equivalent if they have the same number of rows and columns and if the elements of corresponding orientation are equal. Suppose $y_1 = 2$, $y_2 = -3$, and $y_3 = -6$. If we write this set of equations in matrix form, we have

$$\begin{bmatrix} y_1 \\ y_2 \\ y_3 \end{bmatrix} = \begin{bmatrix} 2 \\ -3 \\ -6 \end{bmatrix} \tag{B.5}$$

Transpose

The transpose of a matrix $[a]_{mn}$, denoted as $[a]_{nm}^T$, is the matrix formed by interchanging the rows and columns of $[a]_{mn}$. Thus, if

$$[a]_{32} = \begin{bmatrix} 1 & 0 \\ -6 & 5 \\ 3 & 2 \end{bmatrix} \tag{B.6}$$

then

$$[a]_{23}^T = \begin{bmatrix} 1 & -6 & 3 \\ 0 & 5 & 2 \end{bmatrix} \tag{B.7}$$

Determinant of a matrix

The determinant of a matrix is defined only for square matrices and is formed by taking the determinant of the elements of the matrix. For example,

$$\det \begin{bmatrix} 1 & 2 \\ -5 & 4 \end{bmatrix} = \begin{vmatrix} 1 & 2 \\ -5 & 4 \end{vmatrix} = 14 \tag{B.8}$$

Note that the determinant of a matrix has a particular *value*, whereas the matrix itself is merely an *array* of quantities.

Cofactor

The cofactor A_{ij} of a square matrix is the determinant formed by deleting the ith row and jth column, and multiplying by $(-1)^{i+j}$. For example, the cofactor A_{21} of the matrix

$$[a] = \begin{bmatrix} 2 & 6 \\ 3 & 4 \end{bmatrix} \tag{B.9}$$

is

$$A_{21} = (-1)^{2+1} \times 6 = -6 \tag{B.10}$$

Adjoint matrix

The adjoint matrix of a square matrix $[a]$ is formed by replacing each element of $[a]$ by its cofactor and transposing. For example, for the matrix in Eq. B.9,

$$\text{adj } [a] = \begin{bmatrix} 4 & -3 \\ -6 & 2 \end{bmatrix}^{T}$$

$$= \begin{bmatrix} 4 & -6 \\ -3 & 2 \end{bmatrix} \tag{B.11}$$

Singular and nonsingular matrices

A singular matrix is a square matrix $[a]$ for which det $[a] = 0$. A non-singular matrix is one for which det $[a] \neq 0$.

B.3 OPERATIONS ON MATRICES

In this section, we will examine the operations of matrix addition, multiplication, and inversion.

Addition

Two matrices may be added if both matrices are of the same order. Each element of the first matrix is added to the element of the second matrix whose row and column orientation is the same. An example of matrix addition is shown below.

$$\begin{bmatrix} -2 & 4 \\ 3 & 0 \end{bmatrix} + \begin{bmatrix} 3 & 6 \\ -7 & -2 \end{bmatrix} = \begin{bmatrix} 1 & 10 \\ -4 & -2 \end{bmatrix} \tag{B.12}$$

Subtraction

If two matrices are of the same order, we subtract matrix $[b_{ij}]$ from matrix $[a_{ij}]$ by multiplying all the elements of matrix $[b_{ij}]$ by -1 and then adding it to matrix $[a_{ij}]$. Consider the following example.

$$
\begin{bmatrix} 5 \\ 3 \\ -1 \end{bmatrix} - \begin{bmatrix} 2 \\ -1 \\ 3 \end{bmatrix} = \begin{bmatrix} 3 \\ 4 \\ -4 \end{bmatrix} \tag{B.13}
$$

Multiplication

In order for a matrix multiplication $[A][B]$ to be possible, the number of columns of the first matrix $[A]$ must equal the numbers of rows of the second matrix $[B]$. The product $[C]$ will have the number of rows of the first and the number of columns of the second matrix. In other words, if $[A]$ has m rows and n columns, and if $[B]$ has n rows and p columns, then the product $[C]$ will have m rows and p columns as given by

$$
[A]_{mn} \times [B]_{np} = [C]_{mp} \tag{B.14}
$$

The individual elements of $[C]$ are obtained by the equation,

$$
c_{ij} = \sum_{k=1}^{n} a_{ik} b_{kj} \tag{B.15}
$$

Example B.1.

$$
\begin{bmatrix} 2 & -1 & 0 \\ -1 & 0 & 3 \end{bmatrix} \begin{bmatrix} 4 & 1 \\ 2 & 0 \\ -3 & 2 \end{bmatrix} = \begin{bmatrix} 6 & 2 \\ -13 & 5 \end{bmatrix} \tag{B.16}
$$

Example B.2.   The system of equations,

$$
z_{11}I_1 + z_{12}I_2 = V_1
$$
$$
z_{21}I_1 + z_{22}I_2 = V_2 \tag{B.17}
$$

can be written in matrix notation as

$$
\begin{bmatrix} z_{11} & z_{12} \\ z_{21} & z_{22} \end{bmatrix} \begin{bmatrix} I_1 \\ I_2 \end{bmatrix} = \begin{bmatrix} V_1 \\ V_2 \end{bmatrix} \tag{B.18}
$$

We see that systems of equations can be very conveniently written in matrix notation.

Matrix multiplication is not *commutative*, i.e.,

$$
[A]_{mn}[B]_{np} \neq [B]_{np}[A]_{mn} \tag{B.19}
$$

Observe that the product $[B][A]$ is not defined unless $p = m$. Even a product of square matrices is generally not commutative as seen by the following example:

$$
\begin{bmatrix} 1 & 0 \\ -1 & 2 \end{bmatrix} \begin{bmatrix} -1 & 0 \\ 0 & 2 \end{bmatrix} = \begin{bmatrix} -1 & 0 \\ 1 & 4 \end{bmatrix} \tag{B.20}
$$

If we interchange the order of multiplication, we obtain

$$\begin{bmatrix} -1 & 0 \\ 0 & 2 \end{bmatrix}\begin{bmatrix} 1 & 0 \\ -1 & 2 \end{bmatrix} = \begin{bmatrix} -1 & 0 \\ -2 & 4 \end{bmatrix} \tag{B.21}$$

Inverse

Division is not defined in matrix algebra. The analogous operation is obtaining the *inverse* of a square matrix. The inverse, $[A]_n^{-1}$, of a matrix $[A]_n$ is defined by the relation

$$[A]_n^{-1}[A]_n = [A]_n [A]_n^{-1} = [u]_n \tag{B.22}$$

where $[u]_n$ is the unit matrix of order (nn). The inverse $[A]_n^{-1}$ is equal to the adjoint matrix of $[A]_n$ divided by the determinant of $[A]$, i.e.,

$$[A]^{-1} = \frac{1}{|A|} \, \text{adj} \, [A] \tag{B.23}$$

Consider the following example. Let $[A]$ be given as

$$[A] = \begin{bmatrix} 2 & 1 \\ -1 & 1 \end{bmatrix} \tag{B.24}$$

Then its determinant is

$$|A| = 3$$

and the cofactors are

$$A_{11} = 1 \qquad A_{12} = 1$$
$$A_{21} = -1 \qquad A_{22} = 2$$

The adjoint matrix is

$$\text{adj} \, [A] = \begin{bmatrix} 1 & 1 \\ -1 & 2 \end{bmatrix}^T$$

$$= \begin{bmatrix} 1 & -1 \\ 1 & 2 \end{bmatrix} \tag{B.25}$$

so that $[A]^{-1}$ is

$$[A]^{-1} = \frac{1}{3}\begin{bmatrix} 1 & -1 \\ 1 & 2 \end{bmatrix}$$

$$= \begin{bmatrix} \frac{1}{3} & -\frac{1}{3} \\ \frac{1}{3} & \frac{2}{3} \end{bmatrix} \tag{B.26}$$

As a check, we see that

$$\begin{bmatrix} \frac{1}{3} & -\frac{1}{3} \\ \frac{1}{3} & \frac{2}{3} \end{bmatrix} \begin{bmatrix} 2 & 1 \\ -1 & 1 \end{bmatrix} = \begin{bmatrix} 1 & 0 \\ 0 & 1 \end{bmatrix}$$

$$\begin{bmatrix} 2 & 1 \\ -1 & 1 \end{bmatrix} \begin{bmatrix} \frac{1}{3} & -\frac{1}{3} \\ \frac{1}{3} & \frac{2}{3} \end{bmatrix} = \begin{bmatrix} 1 & 0 \\ 0 & 1 \end{bmatrix}$$

(B.27)

If the determinant of the matrix is zero, then the inverse is not defined. In other words, only nonsingular sqaure matrices have inverses.

Proofs of some theorems on positive real functions

Theorem C.1. If $Z(s)$ and $W(s)$ are both positive real, then $Z(W(s))$ is also positive real.

Proof. When Re $s \geq 0$, both Re $Z(s)$ and Re $W(s) \geq 0$, then Re $Z(W(s)) \geq 0$, also. When s is real, both $Z(s)$ and $W(s)$ are real, hence $Z(W(s))$ is real. Since $Z(W(s))$ satisfies both conditions of positive realness, it is positive real.

Theorem C.2. If $Z(s)$ is positive real, then $Z(1/s)$ is positive real.

Proof. $W(s) = 1/s$ is positive real, hence $Z(W(s)) = Z(1/s)$ is positive real.

Theorem C.3. If $W(s)$ is positive real, then $1/W(s)$ is also positive real.

Proof. $Z(s) = 1/s$ is positive real, hence $Z(W(s)) = 1/W(s)$ is positive real by Theorem C.1.

Theorem C.4. The sum of positive real functions is positive real.

Proof. Suppose $Z_1(s)$ and $Z_2(s)$ are both positive real. When Re $s \geq 0$, then

$$\text{Re } Z_1 \geq 0 \quad \text{and} \quad \text{Re } Z_2 \geq 0$$

so that

$$\text{Re } Z_1 + \text{Re } Z_2 = \text{Re } Z \geq 0.$$

Also, when s is real, both Z_1 and Z_2 are real. The sum of two real numbers is a real number. Therefore, $Z_1 + Z_2$ is positive real.

Theorem C.5. The poles and zeros of $Z(s)$ cannot have positive real parts (i.e., lie in the right half of the s-plane).

Proof. Suppose there is a pole s_0 in the right-half plane. Let us make a Laurent series expansion about s_0,

$$Z(s) = \frac{k_{-n}}{(s-s_0)^n} + \frac{k_{-n+1}}{(s-s_0)^{n-1}} + \cdots + k_1(s-s_0) + \cdots + k_r(s-s_0)^r + \cdots$$

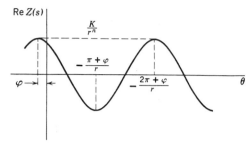

FIG. C.I

where n is real and finite.   In the neighborhood of the pole s_0, $Z(s)$ can be approximated by

$$Z(s) \simeq \frac{k_{-n}}{(s - s_0)^n}$$

We can represent $Z(s)$ in polar form by substituting each term by its polar form; i.e., let $(s - s_0)^{+n} = r^n e^{jn\theta}$ and $k_{-n} = K e^{j\varphi}$ so that

$$Z(s) = \frac{K}{r^n} e^{j(\varphi - n\theta)}, \qquad \text{Re } Z(s) = \frac{K}{r^n} \cos (\varphi - n\theta)$$

which is represented in Fig. C.1.   When θ varies from 0 to 2π, the sign of Re $Z(s)$ will change $2n$ times.   Since Re $Z(s) \geq 0$ when Re $s \geq 0$, it is seen that any change of sign of Re $Z(s)$ in the right-half plane will show that the function is not positive real.   Therefore, we cannot have a pole in the right-half plane.   Since the function $1/Z(s)$ is positive real if $Z(s)$ is positive real, it is obvious that there cannot be any zeros in the right-half plane also.

Theorem C.6.   Only simple poles with positive real residues can exist on the $j\omega$ axis.

Proof.   As a consequence of the derivation of Theorem C.5, it is seen that poles may exist on the $j\omega$ axis if $n = 1$, and $\varphi = 0$.   The condition $n = 1$ implies that the pole is simple and the condition $\varphi = 0$ implies that the residue is positive and real.   It is readily seen that zeros on the $j\omega$ axis must also be simple.

Theorem C.7.   The poles and zeros of $Z(s)$ are real or occur in conjugate pairs.

Proof.   If a complex pole or zero exists without its conjugate, $Z(s)$ cannot be real when s is real.   As a result of this theorem and Theorem C.5, it is seen that both the numerator and denominator polynomials of $Z(s)$ must be Hurwitz.

Theorem C.8.   The highest powers of the numerator polynomial and the denominator polynomial of $Z(s)$ may differ by at most unity.

Proof.   Let $Z(s)$ be written as

$$Z(s) = \frac{a_n s^n + a_{n-1} s^{n-1} + \cdots + a_1 s + a_0}{b_m s^m + b_{m-1} s^{m-1} + \cdots + b_1 s + b_0} = \frac{P(s)}{Q(s)}$$

Network Synthesis

15. M. E. Van Valkenburg, *Introduction to Modern Network Synthesis*, John Wiley and Sons, New York, 1960.
16. J. E. Storer, *Passive Network Synthesis*, McGraw-Hill Book Co., New York, 1957.
17. E. A. Guillemin, *Synthesis of Passive Networks*, John Wiley and Sons, New York, 1957.
18. E. A. Guillemin, *The Mathematics of Circuit Analysis*, John Wiley and Sons, New York, 1949.
19. D. F. Tuttle, *Network Synthesis*, John Wiley and Sons, New York, 1958.
20. J. G. Truxal, *Control System Synthesis*, McGraw-Hill Book Co., New York, 1955.
21. H. W. Bode, *Network Analysis and Feedback Amplifier Design*, Van Nostrand Book Co., Princeton, N.J., 1945.
22. E. S. Kuh and D. O. Pederson, *Principles of Circuit Synthesis*, McGraw-Hill Book Co., New York, 1959.
23. N. Balabanian, *Network Synthesis*, Prentice-Hall, Inc., Englewood Cliffs, N.J., 1958.

Index